"A great portrait of] ... ɔs are the background for ... ven a witch doctor. *A great adventure tale (to) be read again and ..gain.*"
—Steve Geller
Amazon Reviews

"A powerful story of desperation, courage, and friendship."
—Charles Lin
The Internet Review of Books

"Great entertainment!"
—Neil Okrent
Author of *Ticket to Havana*

"Vicarious living at its best!"
—*Bill's Bookshelf*
(Book of the Month)

For six months in 1987-88, Captain Max Hardberger commanded the tramp ship Erika *on a series of voyages to Haiti, Jamaica, Honduras, and the Dominican Republic. This is the story of his desperate adventures as the crew of the* Erika *fought to keep the leaky old freighter trading in one of the riskiest businesses in the world—tramping in the Caribbean.*

Captain Hardberger's textbook, *Deadweight: Owning the Ocean Freighter*, has been called "Required Reading" and "Truth at Last!" by *Fairplay Magazine*.

FREIGHTER CAPTAIN

MAX HARDBERGER

Pioneer Press

GLEN ELLEN

To the Memory of
First Officer Deodath Maraj
Lost at Sea December 6, 1994

ALSO BY MAX HARDBERGER:
Deadweight: Owning the Ocean Freighter
The Jumping Off Place
The Sea Bitch

Cover Design
Gabriel Design Group, Glen Ellen, CA

Cover Art
Detail from "Wailing Wall,"
a 70" X 64" oil-on-canvas painting by Adam Shaw
www.artbyadamshaw.com

Photographs by the Author

Back Cover Photograph: The author onboard the M/V *Erika*
in the Old Bahama Channel, January, 1988

MANUFACTURED IN THE UNITED STATES OF AMERICA

Copyright 2003 Max Hardberger
ISBN 0-9640433-7-8

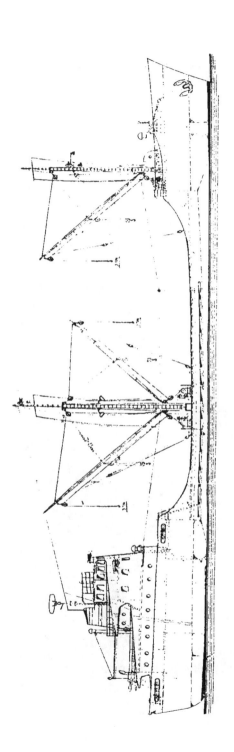

M/V *ERIKA* (ex *SYROS PRIDE*)

Thirteen vessels were built to this design in Groningen, Holland, from 1960 to 1965. The vessel was subsequently lengthened ten meters and the midships cargo gear was removed. Note that there are no exterior passageways along the house, and no accommodations below the main deck. Both are Frisian aberrations in ship design. Also note design freeboard in fully loaded condition (the height of the deck above the sea).

LENGTH	71 m. (228 ft.)
BEAM	9.2 m. (30.2 ft.)
LOADED DRAFT:	4.7 m. (15.5 ft.)

MAIN ENGINE: WERKSPOOR
BRAKE HORSEPOWER: 750
MAXIMUM RPM: 325

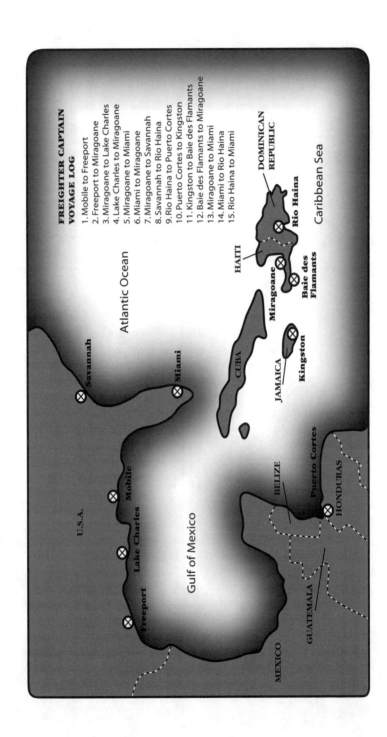

FREIGHTER CAPTAIN VOYAGE LOG

1. Mobile to Freeport
2. Freeport to Miragoane
3. Miragoane to Lake Charles
4. Lake Charles to Miragoane
5. Miragoane to Miami
6. Miami to Miragoane
7. Miragoane to Savannah
8. Savannah to Rio Haina
9. Rio Haina to Puerto Cortes
10. Puerto Cortes to Kingston
11. Kingston to Baie des Flamants
12. Baie des Flamants to Miragoane
13. Miragoane to Miami
14. Miami to Rio Haina
15. Rio Haina to Miami

CHAPTER ONE

I LEFT HOME AT 0600 HOURS, DECEMBER 9, 1987, AND ARRIVED at the Port of Mobile at 0825. The MV *Erika* was at the end of the No. 6 dock, a long, slender needle of a ship, battered and scaly under a fresh coat of gray paint. I parked at the foot of the gangway and went onboard.

The Vietnamese chief mate met me on deck and directed the Arab bosun to take me into the hold. We jumped down through a hole in the hatchboards to the top of the cargo. The hold was hot and dark and stank of rotting cellulose.

The ship had almost broken in half. I could see daylight through a crack in the port side that started at the deck and ended at the wind-and-water strake. The bosun, a slight man in his twenties, played his flashlight over the bales. "Plenty wet cargo, Cap'n," he said.

"I can smell it."

"I thought the ship would crack open like an egg." He studied me. "Are you the new captain, sir?"

"No, I'm the cargo surveyor for the owner."

His narrow shoulders drooped. "I thought maybe we get new captain."

I looked at his drawn face and said, "You got caught in the norther that came through yesterday?"

"Yes, Cap'n. I never thought the Gulf of Mexico could be so rough."

"What's your name?"

"Yussuf al Karim, sir."

"Yussuf, is there food onboard?"

He hesitated. "Not much, sir."

The chief mate dropped into the hold and squatted on his haunches. He was a moon-faced young man with a downy mustache. He sneered at me. "What you think, Mr. Surveyor? You like this ship?"

I regarded him coolly. "I'm here for cargo, First." I turned and climbed down between the bales and the shell plating to the floor timbers. The morning sun glowed hot in the crack above my head, lighting the rust-splattered bales and the orange streaks that ran down the plating to the bilges. Finally I pulled myself back up to the top of the cargo and crawled toward the hole in the hatchboards.

Yussuf had gone topside. The chief mate was still squatting on the cargo. "Very bad ship," he said. "Ship no good, I think."

"This ship brought you into port, First," I said shortly. I lifted myself up on deck and went aft to the accommodations. The starboard hallway had a cold wind blowing through it. I found the companionway leading to the captain's deck and went up. The door to the ship's office was open.

"Hello, Captain?" I called.

No answer. I went through the office into a narrow saloon on the starboard side. There was a table running longships with a half-bottle of Scotch and an empty glass on it. An old man with long white hair and a yellowish handlebar mustache was lying on his back on a bench behind the table, his feet sticking out in a pair of stiff gray socks.

"Captain!" I said loudly. The old man snorted and smacked his lips. His closed eyes were sunken into his veined cheeks. One mottled hand lay motionless on his thin chest. I stood above him for a minute, then went downstairs and aft to the galley. A short, square man with blue-black skin was chopping fiercely at a wrinkled potato.

"Hello, Cookie," I said. "I'm the surveyor. What's for lunch today?"

"We don't have very much, sar," he said. "Potatoes and bacon. I want the agent to come so we can have rice, but he no come yet. We have no coffee, no sugar, no not'ing."

"Where you from, Cookie?"

"Ghana."

"Ah! Many good seamen from Ghana. Well, the owner's coming this afternoon. I'm sure he's bringing money for provisions."

I went back on deck and saw from the angle of the mast that the ship had taken on a starboard list. I went looking for the chief mate and found him smoking in the crew's mess. "Why is she listing, First?" I asked him. "Is there water in the hold?"

He blew smoke at the ceiling. "No water in hold now, Captain. We pump bilges all time when water come in crack. No water now. I sound bilges."

"Any water in the ballast tanks?"

He gave me a wary glance. "Maybe some tank have water. Maybe I sound tanks."

"Yeah. And check with the chief to see if there's a valve open somewhere."

He put out the cigarette. "Okay, Mr. Surveyor, I tell you. There is one big hole in No. 1 starboard double-bottom, and No. 1 tank-top long time no good. Hole in bottom start in storm yesterday. Now chief pump No. 1 starboard every hour, keep water out of hold." He curled his lip. "Maybe I get fire for tell you."

"No," I said, "I work for the owner, Mr. Vance. But we've got to get down to the manhole as soon as possible. I'll talk to the stevedores."

I went on the dock and through a long warehouse to a little office in a trailer. The stevedore foreman was on the phone. He hung up and looked at me. I said, "I'm with the *Erika*. When you get the order to work, pull out of No. 1 first."

"Hokey-dokey," he said. "That was the agent calling. Fiber-Tex says start at 10 o'clock."

"Roger that. We'll have No. 1 open." I went back through the warehouse. A stiff north wind was brewing, rattling the loose tin on the warehouse roof. Wispy little browncaps danced in the muddy wavelets that marched up from the other side of the channel. When I went onboard Yussuf was on the No. 1 hatchcover, wrestling with a hatchboard. I jumped up.

"What's going on, Bosun?" I said. "Where's the rest of the crew?"

He dropped the end of the board and straightened. "The Syrians are leaving the ship. They are packing now."

"The AB's? Why are they leaving?"

"They are afraid of the ship. They are afraid it will break up."

"They're jumping like rats," I said grimly. "Okay, I'll talk to them." I went into the accommodations and through the starboard hallway. The two men, small and dark, alike enough to be father and son, were standing on the fantail with their suitcases and boom boxes at their feet.

"Hello, men," I said.

They nodded to me tensely.

"You know," I said, sitting on a bitt, "the owner's going to fix this ship up. Why don't you fellows stay a few more days and see how it goes, now that the ship is across the Atlantic?"

They shook their heads. "We go now," the older one said. "Plenty bad ship, plenty bad captain. We get money and go today, okay mister?"

"Well," I said, "the owner'll be here later today. Why don't you put your bags back in your cabins until he comes? And the chief mate and bosun need some help with the hatchboards."

"No work hatchboards!" the younger man said. "We go agent office now or I call ITF."

I held up my hands. "Hey, come on, there's no need for that. The agent's on his way."

All seamen know the world waits on the agent. They took their bags back to their cabins. I went back to the No. 1 hatchcover, where Yussuf was still working by himself, and grabbed the other end of the board.

"What you doing, Cap'n?" he asked in astonishment.

"Helping you hump boards. One man can't do this job. Where's the chief mate?"

He shot a bitter look toward the accommodations. "He's hiding so he won't have to work."

"Is that so? Well, I guess it's the two of us, then."

We opened the after half of the hatch, then hauled together on the block-and-tackle to swing the ship's derrick to port and out of the stevedores' way. When the boom was secured, I looked down from the forecastle along the narrow hull. "Hell, Yussuf," I said, "this ship's been lengthened. No wonder she was trying to break up."

"Yes, Cap'n," he said, "I think she was lengthened 10 meters." He slacked the cargo runner. "Her original deadweight was 1100 tons."

"And now she's 1600?" I whistled. "That's a lot of tonnage to add. She must roll like a submarine."

He took off his gloves and shook out a cigarette. "Very bad, Cap'n. We come all the way across Atlantic, no problem. We come in Gulf of Mexico, my God, she want to break up." The cigarette trembled in his fingers. He ducked his head to it.

I looked at the mast. "Well, she's back upright. The chief must have pumped No. 1 down again."

The shore crane came to life with a roar. Stevedores straggled across the dock and climbed down into the hold. Forklifts appeared, and the first bales started coming out of the ship. An hour later the P&I surveyor arrived, a stooped, elderly gent with a brusque manner. He spent half-an-hour in the hold photographing wet bales, issued a report to the master listing cause of damage as seawater ingress, and left.

I watched the stevedores for a while, then went aft to the galley. The cook was out. There was a pot boiling on the stove with scraps of potato and bacon in it. The old captain appeared in the other door. He glared at me.

"I'm the captain," he rasped. "May I help you?"

"Capt. Hardberger," I said. "The owner sent me to inspect the cargo."

"Oh, the fellow from New Orleans." He cleared his throat. "I'm Capt. van der Voort. How do you do?" He stepped into the galley and held out a skeletal fist. I took it gingerly. It felt like a bird's wing.

"Fine, just fine," I said. I gestured toward the pot. "I guess y'all are running a little low on provisions after your long trip."

He snorted. "Not at all. We ran out of coffee because these bloody men drink the stuff like it costs nothing. I bought all the food we needed in Portugal."

The cook came back in. The galley was crowded with three people in it, so I went out. The captain followed me.

"Captain," I asked him, "when is the ship's annual due?"

"It was due on November 29."

"The hell you say! Does Mr. Vance know about this?"

"Capt. Lohren is ship manager. He is coming today. Talk to him." He turned and hobbled along the hallway to the companionway, where he seized onto the handrail and hauled himself up. I shrugged and went on deck. Yussuf was sitting by the gangway, taking tally with the stump of a pencil. We sat together and watched the stevedores working on the dock, burly black men in tee-shirts, sweating in the chilly breeze and cursing each other with good humor.

A gray Nissan pulled up at the foot of the gangway.

"Mr. Dickie!" Yussuf said happily. "I told Binh Mr. Dickie wouldn't leave us here."

A short, stout man with curly blond hair got out and carried a pigskin briefcase up the gangway. I met him at the steps.

"Mr. Vance?" I said. "I'm Capt. Hardberger."

"Oh, great. Good to meet you. Call me Dickie." We shook hands. He saw Yussuf. "Oh," he said, "I met you in Italy. What's your name again?"

"Yussuf al Karim, sir."

"Yes, yes, of course. Has Capt. Helmut been onboard, Yussuf?"

"No sir, we haven't seen him."

"Shit," Dickie said. He turned to me. "Well, Captain, what do you think of the ship?"

I gave Yussuf a look. He excused himself and went down in the hold. I said, "She's ready to sink, Dickie."

"What?"

"She's in bad shape. She almost broke up yesterday."

His jaw dropped. "I thought. . .I knew we had some problems, but. . ." He sagged against the gunwale. "Jesus, I don't need this. What can I do, Captain?"

"Well," I said, "you can fix her or you can sell her. Either way Lloyds has to come onboard. Her annual inspection is due."

He shrugged helplessly. "Helmut is taking care of all that. Helmut Lohren. The guy who bought this ship." He pushed himself upright and ran his fingers through his hair. "I haven't been able to reach him since Sunday, but he said he was going to meet the ship in Mobile."

"Good," I said. "When he gets here, he can arrange for drydocking."

"Drydocking?"

"Lloyds isn't going to renew this ship. She'll have to go into drydock here."

"Christ, how much is that?"

"Hard to say. A hundred grand, more or less."

He paled. "Then I've lost her."

"Dickie," I said earnestly, "if Coast Guard comes onboard, they're going to take one look at that crack and slap a detention on this ship she'll never clear. My advice is to sell the ship and sell her fast."

He thought for a long time. "Okay," he finally said, "I'll talk to Helmut about it. Let's go see the captain."

We went up to the master's saloon. The captain was working on a ledger at the table. The whiskey bottle and glass were gone. He had his shoes on. He stood up and shook Dickie's hand. "Sorry we had problems on the way over, sir."

"Uh, yeah," Dickie said. He held up the briefcase. "I've got the crew wages. Can I put the money in the safe?"

"Of course." The old captain hobbled into the office and pulled a framed picture away from the starboard bulkhead, revealing a small safe. He unlocked the door with one of several keys on a string around his neck. Dickie took out a cloth bank bag and handed it to him. He put it in the safe, locked the door again, and put the string back around his neck.

There were heavy steps on the companionway. A stocky, middle-aged woman appeared in the door, wearing Sunday clothes and carrying a blue, patent-leather purse. "Peter?" she said to the captain.

"Helen!" the captain said. "It's so good to see you." He took a few painful steps. She strode to him and they embraced. He turned to us. "Mr. Dickie, Mr., ah, Capt. Max, meet my wife, Helen."

Dickie stared at him. "I didn't know you had a wife here."

"I live in New Orleans," she said, as if that explained something. There was a prosperous, determined air about her.

The captain cleared his throat. "I'm afraid lunch onboard will not be very tasteful, gentlemen. I have tried to get the crew to be sensible, but they have eaten almost everything." He looked at Dickie. "I bought $1000 worth of food in Lisbon, and they have already gone through it."

"We'll go out to the supermarket," Dickie said. "Can you get a list from the cook?"

"Helen and I will buy some things later. But I was going to suggest that we go out. . ."

"Go out to eat?" Dickie said. "Sure, that's fine. Should we invite anyone from the crew?"

"Oh, no," the captain said, "they are already eating. We can just go."

The cook brought a man into the saloon. He was a thickset Hispanic with an athletic handshake. "Gerhard Castillo," he said. "From the agency." He put his card on the table.

"Just in time," I said. "We've got to sign off the Syrians as soon as possible. They're already threatening to go to ITF."

"Uh oh," Castillo said. "Let me call INS. They're detained onboard, you know." He pulled a phone out of his jacket.

"What's this all about?" Dickie asked.

I told him about the Syrians and said, "Don't cross ITF in Mobile. They'll kill you here. The stevedores won't work if ITF blacklists the ship."

"Jesus. Then get them off."

The agent talked to someone and put the phone away. "INS says bring 'em by on the way to the airport." He looked at Dickie. "I'll need their airfare. That's not included in the *pro forma.*"

Castillo called the travel agent and got the men reservations for the night flight from Mobile to Atlanta, Atlanta to New York, and New York to Damascus. Dickie gave him $3200 for the airfare, and I went down to call them up to the saloon. The old captain paid them off and signed their seaman's books. They left with the agent.

The captain and his wife followed Dickie and me down on deck. Yussuf was taking tally by the gangway. Dickie said to him, "Yussuf, if Capt. Helmut comes while we're gone, tell him we'll be back in an hour."

"Yessir," he said, "I'll tell him."

Helen had a new Dodge conversion van with a raised fiberglass roof and a dinette set. Dickie and I took our seats at the table. She drove west on I-10 until we came to a Denny's Restaurant. The captain was a little groggy at first, but when he got some food in him—he ordered four scrambled eggs—he perked up and gave us a blow-by-blow description of the norther the ship had met in the Gulf. As I understood it, only his heroism and years of experience had saved her.

After we went onboard again and up to the saloon, Dickie said to the captain, "Let me give you some money for groceries. Helen, do you mind driving to the store?"

She said she didn't.

"And I guess I'll pay the crew. Captain, you've got their wage accounts?"

"Yessir."

"You already paid those fucking Syrians, right?" He glanced at Helen. "Sorry, m'am."

She laughed merrily. "I'm married to a sailor. Salty language doesn't bother me in the least."

"Yes," the captain said, "I paid them. For the groceries, 500 will do. That should be plenty." He went to the wall safe and took the string from around his neck. He stuck the key in the lock and opened the door. He looked in. He looked back at us. He reached his hand in the safe and felt around.

"The money's gone," he said in a small voice.

Dickie jumped to his feet. "No!"

The captain took the key out and looked at it, then he looked in the safe again. Dickie reached him in a single bound and pushed him aside. "Goddamn it," he said, "there ain't nothing in here but a fucking pistol."

I closed the companionway door. Dickie turned to me with wild eyes. "What do I do now?"

I shrugged. "We'll have to question the crew. You could call the cops, but they won't do anything. It's a foreign-flag ship. The money's gone, I'm afraid."

The captain said, "Wait. Wait!"

We looked at him.

"I always wear the keys around my neck. The only time I take the keys off is when I go to bed or when I give them to Binh to take Customs around."

"To who?" Dickie asked.

"To Binh, the chief mate."

Dickie's voice rose. "You gave the keys to the chief mate?"

The captain raised his gnarled hands. "It is always done, Mr. Dickie. The chief mate takes the Customs men all around. He must have the keys to show them every part of the ship."

"But he would only have them for a few minutes, right?" Dickie said.

The captain nodded. "But perhaps he made a copy."

I said, "He could make a soap impression in half-a-minute. Then he could carve a copy at his leisure. He could try it out and do more work when he had the original again."

Dickie slammed the wall with his forearm. "This is the fucking end! My ship is breaking up, I'm almost broke, and now the crew wages are gone."

"I'll go get Binh," I said. I went downstairs. Yussuf was sitting on the port gunwale, smoking and watching the stevedores. A bale on the dock had broken its wires. They were gathering the loose sheets of fiber into a rope net.

"Where's Binh?" I asked him.

He blew a mouthful of smoke over the side. The wind whipped it toward the marsh. "I haven't seen him since lunch. He's probably in his cabin."

I sat next to him. A big bulkcarrier in the next slip was loading bundles of steel rods with its own gear. "Look, Yussuf," I said, "I don't know you and you don't know me. I don't know Dickie either. But I want to help him if I can. It looks like this Capt. Helmut ripped Dickie off. Is that right?"

Yussuf flicked the cigarette into the water and turned toward me. "I am Arab, Cap'n. I feel Mr. Dickie is a friend. An Arab will do anything for a friend." He looked up at the captain's windows above our head, but they were closed. He said softly, "Capt. 'elmut came onboard in Taranto to inspect the ship for Mr. Dickie. He got big friends with the captain. For one week they drink all night and sleep all day. Then Mr. Dickie come and buy ship." He bent his head closer. "I think the captain and Capt. 'elmut make monkey business together."

"How much did Dickie pay for the ship?"

"Two hundred thousand U.S."

"Ouch."

He continued, "I know the captain steals money from Mr. Dickie. Mr. Dickie gave him $1000 for food, and the captain bought shit. Maybe he pay only $300."

"Did he buy some good food for himself?"

He chuckled bitterly. "No, that is the wonderful thing. He bought shit, and he eats the shit with us. But of course he is always drunk, so he doesn't know what he is eating."

"That's why you're out of food. He shorted the crew rations."

"And he stole money for paint. Mr. Dickie gave him $700 to buy paint, but he bought house paint." He chuckled again. "We painted the hull in Lisbon and it's already coming off."

The next load of bales came soaring out of the hold, trailing dusty scraps. "What about Binh?" I asked. "What do you think of him?"

He gave a short, angry jerk of the head. "Binh is a bad mate. He knows the sea, but he is lazy. And he steals from the cargo to sell ashore."

"What? Here?"

"No, in the Mediterranean."

"I see." I leaned over. "Yussuf, the wages have been stolen out of the captain's safe. The captain thinks Binh did it. What do you think?"

He stared at me. "Our wages were stolen? Oh, the poor engineers. But I don't know, Cap'n. Maybe Binh could have done it."

"Does he have a key to the safe?"

"I don't know. But you know the captain would give him the keys for the Customs search and then he would get drunk and forget about them. We have bought cigarettes from Binh that he stole from the bonded-stores locker."

"Ah, hah. I see. Okay, thanks." I went into the accommodations and knocked on Binh's door. After a few moments the hook lifted. He was shirtless, a rope of fat ringing his hairless torso. He held a Vietnamese book with a half-nude woman on the cover.

"Binh," I said, "the captain would like to see you."

"Okay," he said. He put down the book and picked up his shirt, buttoning it as he came past me. He left the door open.

When he stepped into the master's saloon the captain straightened up in front of him. "Binh, money is missing from the safe."

"The crew wages?"

"Yes!" the captain said triumphantly. "You have taken the crew wages, have you not?"

"I did not," Binh said. "Not only that, but I want my wages. I want to leave this ship here in Mobile."

The old captain shook his fist in Binh's face. "You, you want your wages, you insolent dog? You have stolen your own wages."

Binh said calmly, "You are accusing me of theft, Captain? I will call ITF."

I stepped up. "Look, Binh, do you want to leave the ship?"

"Yes. I cannot work on this ship. I cannot eat this food any more." He made a spitting sound toward the captain. "It is prison food. You see what we eat today. Rotten potatoes and bacon in a pot of water." He snorted. "Prison food. I call ITF."

"How about this?" I said. "Can we search your room right now?"

He smiled quickly. "You want to search my room, okay. No problem. You call agent after you search my room. Then I sign off ship. And I want my wages before I leave."

"Come on," I said, "let's go."

He and I went downstairs with Dickie and the captain behind us. Helen stayed in the saloon, making a show of looking through the ship's file cabinet. I stood in the door of Binh's cabin while Dickie and the captain searched it. With the three of them inside there was no room for me. The captain went through the clothes in his suitcases. Dickie felt the pockets of his jacket. Then both of them searched around in his closet and in the drawers under his bunk. Binh watched them with ill-concealed amusement. They finally gave up and came outside.

The captain started up the companionway. Dickie detained me with a hand on my sleeve. I followed him back to the fantail.

"Look, Captain," he said, "I need help. What the hell do you think's going on?"

"I think Binh took the money," I said. "Yussuf says the captain would get drunk and give him the keys until he woke up again. And Binh just has a smart-ass look on his face. But he's got to get the money before he gets on the airplane."

"He's a French citizen, isn't he? He can stay in the U.S. as long as he wants."

"Negative," I said. "He came in on a seaman's visa. He's got to leave the country to change it."

"So how do we catch him?"

"We'll pretend he's in the clear. I'll drive him to the airport and search him on the way. Where'd you get the money? From a bank? Could they identify the notes?"

"Yeah. I got it from my bank in Chicago yesterday."

"Good," I said. "I'll give it a try." I left him and went on deck to help Yussuf open No. 2 hatch. We had finished moving the shifting beams, and I was about to go below, when a van turned down the dock and came toward us. I had a sudden chill when I thought it was the Coast Guard—they sometimes arrive in white vans—but it didn't have a CG sticker on the door. The agent, Castillo, bounced out carrying his phone.

"Is the captain onboard?" he called.

"Yes," I said, "he's in his cabin."

I followed the agent up to the saloon. Dickie, Helen, and the captain were there. When I went in Castillo was still shaking hands around. Dickie said, "Mr. Castillo, the crew wages have been stolen from the ship. We believe that the chief mate took them, but we probably won't be able to prove it. Is it true I still have to pay him his wages and his ticket home if I fire him?"

"Yes sir, unfortunately. I am very sorry this has happened. Have you called the police?"

"No. Should I?"

He gave a discreet shrug. "It is up to you. I doubt they will do anything."

I asked, "He doesn't have to be escorted to the airport, does he?"

Castillo shook his head. "No, he can take a taxi." He gave Dickie a careful glance. "But you will have to pay him his wages before I take him to Customs and Immigration."

Dickie said, in a strangled voice, "I'll give it to the captain."

"I'll take him to the airport," I told Castillo, "but don't tell him yet. Bring him back here after you take him to Customs and Immigration."

"He must not come onboard after clearing Customs."

"I know," I said. "Just put him on the dock." I held up a finger. "And watch him closely. He might try to pick up the money after you leave Customs."

He nodded. "I will watch him."

I went down on deck. A few minutes later Castillo and Binh came out. Castillo watched placidly as Binh wrestled his suitcases across the deck and down the gangway, then opened the back of the van for him to put them in. They drove off.

Dickie joined me on deck. I had a sudden, disquieting thought. I turned to him. "Does this ship have a sanitary holding tank?" I asked.

"A what?"

"I gotta check on something," I said, and hurried down to the engine room. Two men were sweating over a Deutz auxiliary engine. A muscular, black-haired man with pale skin and blue eyes was obviously the chief engineer. The second engineer was a big, soft bear of a man with a glossy brown beard. They both gave me curious smiles, but the roar of the other auxiliary suppressed any conversation. I nosed around until I was sure the vessel had no holding tank, then went upstairs.

I found Dickie in the saloon. "I know you've got a lot on your mind," I told him as I went in, "but you've got to do something about the toilet situation."

He was sitting at the table. He looked up. White fingerprints slowly faded on his pink forehead. "What toilet situation?"

"This vessel has no holding tank. If the Coast Guard comes onboard, they'll give you a big fine for discharging sewage directly into the water."

"Oh, great. When are they coming?"

"Nobody knows. Maybe this afternoon, maybe tomorrow, maybe never."

He shook his head stubbornly. "I can't worry about that now. I've got to find some money. Paying that goddamned Binh took every penny I had." He stood up. "I know a guy I can call. I'll be back."

We went on deck together, then he left the ship and drove off. I looked down into the No. 1 hold and saw that the stevedores had reached the floor. There were wet bales at the bottom, but the damage was comparatively minor, and the stevedores had continued discharging without waiting for the cargo surveyor. I went aft and found Yussuf on the fantail. "Bosun," I said, "we can get to work on that hole in No. 1 double-bottom now. The cargo is off the manhole."

He took his empty cup into the galley and came back. "I will get some bags of cement and lower them down to the manhole. How will we seal the hole?"

"With gasket material. I'll get it from the engine room. And get some dunnage. Soon as we get the leak stopped, Allah willing, we'll pour a cement box."

He laughed. "You speak like Moslem, Cap'n." He clapped me on the shoulder. "You help Mr. Dickie, Cap'n, and I will help you."

We started forward. "What's your license?" I asked him.

"AB, sir."

"But you have many years at sea."

"Ten years, Cap'n, but only AB license. I have no time to study for the officer test."

I laughed. "This is a Honduran ship. I can get you a Honduran chief mate's license in 10 minutes."

"Okay, Cap'n," he said. "I'll be your chief mate."

"Not mine. I'm just helping Dickie here in Mobile."

"You come with us, Cap'n. Without you this ship will surely sink."

"That may be true regardless. Do you have four passport photos?"

"Yes, Cap'n, I keep plenty photos for visas."

"Good. Give 'em to Dickie. When he goes back through New Orleans he can get your license and FedEx it to the next port."

As soon as we had gotten the cement lowered into the hold, the old captain and his wife arrived with several sacks of groceries. In the unspoken custom of ships, the whole crew joined in carrying them onboard, making for more stevedores than cargo. Dickie drove up as the last sack went onboard. I was standing by the open passenger door of my truck, checking my pistol. I slid it back into the glove compartment as he walked up.

"I got some money from a friend," he said. "He wired it to the bank while I waited."

"Binh's still gone," I said, "but he should be back soon. I'm taking him to the airport. I'll search him again on the way."

"Thanks," he said. "Look, I gotta be frank. I'm in over my head here. A guy named Helmut Lohren bought this ship for me. He was going to run it. Now his phone is disconnected." He hit the fender of my truck lightly, with his palm. "I think he's hiding from me, the bastard."

I didn't say anything.

"Captain," he said, "how much would you charge me to stay here and get this ship out of port?"

"A thousand a week, plus expenses. What are your plans?"

"What do you mean? I've got to keep her. Who would buy her now? I've got to fix her up."

"Then get the Lloyds man onboard. Call the New Orleans office." I gave him the number.

"Then you'll stay?" he asked.

"Yeah, I'll stay until we get her out of port." Or until you run out of credit, I thought. "I'll need the first week in advance, if that's all right."

He hesitated only a moment. "Sure." He reached into a pocket and brought out a wallet. "Let me pay you here. I don't like doing business in the captain's quarters." He laughed grimly and gave me 10 hundred-dollar bills. I put them in my wallet.

"Okay," I said. "First thing is to get this vessel crewed. Promote Yussuf to chief mate. He's a good man. You can get him a Honduran license in New Orleans. As far as Capt. van der Voort, he's a lush and a thief." I gave Dickie a phone number. "That's Arcadio Munoz in Miami. He's a crewing agent. He'll find you another captain. But be sure to clear the man with me first."

"All right. I'll go out to a phone in a few minutes." He leaned against the fender. "So, Captain, you got a family?"

"Yep. A wife and two kids."

"Oh, yeah? I just had twin girls myself. Or rather, my wife did."

"Congratulations. One of 'em wouldn't be named Erika, would she?"

He smiled. "Sure would. My next ship will be the *Veronika*, after my other little girl."

I gave him a wry smile. "Let's get *Erika* trading first."

The agent's van pulled up. Binh gave us an expressionless stare through the window. "That thieving sonofabitch," Dickie muttered.

"Here we go," I said. "Even smart crooks get stupid sometimes."

Binh got out and hauled his suitcases out of the back of the van. I picked them up and put them in the bed of my pickup. "I'm taking you to the airport," I told him. "I'm going that way anyway."

He frowned. "I want to take taxi."

"Oh, yeah? Well, your bags are coming with me. Do what you want."

Binh turned toward the agent's van, but Castillo was already pulling away. He turned back and shrugged. "Okay," he said, "I come with you."

We got in the truck and I drove off. I headed west on the interstate. Binh sat in comfortable silence. The exit before the airport led north into a rolling pine forest. I took it. He made no comment.

I waited until we were out of sight of the interstate, then pulled off onto a logging road and stopped. I took out my AMT .380 and showed it to him. "Binh, I'm going to search your luggage again. Whether you want me to or not. You understand?"

He looked at the pistol mildly. "Okay, Captain. You can search my bags."

I took the keys out of the ignition. "You wait here. You can watch me through the window, but I don't want you getting out. You understand?"

"I understand."

I got out, put the pistol in my belt, and unzipped the first suitcase. No money and nothing stolen from the ship. I opened the other suitcase. The same. I closed them up and went back around and got behind the wheel. "Binh, put your hands up. I'm going to frisk you."

He spluttered, "But, but I have my wages, Captain. How do you know what money is what?"

"Put your fucking hands up."

He shut up and held his hands in the air. I patted him down thoroughly and counted the money in his wallet. He had $2237. I handed the wallet and money back, put the keys in the ignition, and drove away. Neither of us spoke, but a wide, raw grin kept creeping up his face as we approached the passenger ramp. It got wider and rawer as he got out and pulled his suitcases out of the bed. He gave me a jaunty farewell with a tilt of the jaw and lugged his baggage into the terminal. I drove off.

When I got to the ship Dickie had just finished paying off the crew. He was having a Coke in the galley. Cookie had washed the dishes and laid them out on the drainboard. His cabin was just forward of the galley. Snatches of African music drifted back from the ventilation gap in his door.

I led Dickie forward and gave him the bad news about Binh. He scratched his head. "Maybe he didn't take it," he said. "Or maybe it's still hid somewhere ashore, and he'll come back for it later."

"Maybe. But there's another possibility." I canted my eyes upward.

He nodded. "I thought of that."

"I don't know what to do about it, though. The wife's probably stashed it by now."

"That bastard. He's already drunk, too, staggering around and bragging what a great captain he is."

"Well, I recommend you don't give him any more money for food or supplies." I told him what Yussuf had told me.

He spat into the water. "I forgot about that $700 for paint. So that's why you called him a thief." He looked forward. "House paint, huh? I wonder what he would say if I asked him about it."

"Don't say anything," I advised him. "Pretend everything's okay until you're ready to sign him off. Then give him his money and his ticket and have the agent standing by to take him away."

"All right." He buttoned his leather jacket. "You want to go out for supper? There's a Red Lobster downtown."

I shook my head. "It's better to eat with the crew. They've got some fresh food for the first time in a long time, and you've gotten rid of a troublemaker. You should eat onboard. And buy the crew a beer out of the slop chest."

"Okay," he said. "You take care of it. I gotta call my wife."

I went into the officer's mess and took a seat. Across the hallway I could see Cookie fussing around in the galley. He brought me a heaping plate. I made him take half of it back and told him to bring each crewman a beer, courtesy of Dickie.

The two engineers came in, freshly scrubbed and wearing clean boiler suits. They were talking in Polish as they came down the hall, but when they saw me they became subdued.

I introduced myself. The goateed man bobbed his head and beamed at me. The pale man pointed to his chest. "I am Jacek," he said. "Chief engineer. This is Jerzy, my second. The crew call him Jerry because they cannot say Jerzy. Jerzy cannot speak English."

Yussuf appeared in the door in clean clothes. Jacek frowned at him, but Yussuf took a seat at the table and said, "I am officer now. Chief mate. Binh is already gone."

Jacek said, "Good. Binh was bad man." He translated for Jerzy. They nodded to each other in satisfaction and went back to eating.

Cookie brought cold Portuguese beers for everyone. Jacek took his gratefully and drank half in one long gulp. Dickie came in and sat by me. I looked at the food. It was meat loaf with barbeque sauce, with boiled cabbage on the side. Yussuf and the Polish engineers were digging in like refugees. Dickie picked at his food and pushed it aside. Cookie came out of the galley with two plates covered by napkins and headed toward the captain's accommodations.

After supper I called Honey Buckets, Inc., out of the Yellow Pages. They were still open. The girl promised that a truck would deliver a clean unit shipside by 0800 the next morning.

Yussuf found me in my cabin. I was spreading some threadbare blankets over the frayed and patched sheets on the bunk. "Captain," he said, "I opened the No. 1 manhole. Are you ready to make the cement box?"

I arched my back and stretched out my arms. "I guess so."

We went down into the hold. He had lowered a power cord with an electric saw on the end. Several pieces of dunnage were stacked by the open manhole. We looked down into the open tank. The chief had just finished pumping it out, and water was trickling aft from frame to frame. I climbed into the tank and eased myself through the first lightening hole. The hole in the hull was right under my feet, about the size of a dime, in an area of heavily corroded shell plating.

"It's not too big," I told Yussuf, "but it's going to be hell sealing the leak. The steel is very uneven."

He crouched down behind me and cut a square of gasket material. We fitted it over the hole with a piece of steel plate on top, then cut a board to fit between the lightening holes. With two wooden wedges between the vertical piece and the shoring timber, we started hammering the wedges together to force the gasket material against the pitted surface.

The water slowed to a trickle, but never stopped altogether. We used a second thickness of gasket, then a third, but the water kept seeping in. "I don't know what we're going to do," I finally said. "If we can't stop the leak, we can't put in a cement box. The tiniest leak will cut a channel right through the cement."

There was a shadow above us, blocking the light. We looked up. The old captain stood in the hold, smiling, holding a great slab of bacon in his gnarled hands.

"Use this," he growled. "This is what we used in the old days." He tossed the bacon through the manhole. It landed on the shell plating with a slap. He staggered away. I heard his labored breathing as he hauled himself up the stevedore ladder.

Yussuf and I looked at each other in the flashlight's beam. "Crazy old man," Yussuf said under his breath. "Bacon! Hah!"

I reached through the lightening hole and picked up the slab. "I don't know, Yussuf. It won't matter after it rots away, because the cement will be all around it. And it *is* a lot thicker than the gaskets."

We got the slab of bacon positioned over the leak, skin-side up, and put the steel plate on top of it. We rigged the brace and started hammering on the wedges again. This time when Yussuf shined the flashlight on the plating the leak was stopped.

"I'll be damned," I said. "The old fool knows something after all."

We used boards to make a box around the plate, then mixed up four bags of cement and poured them into it. We left the manhole open and went topside into the cold night air. Jacek was smoking on deck. The cranes on the bulker were still working, turning and dipping, each in its own pool of yellow light, but Jacek was looking the other way, up toward the office buildings beyond the port.

He turned to me suddenly. "Why I cannot go ashore? I am citizen of Poland. Poland is free country now, just like America. Why no go ashore?"

"You're detained onboard?" I said. "That's bullshit. I knew they'd detained the Syrians, but a chief engineer from Poland. . .it's crazy."

"Just to see," he said. "To buy some things. To see America." He put out his cigarette carefully, tucked the butt behind his ear, and went aft.

I went up on the bow and looked back along the length of the ship. I could see the captain and his wife staggering around in the saloon through the lighted portholes. I could see Yussuf unpacking his belongings in the chief mate's cabin on the main deck. I got up and went ashore to call Arcadio Munoz, the crewing agent.

He was in. He always is. He promised to find me two Honduran AB's right away. I told him I would call again in a few minutes.

I called my wife and told her I would be staying at least a week. When I called Arcadio again he said joyously, "Captain, I have two very fine men for you, Manuel Guillen from Cortes and Ricardo Porton from La Ceiba. They are on a Colombian ship in Ft. Lauderdale. The ship is seized, you know, and they must to get off. They have many year on cargo ship, Captain, never fear."

"No, Arcadio," I said, "I do not fear. When can they get here?"

"Tomorrow, Captain, tomorrow."

I found Dickie having a last cup of coffee in the officer's mess. The hard overhead light made his young face haggard. I gave him a slip of paper with the two Hondurans' names. "Send PTA tickets to Miami for these men as soon as possible," I told him. "The agent says they can come tomorrow."

He took the paper and stuffed it in his pocket. "All right. I'll use the phone on the dock." He went out. I poured myself two fingers of coffee and sat at the table, listening to the night sounds of the port. He came back in.

"Here's their flight schedule. They pick up their tickets at the American counter."

I looked at my watch. It was 2200. I went ashore and called Arcadio. Dickie came down to the dock as I was walking back to the ship. We shook hands and he drove off.

I went to my cabin. The floor was hot from the engine room below, but I had left the porthole open, and a cold mist filled the tiny room. I wormed into the damp bedding and fell asleep.

At 0700 the next morning a bright-yellow portable toilet arrived. Yussuf and I used the derrick to lift it onto the starboard deck. Then he got the hooks to open hatchboards. Jerzy came out to help in a pair of shorts and wooden-soled clogs.

I went back to the galley. "Come on, Cookie," I said, "let's help Yussuf and Jerzy with the hatchboards."

He stared at me. "Captain, I am cook. I am not AB."

"Listen, Cookie," I said seriously, "we're short-handed. We need your help for about 30 minutes."

He shook his head and bent over the sink. "I cook, Captain. I don't work them damned hatchboards." He rattled a stack of pans angrily.

"Is that so? Okay, I'll take care of that." I stamped off the ship and called Dickie at the motel. He was still asleep. I said, "That damned Ghanian cook just refused to help Yussuf and me open hatches. You'd better sign him off."

He coughed. I heard the snap of a lighter. "Ah," he said, after a long exhale. "Well, Captain, I haven't got the money to send him home. Can't he stay for a couple of months?"

"You want to run with an extra man in the crew?"

"What do you mean?"

"There's still only three men on deck when the AB's arrive. You can't depend on the second engineer to help. He has enough work in the engine room. The cook's got to help with the hatchboards and during docking. That's the way it is in the Caribbean."

"Okay, Captain," he sighed. "Call your crewing agent and get a cook. I'll be at the ship in an hour."

It was almost 0900 in Miami. Arcadio said he had a Honduran cook with a U.S. visa on stand-by in San Pedro Sula, and could have him flying north that afternoon. His name was Victor Barahona. I called Dickie with the name and he promised to wire a ticket to Honduras.

Yussuf and Jerzy had already gotten the tarps rolled up when I returned. Jerzy went back to the engine room and Yussuf and I worked hatchboards for half-an-hour in a cold wind. Then we went down in the engine room to look for a place to put in a sanitary holding tank.

"No," Yussuf said, after we'd looked around for a while, "I don't think there is anywhere to put a tank."

"You're right," I said. "What the hell we gonna do now? We need to get started on something before the Coast Guard shows up."

He shook his head sadly. "There are so many fish in the sea. . .even in this bay there must be thousands of fish. Do not the fish have to dirty themselves?"

"They do indeed," I said. "They dirty themselves at least as regularly as seamen. But the Coast Guard can't catch them at it."

We went topside and watched the offloading. The stevedores had reached the wet bales at the back of the hold, and were discharging them with nets. The bottoms of the damaged bales had disintegrated into lumps of gluey, rust-colored pulp that splattered over the other cargo, the deck, and the dock. The receiver's surveyor photographed each load as it came out.

Dickie came walking up the dock, picking his way between piles of sodden cellulose. I met him at the head of the gangway. "Captain," he said, "I just borrowed another 50 grand. You think that'll get the ship to Freeport?"

"Maybe, unless something else happens. Like getting a big Coast Guard fine for not having a sanitary system onboard."

"Helmut said that was no big deal," he protested. "He said we could do it later."

I shook my head. "Not in this port. This is the Mobile Coast Guard District. You won't be allowed to leave without a sanitary system."

"All right. How much is it?"

"Well, we have a problem. There's no place in the engine room to put a holding tank, so you'll have to put in an incinerator system. About eight grand, I guess."

"Oh, Jesus," he groaned.

"There's something else we can do on a temporary basis that'll meet the letter of the law. Whether Coast Guard will go along with it is a different matter."

"What's that?"

"You can get a Type III MSD from the local marine store for about $175. It's supposed to be for yachts, but it meets regulations. It's got a little holding tank in the base, like a Porta-Potty, so it would have to be emptied every couple of hours if the crew were actually using it."

"What do you mean? They wouldn't use it?"

"Nah. They keep using the ship's toilets, but, officially, they're using the Type III MSD."

He made a weary gesture. "Just do what you can." He started toward the house. "I put the airline tickets on American Express. That'll buy me some time to pay." He stepped into the hallway. A stiff breeze whistled in from the aft door. I followed him up to the master's saloon.

As soon as we'd shaken hands with the captain, a short gray man came in. He wore a Homburg hat and a blue windbreaker with LR on the left breast. He had a meerschaum pipe clenched in his teeth and a blue flight bag under his arm.

"Good morning, sir," I said. "Lloyds man?"

"That's right." He put the bag down and took the pipe out of his mouth. "Are you the captain?"

I pointed my chin. "There's the captain. I'm a surveyor. This is the owner, Dickie Vance."

They shook hands. "Jupp Arndtsen," the surveyor said. "We spoke on the phone yesterday, didn't we, Mr. Vance?"

"That's right," Dickie said.

Arndtsen said, "What happened to the hull? I understand you have a crack in the shell plating?"

"That's right," I said. "When you're ready, I'll take you down."

"I'm ready now." He unzipped his bag and withdrew a blue boiler suit and a pair of filthy running shoes. I got a flashlight and we went down through the stevedore hatch. Yussuf had opened a rear corner of No. 2 for light, but it was still dark below.

Arndtsen had his own flashlight, one of those $100 titanium jobs. I trailed along as he inspected the rotted shell plating and wasted frames, muttering to himself. When we got back to where we started, he clicked off the light and looked at me in the twilight. "Well, my young friend," he said, "this ship has serious hull problems. When is drydocking scheduled?"

"Um, I don't think Dickie can afford to go into drydock yet. He needs to run her for a few months to raise the money."

"Hmm," he said. He looked around the hold. Maybe the hull looked better from a distance. He said, "I will approve temporary repairs under condition of class. I can make the certificates valid until July."

I nodded. "I'm sure that will be a big help to Dickie."

He took out a piece of chalk in a gold-colored holder, unscrewed the cap, and started forward, marking the areas to be repaired. "You can double between the frames," he said, "from the inside."

"I thought Lloyds didn't permit doubling."

"It will have to come out later, but this way Mr. Vance can sail from Mobile without going into drydock."

I couldn't argue with that. When we came out of the hold, I promised to call him in New Orleans as soon as I'd done the work. He went down to the dock and got in a black Mercedes. A few minutes later, Yussuf was chocking down the tarpaulin and I was stretching my back and looking idly toward the north warehouse when a white van with the U.S. Coast Guard seal came nosing around the corner.

"Oh, my God," I whispered. I spun around. "Yussuf! Belay that! Get something to cover the crack in the deck." He dropped the hammer he was holding. I jerked my chin toward my shoulder as I walked toward him. "Coast Guard! Get that dunnage over there and put it on top of the crack. Hurry, for Christ's sake!"

He walked briskly over to a pile of broken boards in front of the house. He picked up a few of the widest ones and brought them to where I was standing. Four uniformed men got out of the van. He placed the boards over the crack.

I struck a casual pose and said out of the side of my mouth, "Get down in the hold while I delay them in the saloon. Hide the crack in the side with something."

The lead man was coming up the gangway with a black briefcase, a pink young petty officer in Corfam shoes. I walked across and jumped to the deck. He came down the steps and shook my hand. The others, two teenagers and a big man in his mid-30's, crowded onto the deck behind him.

"Lieutenant Randy Sayles, U.S. Coast Guard," the man said. "We're going to make a Port State Control inspection of this vessel. Are you the captain?"

"No sir, he's upstairs in his quarters. I'll show you up."

I led the way up the companionway and into the captain's saloon. He was upright and reading a newspaper. He put it down and greeted the Guardsmen cordially. They ranged themselves on the other side of the table and put their notebooks on it.

"Captain," Sayles said, "we'd like to take a look at your documents."

"Could I get you gentlemen something to drink?" I said. "Coke? Coffee? Tea?"

They all wanted Cokes. I ignored the captain's small refrigerator and went downstairs. The crack in the deck was covered with a loose pile of boards and some scraps of tarpaulin. I went into the hold. Yussuf had just finished covering the crack in the hull with dunnage. He followed me out of the hatch. I bent close to his ear. "Lock up this hatch," I told him, "and make yourself scarce for a while."

He nodded. I went down in the engine room and had the chief close and lock the toilets' overboard discharge valve. Then I had him make a quick entry in the Oil Record Book showing a sludge-tank pump-out in Lisbon. I finally got back to the saloon with four Cokes and glasses of ice.

Sayles was writing furiously on a detention form. One of the teenagers was studying a book of CFR's and the other was poring over the ship's documents like they meant something to him. The middle-aged man had his arms spread out on the seat-back and his legs stretched out under the table. He was looking at the ceiling.

Sayles glanced up. "Are you a crewman onboard, sir?"

I shook my head. "Port captain for the owner."

He turned to van der Voort. "Captain, you will not be able to depart this port until you have current certificates onboard. Do you understand?"

"Yes, sir," the captain said. "The owner has already spoken to the class surveyor."

"Now we'd like to go over the rest of the ship. Can you call the chief mate?"

Van der Voort opened his mouth, but I said, "The crew's off-duty now. I can show you around."

Sayles looked at the captain. "We'd like to have one of the crew with us, Captain. Maybe you can come."

Old van der Voort struggled to get out of his chair, then looked up redfaced. "My legs aren't so good any more, I'm afraid."

Sayles said, "That's okay, Captain. Mr. . .ah. . ."

"Hardberger," I said.

"Mr. Hardberger can take us around." The Guardsmen slid out from behind the table. I led them down the companionway and into the hall. "Engine room first," Sayles ordered.

The ship was on the harbor generator, and the engine room was cool and quiet. Jacek kept it clean, and they didn't find any problems until we got to the oily-water separator, an old Smeralda unit with more pipes and valves than a steam locomotive. Jacek was following us around in his bikini underwear. Sayles pointed to the separator. Jacek said, "Separator no work now. Only small problem. . .electric problem. Motor no start."

Sayles nodded and made a note. The others stared at the thing dumbly. Sayles looked around and said, "Where's the sanitary holding tank?"

"The ship doesn't have one," I said reluctantly. "That's one of the things I have to deal with for the owner."

"No holding tank? This vessel may be in for a big fine, Mr. Harberg."

"Hardberger. Well, sir, there's a portable toilet on deck, and the overboard discharge has been locked since the vessel left international waters. There's really no basis for a fine."

He gave me a sour look and didn't answer. We walked around the engine room some more, but he issued no more detentions. Back on deck, the Guardsmen dutifully climbed over the boards Yussuf had laid on the crack as they made their way forward to the forecastle. None of them even glanced at the stevedore hatch.

Sayles didn't find anything wrong with the deck plating as we walked forward, but when we got into the forecastle he led the trainees on a teaching tour that showed them overhead lights without their glass covers and the harbor generator without a belt-guard. He showed them how to write up deficiencies. He was very thorough about it.

He wasn't interested in the hold. He led the party aft along the starboard deck and up to the master's saloon. The captain straightened up as we came in, rubbing his eyes. The Guardsmen took their places behind the table as before, and Sayles finished the detention form. By writing large and listing many small items separately, he managed to fill two pages. He handed them to the captain.

"Captain, I am required to advise you that this vessel cannot move from this dock until the detention has been removed. The vessel may not take on or transfer bunkers. This order is issued under the US Coast Guard's Port State Control authority as granted by the IMO."

He paused. The captain and I were suitably impressed.

"When these deficiencies have been corrected, please give the Captain of the Port a call. The number's on the front of the page. We'll come back for a reinspection." He nodded his head at us and went out, followed by his ducklings.

When Dickie got back I told him his vessel had been detained by the Coast Guard. I read the items off the list and explained what it was going to take to clear each one. "Except for the sanitary system," I concluded, "we got off easy. It's the welding for Lloyds that's going to hurt us. We need to find a welder locally who can supply the men and machines."

"How do we find a local welder?"

"Yellow Pages. I'll be right back." I went down to the pay phone and thumbed through the crumbling, swollen directory. For no good reason I chose Tiny's Welding Shop, Specialists in Marine Fabrication. A man with a deep voice answered the phone. "Hell," he broke in, when I started telling him what we needed, "y'all just come on out and see me. I ain't hard to find."

He gave me directions. I went back and got Dickie. We drove to Tiny's Welding Shop on the west side of town. Tiny was a big, black-bearded man with a glossy ponytail that hung down to his waist. He wore a bright-colored cap spotted with burns. "Just tell me how many men I need," he roared, "and I'll be there. I got four machines of my own, and I can rent as many more as I need."

Dickie looked at me. I said, "We need about eight to 10 welders. We'll provide the helpers. There's one welding machine on the ship, and we've got a crewman who can weld, so you should provide eight or nine men and machines."

"Okay, far out. Who buys the rods?"

"You buy 'em. You can get the best price. We'll supply the steel."

"Right on. When we start?"

"Tomorrow morning," I said. "I'll get the steel delivered today."

That afternoon I went to a Rent-All place on the west edge of town, a vast enterprise catering to the construction trades, and rented six sets of three-level scaffolding. Their truck was out, but they promised to have the scaffolding shipside by nightfall. Then I went to Weston Steel, a big, dusty facility north of the interstate. The salesmen sat in tiny cubicles wired to their phones. The receptionist didn't know what to do with a walk-in customer, but she finally led me to a pleasant young man with sweaty palms. He let me into his stall reluctantly. We sat with our knees almost touching.

The steel order was complicated by the fact that the ship's Frisian builders had not tried to put the frames on a regular spacing. There was a range of about 10 centimeters among them. To have each piece custom-cut would have cost a fortune, so I divided the differences into three sizes and ordered the appropriate number of each.

When I left the steel yard a cold northeast wind was racing across the coastal marshes. It smelled of rain. I called the sheriff's office from a pay phone and asked if they had a prisoner work program. They did indeed. I was directed to the county detention facility, a haphazard collection of WW II-era barracks on an old airbase west of town. Concertina wire had been stretched between tall steel poles around the buildings, giving the place a sense of wartime urgency.

A stocky woman in a portable office building outside the wire had me fill out a form. I ordered 10 men for 0800 hours in the morning. She said a sheriff's van would deliver them. The price was $3.45 per hour, per man.

Mid-South Marine was a huge, low building on the tracks south of town. It was the only place in town with a Type III MSD in stock. I paid $197.80 and carried it out to the car.

On the way back to the ship, I almost passed up a small auto junkyard. I skidded in and bought four auto jacks for $3.00 each.

By the time I got back to the ship, the sun had fallen below the lumpy, wet clouds. The rental company truck was backed up to the edge of the dock. Yussuf was working the levers on the derrick. The vessel had a slight port list, away from the dock, and he was having a tough time of it by himself. I parked ahead of the bow and walked to the gangway. The truck driver was standing on the bed clapping his gloves together, waiting for the hook.

Yussuf and I lowered the scaffolding into the hold, then I got the MSD from the truck and put it in the port-side oilskin locker, a small closet just inside the door. The agent arrived and took away the Ghanian cook. I sat on the starboard gunwale and watched as they drove off. A few minutes later a taxi pulled up and three Hispanic men got out. They came up the gangway with an experienced roll in their gaits.

"*Buenas tardes*," I greeted them. "Good to have you onboard. I'm the port captain. Put your bags in the crew's mess and report to the captain upstairs."

They bowed and shouldered their duffle bags. One of the AB's, Manuel, was a short, chubby man with a round clown's face. The other, Ricardo, was a tall young man with very dark skin and a solemn manner. Victor, the replacement cook, was a soft-looking middle-aged man with a full head of glossy black hair. They filed into the accommodations.

I went looking for Jacek and found him drinking a cup of coffee in the officer's mess. He was covered in grease and had put a rag on the seat before sitting down. I slid onto the bench across from him.

"You look tired, Chief," I said.

He nodded. "Twenty-six days, no fix nothing. Only run, run, run. Now in port, we fix everything."

"How about the separator? Have you looked at it?"

He winced. "Separator big problem."

"How so?"

"Separator never work since I join ship one year." He shook his head. "Never use separator. I tell Coast Guard one small lie."

"What's the problem with it?"

He lit a cigarette. "Problem in control box. Lights come on, but no clean water. Oil-water go overboard."

"Well, it's got to be fixed or replaced. The Coast Guard's issued a detention for it."

There were heavy footsteps in the hallway. Dickie stuck his head in the door. "What's the problem now?" he asked.

I told him.

"What does that mean? Small problem, big problem?"

"Ten-thousand-dollar problem. That's what it'll cost to replace the separator. The company that made that unit has been out of business for 10 years."

He sat down heavily. He had just gotten a haircut, a trendy bowl cut with white sidewalls that made him look like a dissipated Capuchin monk. "Fuck," he said. "I can't borrow any more money, I just can't. The money for the what-you-call-it is just going to have to come out of what I've got."

"I'll take a look at it," I said. "Maybe we can do something."

Yussuf came in and poured a cup of coffee, raindrops glistening in his wiry hair. His thin face was lined with fatigue. "Want me to start setting up the scaffolding, Captain?"

I shook my head. "You've done enough for today, First. Close up the hatch and knock off the crew. I'll get the prisoners to set up the scaffolding. But don't secure the derrick. We're going to need it when the steel gets here in the morning."

He nodded, wiped his face, and went out. Jacek turned to Dickie. "Mr. Dickie," he began, "you know, my wife never leave Poland before. Thirty winters in Poland. . .she ask if she can come on ship for one or two voyage. Now government change, okay to leave. You let her come on ship?"

Dickie looked at me. I nodded.

"Sure, Jay-Sek," he said, pronouncing the chief's name phonetically. "It's okay."

"*Yacht*-sek," I corrected him. "The usual rate is six dollars a day for meals when an officer brings his wife onboard."

Jacek nodded energetically. "No problem, Captain, no problem. She come soon. What port we go now?"

Dickie said, "I think I have a cargo from Freeport, Texas, to Miragoane, Haiti. I'm supposed to find out tomorrow."

"Haiti, huh?" I said. "Hope you're getting a good rate." I turned back to Jacek. "I'll let you know tomorrow. You can call your wife on the agent's phone the next time he comes."

"Okay. When agent come I call her. Pay from salary end of month, okay?" He got up abruptly, stubbed out his cigarette, tucked the butt behind his ear, and slid out from behind the table. He jammed his feet into his clogs and clomped off to his room.

Dickie looked at me. "Is he drunk again? Helmut said he's a drinker."

I shook my head. "I think he's pissed off about being detained onboard. I don't blame him. Stupid INS policy." I went to the urn and poured a cup of coffee.

"That's too bad," he said absently. He got up and poured himself a cup. "Where's the captain? I knocked on his door, but he didn't answer."

"Probably drunk. I haven't seen him since the Coast Guard was onboard."

He'd overfilled his cup. Boiling coffee slopped on his wrist when he started to sit down. He yelped and dropped the cup, sending steaming rivulets across the scarred table. I pulled a handful of napkins from the dispenser and dammed the flow.

"Put some ice on it," I suggested, but he merely stood and cursed and waved his hand in the air.

Finally he refilled his cup and sat down. "Will the welding be finished in time to reach Freeport by the 15th?"

I thought. "More like the 16th. I think we can finish by Friday. The ship can sail on Saturday if Arndtsen issues the certs."

He shook his head doggedly. "The ship has to finish by Thursday. It has to be in Freeport on Saturday or we miss the lay/can."

"Push it back. Better now than later."

He got up. "Well, let's see how it goes tomorrow." He went out.

I sat by myself in the darkening mess, watching the lights on the eaves of the warehouse come on one-by-one. A ship somewhere in the port sounded five blasts. There was a low rumble as it started its engine in reverse.

I walked aft to the fantail. It was the bulker, sailing out. I watched its super-structure slide along behind the roof of a warehouse to the east, its aftermast glittering with lights. Above it a waning autumn moon slowly mounted a bank of cloud. A hard wind was blowing from the north. The ship's lights sank out of sight. Its engine throbbed up slowly. I went to my cabin.

The room was cold and dark. I undressed without turning on the light and climbed up in the bunk. A conveyor belt rattled steadily in the distance. I felt my breathing lengthen, and finally, like a mountaineer losing his grasp, I fell into sleep.

The rumble of trucks woke me at dawn. I dressed in the chilly half-light. Tiny the welder was standing on the dock in an orange boiler suit, looking like a bearded pumpkin. Lined up behind him were half-a-dozen trucks, some with welding rigs on the beds and some pulling trailer units. Men in peaked hats were yelling at each other and pouring coffee from battered Thermos bottles.

Tiny saw me on deck and came up with a steaming mug. "Morning, Captain. You ready for us to get hooked up?"

"Ready. We'll pop open some hatchboards now to get your gear in. The steel is coming any minute. It's already cut, so all we got to do is weld it in."

He came up the gangway awkwardly and stepped down to the deck. "You say this old ship came across the Atlantic?"

"Yep."

"You guys got balls,"

"Well, I didn't come with the ship. The owner just hired me to ramrod the repairs." I jumped up on the hatchcover. "Look, my crew were too tired last night to set up the scaffolding, but I got six prisoners coming. I'll get them started. . ."

"Prisoners? Is that what you said?"

"Yeah. I got 'em from the jail at the old airbase."

"Holy shit. Fucking jailbirds." He put down his mug and climbed up onto the hatchcover beside me. We looked down through the opening. Yussuf and Manuel were pulling scaffolding sections into place on the floor. The welding engines on the dock started up one-by-one, rumbling and shaking and sending puffs of blue smoke across the empty slip. The welders came up the gangway with their lunchboxes and helmets.

Jerzy came lumbering out of the accommodations uncoiling welding leads, grinning madly. He threaded the leads along the deck and lowered them into the hold. "I work too, okay?" he said, pointing down.

"Okay," I said. I pointed to my eye, then all around in the hold. "You keep eye on work, okay?"

He chuckled fiercely and disappeared down the stevedore hatch. A Weston Steel Company truck arrived and Yussuf worked the derrick to lower the plates into the hold. After a few minutes the welding-machine engines went to work, bogging down and revving up as the welders started burning rods. A white van full of men appeared. It had "Mobile County Detention Facility No. 2" stenciled on the side.

"Well, Yussuf," I called out, "here come our prisoners."

The van stopped and the men piled out with paper lunch bags. They were an ordinary bunch of young men, white and black, dressed in khaki shirts and blue jeans. They came on deck single-file and stood waiting for orders. I handed them over to Yussuf and he took them down into the hold. The driver of the van, a brusque young deputy with a blond mustache, explained that I was to fill out a form for each man at the end of the day and to pay in cash on the spot. He made me sign a form and left.

Tiny heaved himself out of the stevedore hatch like a cork out of a bottle. "We got a problem, Cap."

"Yeah?"

"That steel on the sides ain't thick enough to weld to. We're burning through to the outside."

I nodded. "I figured that was going to happen here and there. Is it all bad?"

He shrugged. "We're just getting started. I got a couple of places where we done burnt through already."

"We'll just have to weld the plates directly to the frames."

He laughed shortly. "Them frames ain't too good neither. I guess you seen that. Plus them plates don't fit exact between the frames. We might have to put in some strips to bridge the gaps."

I shook my head sadly. "Then I guess you'll have to select through the plates for the ones that fit the closest. It ain't gonna be pretty, but what can we do?"

He patted me on the shoulder. "Don't worry, Cap," he said. "We'll get it done." He maneuvered his belly through the stevedore hatch and sank out of sight. I went down to the dock and walked along the quay to the bow, inspecting the shell plating. The gray paint job, only a month old and already peeling, helped hide the wastage, but the crimping of the plating around the frames was a dead giveaway. The only good metal on the shell was the center section, added when the vessel was lengthened, and even that was starting to blister.

I could follow the progress of the welders inside the ship by looking at the lines of scorched paint on the outside. A ragged, dime-sized hole in the plating, filled with flickering light, showed where a welder had burned through. I stepped up on the breastlog and leaned over far enough to put my little finger through the hole. The steel was as thin as tin foil.

I was half-way up the gangway when Dickie's rented Ford came nosing along the dock and pulled up at the foot of the gangway. He was wearing a nylon windbreaker with crossed golf clubs and a pair of double-pleated khaki slacks. There was a spring in his step.

"Good morning, Captain," he said. "How's the work going?"

I pointed my chin at the machines roaring and backfiring on the dock. "We've got eight shore machines, the ship's welding machine, and a tenth machine running off service power. As you can hear, they're hard at work."

"Excellent. Can you finish by day after tomorrow?"

I shrugged. "Without problems, maybe."

He peered at me anxiously. "We got to do it. The broker says they can't extend the lay/can past the 15th."

"What's today? The 11th? No way. It's a day and a half steaming, you know."

He hit his forehead with his palm. "I gotta get that money. The ship has to be there by midnight on the 15th."

"The charterer is a Haitian," I said. "Don't worry about being a day or two late." I saw Jacek coming on deck with a hand-pump. I went over to him. "Jacek, when you call your wife, tell her to plan to arrive in Houston on the 16th. The agent will pick her up at the airport."

"Thank you, Capt. Max." He started pumping lube oil from a drum lashed on deck. I went down in the hold with Dickie right above me. The two welders who had been working forward were standing around smoking cigarettes while Yussuf, Manuel, and some of the prisoners moved their scaffolding to the next frames aft. Dickie and I walked up the slight incline of the hold, picking our way over tangles of wires and welding leads.

Tiny came aft to meet us. "This ship really going to all them islands in the Caribbean?" he demanded.

"That's right," I said.

"Dang! They got any pretty women on them islands?"

"They're all beautiful "

Huh." He looked off into the distance. "Always wondered what it would be like working on a ship."

"Why don't you come along? We're going to need some welding."

He canted his head. "How much a welder make on this ship?"

"I can pay you. . ."—I gave him a sly grin—". .oh, hell, you're a good welder. I can pay you $800 a month."

"What? Are you shittin' me? That's what the crew works for on this ship?"

"That's the going wage for a welder."

"Hell," he said, "I couldn't pay child support to a single one of my ex-old ladies on that." He snorted and spat on the floor and went aft to yell at one of the welders.

I said to Dickie, "The real bitch is that all this work is going to be wasted. I can promise you that the next Lloyds man who comes onboard is going to take one look at this mess and tell you to crop it all out."

"There's no time for anything else," he said. "I've got to get this charter or I'm sunk."

"Hey, I'm just the port captain. Speaking of which, here's the accounts for the money I got on Tuesday. I've got $320 left." I handed him two handwritten sheets. "And here's a list of what we're going to need before we leave."

He studied the list carefully, his manicured fingers brushing the nape of his neck. "This is what owning a ship is all about," he grumbled. "I'm just figuring it out. It's about paying bills. One goddamn bill after another."

We welded for three days. A couple of welders went home at noon on the first day because Tiny didn't like something they'd done or didn't do. Two more came on after lunch. A couple of prisoners didn't come back the second day, but fresh ones took their places.

The weather deteriorated throughout the second day. In the late afternoon, with staging over the port side to crop-and-replace some paper-thin shell plating, a freezing rain began that soaked us to the skin. We worked on under a hastily rigged tarpaulin. Two more welders walked off the job.

When we quit for the day at 2100 hours, I took a hot shower and went down to the galley. Victor was sitting on a bucket shelling peas, but he insisted that I take a seat in the officer's mess, and served me supper. I had just started to eat when I heard strange footsteps in the hallway and looked up to see two of the prisoners come in, a pink-haired boy named Red and a goateed black man. "Hey," I said, "what's up, guys?"

"We got a problem, Captain," Red said somberly. "The WRA says we gotta get paid for the overtime we done." He sat down across from me. Goatee remained standing.

I rubbed my eyes. "The who?"

"The WRA. The Work Release Administrator."

"I didn't agree to overtime."

"Yessir," Red said, "but, you see, that was a mistake. Gary—the guy who drives the van in the mornings—he didn't know we was going to work overtime. When we told him today how many hours we worked, he said, well, we gotta get paid overtime."

I shook my head. "I already paid what I agreed to pay."

Red scowled. "Man, you want us to go back to the state farm? Cause that's what's gonna happen if we don't get that overtime."

I stood up. "If there is any problem with the payment for your work, I'll call the WPA—the WRA, I mean—in the morning. I'm not going to pay you guys money just on your say-so."

Goatee squared off in front of me, a head taller. "You gotta pay us now," he growled. "We gotta take that overtime back with us."

"Oh, yeah?" I said. "Or what?"

He didn't answer. Red said, "We didn't want to have to do this, man, but there a deputy out in the van. You want to, we'll get him to come in and settle it."

I jumped back. "You will, will you? What's he's gonna do, collect overtime at gunpoint? Then get his ass in here."

They went out. A few seconds later Red came back with a short, swarthy deputy in a cowboy hat and starched uniform, his gunbelt full of accessories. The deputy stopped in front of me in the hall and spread his legs. "You the captain of this boat?"

"I'm the port captain," I said.

"You hired these men?"

"I did."

He nodded like he had scored a point. "Did these men work more than eight hours per day?"

"They did."

He nodded again. "Then you gotta pay them overtime. That's the law."

"Is that so? Well, I'll get it all cleared up in the morning when I call the WRA."
He shook his head. "Prisoners get paid daily." He spoke over his shoulder.
"How much overtime all together?"

"A hundred and twenty-eight dollars," Red said.

I turned to go back to the mess. "Give the bill to the WRA and I'll discuss it
with him tomorrow."

"Hold it!" the deputy barked. "I can take you in right now if you wanna get
smart, mister."

I turned around. "Listen," I said carefully, "I don't want anybody to lose his
job behind this bullshit. You're on a Honduran freighter, deputy. You're not even
supposed to be here. You arrest me tonight and tomorrow morning the State De-
partment will be calling your sheriff. Tomorrow afternoon you'll be standing in
line at Wackenhut."

He didn't like the part about Wackenhut. He turned on Red. "Why didn't you
tell me that? Hell, you know I ain't got no authority on no Honduranian boat.
Come on, jailbird, let's go." He brushed past Red and went outside. Red shot me
a bitter look, worked his mouth a couple of times, and followed the deputy out.
The van cranked up and pulled away. I called the detention facility and left a
message on the answering machine to cancel all prisoner labor on the *Erika* until
further notice.

After breakfast the next morning I took my coffee down to the engine room. It
was cold and quiet. Jacek was lying on his stomach on the floor plates forward of
the main engine, working on something in the bilges.

"Jacek," I said, "we've got to do something about the oily-water separator.
The Coast Guard won't let us leave until it's fixed, and a new one costs 10 grand.
Dickie hasn't got 10 grand."

He sat up, a cross-hatch of black grease on his bare chest. "I think no fix old
separator, Captain."

"Yeah, you're probably right. No way to get parts. But I got an idea. Come
over here."

He wiped his hands and listened as I explained. Finally a crafty grin spread
across his sooty face. "You think they no catch us, Captain?"

"I hope not."

"Okay, I fix for you. Come back two hours."

When I went back down, he had a clear plastic tube running up the inside of
the separator's angle-iron support. He had drilled a hole right through the hous-
ing of the separator, and had run the tube up to the discharge sampling line. It was
hooked into the ship's fresh-water supply below the workbench. He had installed
a brass valve on the tube at the other side of the washbasin, hidden by the towel
rack.

"What's this for?" I asked.

"You watch, Captain," He pulled down some wires from the back of the separator's control panel. "Okay, I stand here. Jerzy stand there at washbasin. Nobody see me touch wires from control panel, okay?" Jerzy took his position by the wash basin. Jacek pushed the start button on the panel, and the pump motor started. I could hear water splashing overboard.

"See water sample?" Jacek said. He turned the valve on the sample discharge line. Jerzy turned the concealed valve and clean water poured into a clear plastic cup.

"Clean water, Captain," he said proudly. "Now come dirty water."

He touched two wires together behind the panel and the red light came on. Jerzy closed the sample valve.

"Not bad," I said, "unless they see you touching those wires together."

"No worry, Captain. I fix switch on floor. I push switch with foot. Coast Guard man see nothing."

"Okay, Chief. I'll tell 'em to come this afternoon."

I went topside and watched as the welders arrived for the last day. We had a harder time of it without the prisoners, but Yussuf and I pitched in as welders' helpers, and by 1100 hours the job was finished.

I made a quick trip to a ship chandler south of the port and found glass covers to fit the lights in the forecastle. With these installed, and the other petty detention items already taken care of, we were ready for reinspection. I called the office of the Captain of the Port and scheduled it for 1400 hours.

After the shore welders had rolled up their hoses and leads, and hooked the machines to their trailer hitches, Tiny came aft to stand in front of me. We'd already calculated accounts, so I had the payment ready in cash. I handed the envelope to him. He rifled through the hundreds, put the envelope away, and stuck out his hand.

"Captain, it's been a real pleasure."

"Likewise, Tiny. You did a hell of a job. Sure you don't want to sail with us?"

He smiled. "You guys gonna miss winter altogether, ain't ya?"

"That's right. Nothing but palm trees and coconuts for the *Erika*. And naked island girls, of course."

His eyes floated down to mine. "Right. And bustin' ass welding on this old bitch for $800 a month." He laughed. "I was thinkin' about it las' night, I sure was. But I done got so many people dependin' on me, what with two ex-wives and all them kids, not to mention my welders, I just cain't do it." He leaned closer. "Are you taking the ship over? You ain't lettin' that drunk-up old captain have this ship after all the work we done put into it?"

"No, Tiny," I said, "I've got a business to run, such as it is. It's up to the owner to find another captain."

He gave me a two-handed shake. "Well, you come see me when you get this way, Captain."

"Will do."

He bustled down the gangway, the chrome chain on his wallet flashing and jingling, and got in his pickup truck. When he left the dock was empty. Scraps of cellulose spun and tumbled across the concrete and fluttered into the water.

I went in to lunch. The chief had just finished eating. I told him, "The Coast Guard's coming this afternoon to reinspect the oily-water separator. Is it all ready?"

"Yessir," he said. "I have the switch for the controls on the floor. Jerzy and I will be ready for them."

"Good. Leave ship's service power on one of the main generators. I want the engine room hot and noisy while they're down there."

He grinned. "Yessir. I can promise that."

The Guardsmen came at 1400 hours, three men in a small white car without markings. They marched up the gangway at exact spacing and ranged themselves on deck. None of them had been onboard for the first inspection. I had bought some sheets of 3/8" steel for ongoing plate replacement, and Jerzy had just finished cutting them to store on the port deck amidships. They also happened to conceal the welded repair. I came across the hatchcover and took off my gloves. The Coasties shook my hand with military precision and followed me downstairs, their service brogans clomping on the metal rungs.

The chief was sharpening a chisel at the grinding wheel. He nodded when I bent close and made a show of telling him to start up the oily-water separator. Jerzy came over, ostensibly to watch the action. He washed his hands at the basin and stood by it as Jacek pushed the power button on the control panel. The red light flickered a couple of times and went out. The machine's discharge pump started with a click and a whine.

"Water clean," the chief yelled at the Guardsmen. Jerzy opened the hidden valve. The ship's drinking water flowed into the sample cup. The chief pointed to it proudly.

One of the Guardsmen bent to my ear and said, "Now show us that the bypass switch works."

"Okay." I repeated the order to the chief. He nodded and went to the piping manifold. He pointed to a brass plate on the forward bulkhead that said, "Sludge tank #2," opened the valve, and came back to watch the control panel. His foot crept toward the switch, out of sight under the corner of the workbench. A second later the red light came on and solenoids clicked on top of the machine. We could hear splashing in the bilges below. The Coasties looked at each other and nodded.

After that, they inspected the portable toilet, the lights in the forecastle, and the other detention items, wrote out a new Report of Inspection with the detentions cleared, and left the ship. I took three beers down to the engine room, where the engineers and I drank a toast to the Defenders of America's Coasts.

Arndtsen came onboard the next morning. The crew were at breakfast. He and I went down into the hold, he approved the repairs, and we went aft to the officer's mess. He stamped the certificates and slid them across the table. "She's due for drydock in July," he said. "I have extended her class until then."

"Very well," I said.

We stood up and shook hands. "Make sure she gets plenty of work before July, Captain," he warned me. "There are many class items coming due, and there will be no more drydocking extensions."

He went down to his Mercedes and drove off. I went up to the master's saloon. The captain was lying on the floor under the table, his head thrown back, his mouth wide open. An empty Scotch bottle stood sentinel over him. Dickie appeared at the foot of the companionway as I was going down.

"Captain is blind drunk," I said.

"Oh, shit. I just came from the agent's office. The pilot'll be here in an hour."

"It'll take that long to wake him up."

He gave an angry shake of the head. "I wish I had signed off that old lush when the ship first got here. Now I don't have time to find another captain."

We went into the saloon. Dickie took a bottle of ice water from the refrigerator and splashed it in the captain's face. The old man shook it off, turned on his side, and started snoring.

After a few more tries, we went downstairs. "I don't know what to do now," Dickie said. "Can Yussuf take the ship to Freeport?"

"No," I said. "He's not even an officer." I regarded him somberly. "Listen, Dickie, I'll take the ship to Freeport. I'll tell the pilot I'm the captain. He won't know any better and he won't care. We're sailing coastwise, so I don't need to sign on the articles. I gave you the phone number of that crewing agent in Miami, Arcadio Munoz. You've got three days to find another captain."

He brightened. "Damn, Captain, you did what you promised in getting the ship out of Mobile, and now you're going to get it to Freeport." He grabbed my hand and pumped it. "I sure do appreciate it."

I nodded. "I'll need to get paid for another week," I said. "That's another $1000."

He sobered. "I don't have that much left, I really don't. You can see how close it's gotten. Wait a sec, though. . .I think I can get some more money on my American Express card. Maybe I can get that much. I'll be right back."

He hurried to his car. Yussuf was on the dock, piling up the last of the scaffolding. "First," I said, "looks like I'm going to have to take the ship to Freeport. The captain is passed out drunk and we can't wake him."

He nodded. "He was up at 0400 this morning. I went in the galley to get a drink of water. He was making himself a plate of eggs. He was so drunk he dropped an egg on his foot and didn't even notice."

"What a shithead," I said, and went up to the wheelhouse. I was checking the compass and radar when Dickie drove up. He came in and gave me 10 hundred-dollar bills.

"I had an idea while you were gone," I told him. "You've got to go back to New Orleans anyway. Why don't you turn in your car here, drop my truck off at my house, and take a cab to the airport?"

"That's a good idea," he said. "I'd forgotten about your truck."

"And while you're in New Orleans you can go by the Honduran consulate and pick up a chief mate's license for Yussuf."

"All right. I can do that." He went to the phone and called the car rental company. They had an office in Mobile, and for $50 extra he could drop the car off. I followed him to the office in my truck and took him back to the ship. The pilot drove in the front gate ahead of us. I followed him to the ship and parked. The crew had taken up the gangway and lowered the pilot ladder.

I opened the glove compartment and took out my AMT. Dickie looked at it. "Doesn't the ship have a pistol?" he said. "I saw it in the safe."

"That's the ship's pistol. This is mine." I gave him a thin smile. "An important distinction to a Southern boy."

"Yeah? Anyway, I'll have another captain waiting for you when you get to Freeport. I guess ol' van der Voort already gave the money he stole to his wife, so it wouldn't do any good to search him."

"Maybe," I said, "but I still think Binh did it."

The pilot was already in the wheelhouse. Yussuf came on deck to toss down an envelope for Dickie. It held his passport photos. Dickie and I shook hands. I climbed up the pilot ladder.

The pilot was talking on his walkie-talkie when I arrived on the bridge. He was a genial, middle-aged man with a shock of prematurely white hair. "Are you the master?" he asked.

"Yes, I am."

Yussuf was busy testing the steering. He didn't look up.

"Very good," the pilot said. He took out a handheld VHF. "Single up."

Yussuf made a signal to the forecastle. The linesman on the dock lifted the heavy eye off the bollard and the windlass on the bow ground to life, piling the hawser on deck. I could hear the capstan on the afterdeck turning as well.

The pilot looked aft, gauging the distance to the turn of the quay. "Hard-a-Starboard," he ordered, "and Dead Slow Ahead."

"Hard a-starboard and Dead Slow Ahead," Yussuf repeated, working the engine-room telegraph and spinning the wheel at the same time.

The telegraph rang as the engine room answered the order. The main engine coughed to life. I watched the rpm's stabilize at 100. "Stop Engine," the pilot ordered.

Yussuf signaled "Stop Engine," and the popping died. The stern of the ship swung slowly out into the slip as the spring line pinned the bow to the quay.

"Cast off all lines," the pilot ordered. I leaned out the wheelhouse window and whistled to Manuel on the foredeck. The linesman cast off the spring line and started walking toward his golf cart.

"Midships," the pilot said. "Dead Slow Astern."

The ship drifted sideways. The engine rolled over a couple of time and started in reverse. The ship backed across the slip like a Cadillac.

"Stop Engine," the pilot said. "Port 10. Dead Slow Ahead." The engine stopped and started in forward. Boiling brown water checked the sternway, and slowly the bow came to port.

A pickup truck came barreling around the corner of the warehouse just as we were turning into the channel. It was Tiny. He stopped at the end of the quay, flashing his lights and blowing his horn, until the ship passed him and turned south toward Mobile Bay. I could still see his headlights flashing as we passed out of sight.

There was a short chop in the bay that bumped against the port side of the hull. The pilot gave Yussuf a point to steer for and went to sit on the stool on the starboard side. He shook out a cigarette, held out the pack to Yussuf, and lit up.

As we gained some distance from the low, marshy shore, the pilot called for Full Speed Ahead. The old ship trembled as the engine slowly revved up. The wind was behind us now, blowing in cold and raw. The pilot got up and closed the starboard door.

We slid out between an old Spanish fort on the left and the tip of Dauphin Island on the right, out into the blue Gulf, a steady wind blowing from dead astern. The air was so clear I could see whitecaps on the horizon. They gave it a jagged edge, like torn paper.

The pilot boat came roaring up behind us so suddenly it scared me off my stool. It churned up on the port side and circled in front of the ship. The pilot gave me a chit to sign and went out. With his bag swung around to his back, he climbed over the bulwark and down the pilot ladder. The seas coming off the beach were short and confused, and he had to wait almost a minute until the boat took a good roll and put the catwalk under his feet. He stepped across, the boat sheered away, and the growl of its engine died as it turned toward land.

I looked at Yussuf. "Well, that's that, First."

"Yessir. Mobile finish now."

I had already laid off the course. "Hold on 213 until we get offshore," I told him. "The course to Freeport is marked on the chart."

"Yessir."

The telegraph rang. I looked at it blankly. Yussuf said, "We go tailshaft generator?"

"Oh, that's right. Sure, absolutely."

He answered the ring, and the lights flickered. The generator engine died with a heavy rattle. Now we could hear the main engine thumping along far below, its exhaust making a soft pockety-pockety noise in the funnel.

"It's 1015," I told Yussuf. "Go below and get some rest. I'll call you about 1400. That way we'll both have a four-hour watch."

"Yessir."

He set the autopilot, put away the binoculars, wiped the windows, and checked the oil in the steering reservoir. Then he picked up an empty coffee cup and went out the starboard door. He stuck his head back in.

"Good to be at sea, Captain," he said.

I looked around the horizon. Dauphin Island was now a thin necklace of white dunes off the starboard stern quarter. A yellowish mushroom over Mobile cloaked the scattered skyscrapers and dimmed their brilliance. I looked ahead to the open sea.

"Damned good, First," I said. "Damned good."

CHAPTER TWO

THERE WAS NO TRAFFIC EXCEPT FOR TWO LARGE BULKCARRIERS hull-down off the port bow, heading east. I climbed up into the starboard stool, put my feet on the dashboard, and watched the bow rise and fall on the short sea. The wind heeled the empty vessel to port. The steering gear whined as the hydraulic pumps worked the rudder arm. The bulkcarriers disappeared. The cold blue horizon stretched unbroken around the ship.

Yussuf came up to relieve me at 1400, and I went down to lunch. Jacek was there, smoking a cigarette and drinking coffee. "Jacek," I told him, "you can unlock the sanitary valve now. We're more than 12 miles offshore."

He smiled through the grease. "Very good. Everybody tired of using that, that thing in the closet. Very bad smell there, Captain."

"Yeah, I know. I'll get Manuel to clean it out. We won't have to use it again until we come back to the States."

He drained his coffee cup, gave me a formal little nod, and went down to the engine room. Victor was all smiles when he handed me my plate.

"Happy to be at sea?" I asked him.

"*Sí, Capitán, muy contento.*"

I went to my cabin. I had been carrying my pistol around since I came onboard. I stashed it under a pile of electrical spares in the closet and got into the bunk, but the pitching of the ship kept me from sleeping. At 1700 hours I got up and put on my clothes. The bow rose over a crest and fell heavily into the trough behind it, sending a deep, sick shudder through the ship. I was about to run up to the bridge to tell Yussuf to slow down when I heard the bridge and engine-room telegraphs communicating. The auxiliary engine started and the main engine slowed.

A damp, heavy wind was bullying out of the northwest as I stepped into the wheelhouse. Yussuf was at the radar. I wished him good evening and went into the chartroom. We were 70 miles off the Louisiana coast. I glanced at the binnacle. "Anything interesting?" I asked.

He shook his head. "Plenty traffic. Ships, fishing boats, tankers, everything."

"Yeah. We'll be out of the shipping lanes in a couple of hours, and then it'll be mostly shrimp boats."

He finished the day log and took his coffee cup downstairs. I checked the course and position and went out to sit on the port wing. The sky was overcast again, with the gray sea and sky meeting unseen in the distance. Whitecaps boomed against the sheer face of the hull, sending sheets of spray over the deck. The ship took a quick, hard roll that sent ashtrays and abandoned coffee cups flying. I propped myself between the dashboard and the door and held on while the autopilot fought the waves.

Red and green lights appeared ahead out of the darkness. I called on the VHF and talked to the vessel, an offshore supply boat, and we both altered course to starboard. Somewhere a long way away two Vietnamese fishermen were chattering on Channel 16.

The satnav receiver failed to get a fix on the next pass, so I continued navigating on radar and dead reckoning. Three passes later I got a good fix and calculated the ship's speed at only seven knots. I noted the sea conditions carefully in the day log. The barometer was low, but steady.

The night dragged on. I checked the compass against the rigs we passed, tested the VHF and SSB, plotted fixes, and calculated a revised ETA to be passed on in the morning. I paced back and forth in the narrow wheelhouse. The wind held steady and the ship rolled along. Yussuf relieved me at midnight, and when I came on watch again at 0600 we were past Lake Charles and within eight hours of Freeport. I called the agent by VHF Marine Operator and gave an ETA of 1700 hours. He told me to call the pilot station on Channel 13 when we reached the seabuoy.

At 1200 hours Yussuf came up, freshly showered and carrying a cup of coffee. I ate a light lunch, took a long, hot shower, and retired to my bunk. I was climbing into it when the vessel took a sudden lurch to starboard. She rolled so heavily I could see green sea through the porthole. I flew across the cabin.

The ship had lost almost all headway. The bow rose into the air again and fell back in the sea with a crash. I climbed to my feet, got dressed, and went up on the bridge. Yussuf was about to telegraph the engine room to reduce speed, but I told him to leave the speed alone—we were already four hours behind schedule—and to turn the bow toward the south to get out of the eye of the wind. After a few minutes on the new course, the ship's motion eased and we increased rpm's to 170.

There was a noise behind me. I turned. The old captain appeared in the starboard door in a shortsleeved boiler suit, his hair wild, his mustache skewed, his eyes like holes in a snowbank.

"Where are we?" he croaked.

"Six hours from Freeport," I said.

"You're not the captain of this ship. You're on this ship illegally."

"Captain, I am the owner's rep onboard. I want you sober and on the bridge when we take on the pilot. I don't need you until then. Go back to your cabin."

He hesitated. The ship heaved again and slammed its forefoot into a trough. He worked his mouth. "I'll be in the saloon if you need me," he finally said. "I have the ship's papers to catch up on."

After he left, I laughed. "Ship's papers! Who does he think he's kidding?"

At supper I found the captain in the officers' mess, eating a big meal. There was color in his leathery cheeks, and his eyes were focused.

Dark fell as we approached the Texas coast. Yussuf stayed in the wheelhouse while we threaded our way through the oil rigs. The captain came into the darkened bridge. I went up close to him. He didn't smell of whiskey.

"All right," I told him, "I'm going below. If anybody asks about me, I'm the owner's rep who's sailing with the ship." I went down to my little cabin and lay in the bunk while the pilot took the ship into port and berthed it. I could hear the clanging of the telegraph as the bridge rang for Finished with Engine. After a few minutes I went on deck.

We were coming from a U.S. port, so the dock was deserted except for the agent's boy and the lineshandlers. I called Dickie from a pay phone on the quay as soon as we were tied up. "The captain sobered up just in time to bring her in," I said. "We never saw him before then."

"No problem, Captain, no problem," he said. "I've got another captain standing by. His name's Rudolfo Gomez. And I already wired old van der Voort's wages to the agent."

"I know Rudy," I said. "You don't want him."

"Rudolfo? Really? You sure?"

"I know him, Dickie. You can ask anybody on the Miami River. They call him 'Rollover Rudy' because he lost the *Ceriane Z.* and the *Heide*, both by rollover. He's an idiot."

"Well, okay, if you say so. Shit. . .I couldn't find anybody else."

There was a silence on the line. A woman's voice swirled and eddied in the wires.

"You sure you can't sail as captain?" he finally asked. "I really need somebody like you to get this ship straightened out."

"How much do you pay the captain?"

"I'm paying van der Voort $2500 plus 2 1/2 days' vacation pay."

"I'd have to get $3000, but you can forget the vacation pay."

"That's fine, that's fine."

"All right. I'll sail as master for a couple of months."

Yussuf was smoking and drinking coffee in the officer's mess when I went onboard. He had the ports open and the wind was blowing the smoke into his eyes. I sat down. "I told Dickie I'd take over the ship for a couple of months," I said. "He can't seem to find a good captain."

"That's great news. When old captain go?"

"Tomorrow. And we have to make sure he doesn't try to sabotage the ship. I'll talk to you later about that."

"Well, Captain, the crew and I will be very happy to have you onboard. Now the Polish engineers will not be so scared of going to Haiti."

Just before 0700 the next morning the cargo surveyor arrived. He was a wizened little man in a spotless boiler suit. He went down into the hold with Yussuf and came back five minutes later to hand me a written note requiring that the hold be swept again before loading. I stared at him, but he stared right back and assured me that the hold was fine. I shrugged and pocketed the note.

I found Yussuf already handing out brooms in the hold. "Can you believe that?" I called down from the deck. "We've got acres of bare rusty steel in the hold, and all the surveyor wants is a little sweeping."

He grinned up at me. "He never looked around, Cap'n. He just came down and said to sweep up."

"He was paid off by the shipper, you can be sure of that. But I want you in the hold all the time we're loading, Yussuf, to make sure Kraft paper gets put against the steel."

"Yessir."

The stevedores were starting to arrive, riding on the backs of forklifts. The agent came onboard just as the first sacks were being lowered into the hold. I was standing on the hatchcover when he came up the gangway. He was a man about my age with a thick round cap of glossy black hair combed low over a narrow forehead. He watched the stevedores jumping around with the first energy of the day.

"Captain," he said, "I have two faxes from the owner." He glanced toward the saloon windows. "Has the captain been informed that he's signing off?"

"Actually, no. It's kind of a last-minute thing. He's Dutch, so there should be no problem with him making his own travel arrangements."

"Good. Do you know anything about the chief's wife?"

"I know she's coming to join the ship, but I think she has to be delivered by INS, since she's Polish."

He shook his head. "I called INS this morning. They said I could have her picked up."

"I've got to rent a car and go to Houston anyway. Can I pick her up and save the agency charge?"

He didn't like me saving the agency charge, but he said, "Well, I guess that's all right."

The chief's wife was arriving at 1330, so I had plenty of time. I left Yussuf in charge and went with the agent to a car-rental office. All they had was a scratched-up Cordoba, so I took it. After a swing by a grocery store to pick up fresh meat and bread, and by a hardware store for bolts and hand cleaner, I returned to the ship. Several cars were parked on the dock, and the loading was proceeding apace.

Yussuf met me at the head of the gangway. "The charterer is here."

"Who's that? The Haitian?"

"Yessir. He's in the saloon."

"Fine." I dropped off the groceries and supplies in the galley and went up-stairs. An old, frail-looking brown man in expensive rayon clothing was sitting at the table staring out over the deck. He stood up when I came in.

"Capt. van der Voort?"

"No, I'm Capt. Hardberger. I'm taking over command of the vessel today."

"I see. I'm Pierre Bonvillain, the charterer."

"Pleased to meet you. Have you had coffee? Want a Coke?"

"Coke, please." He looked around the saloon. "Has the other captain signed off already?"

"Not yet. He's in his cabin." I pointed toward the bulkhead with my chin. "I think he's sleeping." I got Mr. Bonvillain a Coke from the captain's fridge, then tore two sheets of paper from my notebook and scribbled out two Notices of Relief.

There was a thump from the other side of the bulkhead. The door to the master's cabin flew open. Van der Voort stood in the doorway in a long tee-shirt, his wasted legs as mottled and white as a corpse's. "You. . .you take command of my ship, do you?" he croaked.

Bonvillain stared at him, then cranked his head around to stare at me. I said coolly, "The captain hasn't been informed that he's being relieved."

Van der Voort staggered across the small office and into the saloon. "You're goddamned right I haven't been informed."

Bonvillain half-rose. "I am the charterer. . ."

The old captain snarled, "So what?"

Bonvillain sat down. I said, "Captain, it gives me a regrettable pleasure to inform you that you're being relieved of command as of this moment, 0830 hours, December 16, 1987."

Another netload of cargo came onboard. The ship rocked a little. I handed the captain the fax from Dickie and his Notice of Relief. He read them slowly and put them on the table. "Okay, fine. Okay, then." He looked at Bonvillain and blinked. "Sorry about all this. Not Mr. Dickie's fault, you know. Fine young man."

He walked back to the cabin and turned around. "Do you have my wages?"

"The agent has them," I said. "He'll be here at 1100 hours to take you to Customs and INS."

He nodded shortly and closed the door. I looked at Bonvillain. "That takes care of that. Now, how may I serve you?"

"Well," he said, "everything is going well with the loading, praise God."

"Yes, praise God."

"How many tons do you think you will be able to carry?"

I thought. "We're 1615 deadweight, subtract 100 tons for fuel and constant, so I guess about 1500 tons. . .30,000 bags."

He nodded, pleased. "Very good, Captain. And no cargo damage?"

"No cargo damage. I don't allow it."

He smiled weakly and sipped at the Coke. "I have another item of cargo to go onboard."

"Yes?"

"A Mazda Montero. I will bring it to the ship tonight."

"Fine. We've got the lashings. . .we'll put it on No. 2 hatchcover."

He hesitated. "Em. . .it must to go in the hold. In the cargo."

"In the cargo? What do you mean?"

He crossed his legs delicately, the thin material of his slacks falling loosely around his old shanks. "You know, Captain, Haiti is very bad right now. The port, Miragoane, now run by bad men. Maybe they steal my car."

"So you want me to smuggle a car into Haiti."

He threw up his hands. "Oh, no, Captain, don't worry about a thing. I will handle it. Smuggling? Well, you see, Captain, there is no government in Haiti. You cannot go through Customs, because someone in Customs will steal the car. It will disappear and no one will know where it went."

I grunted. He became agitated. "It is nothing to do with the ship, Captain. I will take care of everything."

I stood up. "I must call the owner and advise him of this request."

"Of course, of course, call Deekie, call him now. I talk to Deekie las' night, you know. A very nice young man, although I have not the pleasure to meet him."

I nodded, excused myself, and went out. I found Yussuf on deck. "Look, First," I said, "the old captain's signing off. I want you to stand by near the office until he leaves to make sure he doesn't sabotage the ship or steal something."

"Yessir."

"Watch him everywhere he goes. He may have those stolen crew wages hidden somewhere. I doubt it, but watch him."

"Yessir." He went inside.

I went down to the dock and called Dickie from the pay phone. I relayed Bonvillain's request.

"Well, what's the problem, Captain?" he asked. "Make him sign something saying I'm not responsible for damage to the damn thing."

"That's not the problem. If we get caught with unmanifested cargo onboard, the ship can be seized and I can be put in jail."

He didn't say anything. I could hear sheets rustling. A woman murmured in the background. Finally he cleared his throat and said, "Captain, you're just going to have to let him do what he wants right now. I've got to keep this charter long enough to pay some bills. Just use your best judgment when you get to Haiti."

"Very well," I said. We hung up and I walked back to the ship.

The sun was high above the American Rice Company warehouse to the east of the quay. A pitiless wind was still driving out of the northwest. The loading was going quickly, with four trucks on the pier and the groundmen standing around with pallets slung and ready to go onboard.

I told Bonvillain that I would take the car. He pumped my hand and left. The captain came out of his cabin, fully dressed, his hair wet from a shower, just as the agent arrived with the money. I paid him his wages and signed him off the articles.

He went into his cabin and I went on deck to watch the loading. There were a dozen men in the hold, stripped to their pants, carrying the 110-pound sacks from the landing point to the growing stacks of bags in the corners. At 1100 hours the agent arrived and Capt. van der Voort emerged from the accommodations with two large leatherette suitcases. He dragged them down the gangway to the agent's car. The agent put them in the trunk for him. Yussuf joined me at the gunwale. The old man got in the passenger seat and they drove off.

"Well, First," I said, "that takes care of that. Let's go to work." I told him about the Mazda we were going to smuggle into Haiti.

He shook his head. "No problem for the crew if we are caught, Captain, but maybe plenty problem for you."

I spat. "Well, Haiti isn't like the rest of the world. That's why I agreed to do it. But I'm going to have a proper export permit and Bill of Lading to leave this port with, you can be sure of that. If they blow overboard on the voyage, well, *c'est la mer, n'est-ce pas?*"

He laughed and went back to stand with the stevedores. I went down to the dock phone and looked up mattress wholesalers in the phone book. A cigarette-voiced woman at a mattress factory in Houston told me they had every kind of mattress from the cheapest to the most expensive. They were so busy building mattresses she didn't have time to talk to me, and I should just come down with my retail license. She agreed to take a copy of the ship's registration instead.

As I was going out Jacek met me in the hallway, wiping his hands on a paper towel. "Captain, you captain now?"

"That's right, Chief."

There was a quick white smile in his heavy black stubble. "Very good, Captain. You go Houston now?"

"Yeah. I'm going to pick up Mrs. Jacek at the airport. Long time no see, eh?" I chuckled. "I hope Secundo can manage the engine room for a couple of days by himself."

"No, Captain," he said seriously, "I do my job all time."

"I know, Jacek, I know. Now, is there anything I can get for you while I'm out?"

"Rags, Captain, rags!" He held up the paper towel and shook it at me.

"Okay, Chief, I'll get 'em," I promised.

He glowered at me in reply and stomped off to the engine room. I left the ship and drove north along the flat coastal plain. The mattress factory was a sagging steel building at the back of a deserted industrial park near Hobby Airport. I was led through a series of dark, dingy offices to the woman I'd spoken to on the phone. She was a leathery specimen in a low-cut business suit and a Superglue hairdo. Her handshake was as hard as a stonemason's.

"Cheap mattresses for Haiti? You'll want Seconds and Rejects, then. Okay, come on." She strode out from behind her desk and led me to the factory floor, her haunches marching under her suit. There were about 400 Mexican women working huge, stand-up sewing machines, and a gang of young Mexican men carting supplies and finished mattresses along the wide aisles.

"Singles, twins, queens, or kings?" the woman asked over the noise, talking over her shoulder.

"All kings."

We stopped in front of a roll-up door. She flung it up and gestured toward a disorderly pile of mattresses. "S&R warehouse. Every king in it $33.00 and you load."

I looked at them, couldn't see any obvious flaws, and told her I would take 40. She pulled down the door, told me to bring cash, and let me find my own way out.

The rags were a little harder to find. The first few places I called had only synthetic rags. Engineers hate synthetic rags. I finally bought 100 pounds of all-cotton rags for $1.10 a pound at a used-clothing warehouse only a few blocks from the mattress factory.

I had to drive all the way to Intercontinental Airport to pick up Jacek's wife. The terminal was packed. She came through the security gate, saw the sign I was holding, and came up with her hand out. "I am Daniela. You are agent, no?"

"No, I'm the captain of the ship."

"Oh, Captain, very glad meet you. Very glad be America." She was a big, sturdy blonde woman in her early 30's. She looked up at the lofty ceiling of the terminal. "Very glad America. First time. My sister live Cincinnati." She looked like she was about to get teary-eyed. I hustled her down to the baggage-claim area for her threadbare carpetbag, then led her out to the rental car.

She got in and looked around. "Very nice car. I only. . .see such car on television. Never I in such car."

We didn't talk much on the way back to the ship, but when I stopped to get some groceries at a huge supermarket on the edge of Freeport, she came in with me. The fruit-and-vegetable section was in the front, and she stopped short when we walked through the doors. Before us were two long inclined displays of shiny apples, oranges, grapefruit, lemons, pears, plums, grapes, carrots, lettuce, and everything else.

"Hoh!" she said. "I am shock! I am shock! So much food. . ."

We started walking down the aisle. The store was busy, but she never noticed the other shoppers. I slung bags of apples and oranges into the basket while she stared at the stacks and trays all around us. Then a timer turned hidden nozzles on, and a mist began to spread over the fruit.

"Oh," she said quietly, "oh, my." I looked at her. She was crying.

When we got to the ship, Daniela left her bags in the car and ran onboard. As I came into the hallway Jacek was coming out of his cabin in shore clothes, his hair slicked back. He smiled at Daniela shyly and let her hug him. She almost lifted him off the floor. As I was going aft I glanced into his cabin and saw that he'd cleaned it as neat as a spinster's parlor. The centerfolds were gone from the bulkhead.

I went back on deck. The same stevedores were still on the job, but they weren't working as fast. Yussuf was sitting on the hatchcoaming. "We'll be finished to-morrow night," he said.

"Looks like it. Don't forget to leave a hole in the cargo for the car. And put some tarps under it to keep oil off the rice."

"Where do we put the car?"

"In Number 1. We have to put it right under the derrick."

After supper I walked along the dock, checking the drafts and the dock lines, then went out to the end of the quay and sat watching the sun set over the western horizon, as flat and distant as the rim of the world. The night stevedores arrived, laughing and joking as they waited. The day shift filed off in exhausted silence and drove away. Another truck discharged its 20 tons and growled off toward the road. Night fell over the marshes, and here and there frogs began to call to each other. The ship was an island of light and movement in an ocean of dark.

When I went back onboard Yussuf and Manuel were smoking cigarettes on the No. 2 hatchcover. Yussuf said, "The chief's wife is screaming in the chief's cabin."

"Screaming?"

He laughed. "Screaming."

Manuel grunted. "Fockee, fockee!"

I stepped down to the deck. "You guys are terrible. Tell you what, though, I'd hate to be the man to tell her no. You see the size of those arms?"

I went into the accommodations and waited for Yussuf in the officers' mess. He got a plate from the back of the stove and came in. He sat down heavily. After a few moments he picked up his fork, gave me a weary smile, and started eating.

"So what part of Egypt you from?" I asked.

"El Roda, in the western desert. My father has many goats and horses. He was very sad when I ran away to sea."

"How old were you?"

"Sixteen." He washed down a piece of chicken with a gulp of beer. "I learned to read when I was very young, at the Government school. I read books about the great sailors, Magellan and Columbus and de Gama. And the more I read about the sea, how clean and vast it is, the more I hated the smell of goat shit." He speared another piece of meat left-handed, European-fashion, and took another swallow of beer. "I caught the train to Alexandria, and there were more ships there than I thought could be in the whole world. I found a job the first day, as AB on a Turkish bulkcarrier." He shook his head. "That was a brutal job, Captain."

"I bet."

"And you, Captain? You ever sail the Mediterranean?"

"No, just this side. You been to the Caribbean before?"

"No, sir. We called Rio from Lagos once, but except for that this is the first time."

Jerzy came in wearing his ear protectors around his neck like a talisman, holding a Coke. He bobbed and nodded and grinned and got his plate from the stove. Victor was up and puttering around in the galley, so he brought Jerzy a glass of ice. Jerzy pointed his fork at Victor and said, "You good man."

Victor smiled blankly. I translated. He bowed to Jerzy.

"You good. . .cookie!" Jerzy said.

I translated again. Victor pointed to Jerzy. "*Tu. . .buen soldadero.*" He made a welding motion with his hand.

Jerzy grinned with simple pleasure.

Victor said, "Captain, your cabin is ready. I cleaned it and changed the bedding." He wrinkled his nose. "Old captain plenty *sucio.*"

I thanked him and went upstairs one step at a time. The captain's cabin was small and cold and smelled of disinfectant. The double bunk ran athwartships. I let my clothes drop to the floor and tumbled in.

The next morning I rented a Ryder truck and got to the mattress factory by 0900. They were working hard. It looked like they had been working all night. The same double-breasted dragon led me to the same storeroom, where I chose 40 of the wildest flower-print king mattresses I could find. She scrawled out an invoice and pointed me toward the cash desk, let me shake her muscular paw again, and disappeared into her cave.

I had a lot of errands to run, including finding European engine-room stores, and got back to the ship in late afternoon. Yussuf and the AB's helped me wrap the mattresses in plastic and load them into the forecastle. They filled it to the point that we could barely squeeze out.

"Captain," Yussuf asked, after he locked the forecastle door, "why Haitians buy so many mattresses?"

We started aft for the accommodations. "Well, First," I said, "you got eight million people in Haiti, and most of them never slept in a bed before. Now that Baby Doc's gone, they're getting access to the outside world, and the first thing they do when they come down from the mountain is buy a bed."

I checked my watch and saw that it was suppertime. We went back to the officer's mess, where Jerzy was already deep into a bowl of Victor's ginger beef stew. Jacek came aft to the galley and laid out a serving tray with stew, silverware and napkins, gave us a happy bow from the door, and carried it back to his cabin. The three of us smiled among ourselves.

Shortly after dark, I went on deck to check the stowage. Yussuf was sitting on the port coaming of the No. 1 hatch. I climbed up by him. At that moment a huge gout of fire shot out of the generator stack at the top of the funnel. We turned and stared. The ball of flame wraithed away into the night, followed by a thick column of blue smoke.

"Ah, shit," I said. "One of the generators just cratered."

Yussuf listened. "The MWM."

I made my way to the engine-room door. Jacek was hurrying down the ladder ahead of me, stark naked, his black hair sticking straight up. The engine banged and shook to a dead stop. The lights faded to blackness. A second later the emergency lighting came on, an array of weak yellow bulbs tucked among the pipes and wiring trays overhead.

Jacek had a flashlight in his hand. Its arrow of light bounced off the machinery. He was calling to Jerzy in rapid Polish. I came up behind them. Jerzy opened the valve on the starboard air receiver. Jacek pulled the starting handle and the Deutz rattled and sputtered. He cradled his flashlight under his arm, aimed a spray of ether at the intake, and tried again. This time the old engine barked, shook, spat flame, and started. Jerzy was already at the main panel, and as soon as the rpm's stabilized he switched the system over and the main lights came on. Still naked, Jacek grabbed a handful of tools from the bench and started tearing off the MWM's accessories. Jerzy grinned at me and lumbered over to help his boss.

I went back up into the cold night air and took over the loading watch from Yussuf. He trudged off to bed. About 0300 Jacek came on deck, now wearing an old blue boiler suit, and showed me some broken parts in his blackened hands. "Timing chain break, Captain. Two exhaust valves break, plus one connecting rod bent." He held out the rod. It was bent exactly in the middle, as if made of putty.

"Huh. I don't guess there's an MWM dealer in Freeport. Maybe in Houston, but. . ."

"No problem, Captain. We have spare parts. I fix already, but I no have torque wrench. Must torque heads, you know, Captain."

"No torque wrench? You never had one?"

"No have, Captain. Have torque wrench in Mobile, but disappear. Plenty tools disappear in Mobile, you know, Captain."

"Probably those fucking prisoners. Well, I'll go buy a torque wrench. It'll be in foot-pounds, though."

He waved a grimy hand. "No problem, I make change to meter."

"Can we still sail at 10 o'clock?"

"We sail on other generator, Captain. I fix at sea."

I put a hand on his shoulder. "You're a good man, Jacek."

Just before dawn a white Mazda Montero glided along the dock and stopped next to the bow of the ship. Bonvillain got out and came up the gangway.

"Captain," he said, without preamble, "we must load the car now."

I looked down in the hold. The stevedores had left a hole in the cargo forward for the car. I turned back. "Where's the export permit and B/L?"

He got the documents and we went up to the saloon. Everything was in order, so I allowed him to load the car. The derrick dropped it neatly in the hole, the crew placed bags around it as dunnage, and timbers were laid across the top so that more bags could be used to cover it. We finished just as a clear, hard dawn broke.

At 0700, when Yussuf shuffled into the galley for coffee, I was warming my hands over a fresh cup in the officer's mess. "We're done, First," I called to him. "Go back and get another half-hour of sleep. We sail at 1000 hours."

He poured himself a cup anyway and gave me a wide, white smile. "Very good, Captain. Very good."

I had left my pistol in the closet of the spare cabin. I retrieved it and took it up to the master's cabin. After looking around for a while, I finally stashed it in the overhead air duct, at arm's length.

At 0800 I took Victor with me to the Country Market to stock up on more food, and when we came back the agent was waiting for me in the saloon, looking natty in a tight cowboy shirt with pearl buttons. He shook my hand heartily.

"Good to see you again, Captain. All ready to sail?"

"We'll be ready by 1000, I believe." I sat down and looked at the documents on the table.

"Here's the Bills of Lading." He slid them across.

I glanced over them. "So we loaded 30,420 bags. Not bad." I underlined the exclusions at the bottom of the forms and signed them.

He handed me a UPS envelope. "This came yesterday." He collected his copies of the Bills of Lading, gave me my clearance, and left the ship. I opened the envelope. It was Yussuf's Honduran First Mate license. I took it to him in his cabin.

A woman in a black Jeep dropped the pilot off a few minutes before 1000, and the lineshandlers arrived on the hour. Jacek already had oil up. Yussuf sent Manuel and Ricardo forward when he saw the pilot arrive.

The pilot came on the bridge, a slim young man sporting a diamond-studded Rolex on his hairless wrist. He unlimbered his walkie-talkie, muttered to someone, and gave the sign to single-up. I motioned to Manuel, and the bow and stern ropes dropped into the water. The pilot and I went out on the port wing and watched as the windlass and capstan pulled the end-loops out of the water and through the chocks. He gave Yussuf the order for Hard-a-Port and Dead Slow Ahead.

A few minutes later we had put the barrier islands astern and the pilot was climbing over the side. Dozens of fishing boats criss-crossed the fairway in front of us, their outriggers flying and their nets in the water. The VHF rattled with Vietnamese chatter. The pilot boat roared away. I went out on the port wing to look back. Already the barrier islands had shrunk to green dots on the blue horizon. The tanks and cranes of the port were low behind the islands.

At 1800 hours the next evening I took a hot plate of Creole chicken and a cup of coffee up to the bridge. The bite had gone out of the wind, but it still hummed out of the northwest at a steady Force Four. We were in the open ocean, loping along with long swells overtaking us from dead astern. The smoke from Yussuf's cigarette drifted lazily out of the front windows and forward over the deck.

"All okay, Captain," he said.

I put my cup and plate on the shelf by the steering station and glanced at the compass, then stepped over to the radar. There was one large target, to the northeast, passing abeam of us. I could see her dimly on the murky horizon, a big RO/ RO, her lights just starting to twinkle.

Yussuf tossed his cigarette over the wing and we went back to the chartroom together. We were northwest of the tip of the Yucatan Peninsula. The satnav was showing another pass coming up, so we waited for it and got a "Fix OK." We were making 10 knots.

Yussuf went below and I ate my supper. After that, I walked around the boat deck, checking the running lights. A pale half-moon was already high in the empty sky, pouring a trail of silver across the gunmetal sea. I sat on the starboard wing of the bridge for a while, but the air still had a whiff of winter in it, so I went back inside and raised the windows. The VHF was now silent except for an occasional burst of static and the ghosts of Mexican radio chatter.

At 1130 I walked by the radar and glanced at the screen. There was a small round blip moving from right to left at a high rate of speed. I stopped and stared at it. Much too fast for a ship. I felt the hair on my neck start to rise as I watched the blip coming steadily toward us. I snatched up the binocs and ran out on the starboard wing.

A tiny smudge showed in the darkness to the south, just above the horizon. A minute later a big airplane emerged from the night, a twin, flying just above the water, all lights out. It continued on its course, coming so close as it crossed the bow that I thought I could see the pilot's head in the cockpit. The sound of its engines drifted past, then the plane was swallowed up in darkness again.

At midnight Yussuf relieved me and I went down for a midnight snack. Jacek was drinking coffee and smoking in the officer's mess, but he was uncommunicative, so I ate in silence and read a tattered copy of *¡Hola!*.

I woke at dawn. The small cabin was hot and stuffy. I got up and opened a window, and warm, sweet tropical air poured in. A brilliant sun was rising out of sea off the port bow. I dressed in clean clothes, got a cup of coffee, and went up to the bridge.

Yussuf had pulled a stool up to the front windows, and was sitting back with his bare feet stuck out. He started to get up when I came in, but I motioned him to relax.

"Into the tropics at last," I said.

He stood up anyway. "Very nice watch, Captain. Only two ships, far away. Speed 10.5 knots."

"Good." I checked the radar. "That Isla Contoy on the radar?"

"Yessir."

"Excellent. About time to turn, isn't it?"

"Yessir. I was just waiting for you to come on watch." He went to the autopilot and turned the knob. The bow sheered toward the south and steadied on 168°. We went out on the starboard wing and watched the low Mexican coast sliding backward along the horizon. A wrecked ship lay broken on the reef just east of Contoy, so high out of the water that her whole prop was showing. Her eight sets of union-purchase derricks were now splayed like jackstraws over the lee side. The surf had stove her in to seaward, exposing great rusted frames and a ruined, cavernous hold. Yussuf and I studied her silently through binoculars as we steamed past.

He went below. I charted our course along the Cuban coast toward Haiti, keeping well off the 12-mile limit. In mid-afternoon I altered course to the east as we passed Isla Juventud. As the Isle of Pines, it had been Castro's snake-pit for journalists and other counterrevolutionaries, and had earned such a fearsome reputation that he had decided to change its name. But only a quixotic wit like Castro could have come up with the Isle of Youth.

The next day found us off Cayman Brac, close enough to catch sparks of light as the sun flashed on car windshields. Jamaica slid astern unseen off the starboard side. A heavy wind sprang up as we approached the Windward Passage, a wicked, turbulent wind out of the southeast. The bow struggled up the faces of the swells, now streaked with white foam, and settled solidly into the troughs. Sheets of spray tore across the deck and hatches. I left the bridge to Iron Mike and went down to the main deck to fetch a slicker suit.

Working my way forward, with warm spray shooting up my sleeves, I checked the tarps and the stevedore hatches. All appeared tight. I went back to my cabin, changed clothes, and went up to the bridge. Yussuf was perched on the port stool with a cup of coffee and a cigarette. We talked for a while, then he jumped down and grabbed the binocs out of their case. He ran to the starboard wing and trained the glasses on something bobbing in the sea.

I followed him with the other pair. After a moment the ship heaved up on the roof of a swell and I could see what he was looking at. It was a Jamaican fishing skiff, about 20 feet long, with four black men in it. As we came closer I could see the dreadlocks on their heads, baled into nets. They were waving their shirts at us.

"They are in trouble, Captain," Yussuf said.

"No kidding. If they're depending on us, they're really in trouble."

"We don't pick them up, Captain?"

I put the glasses down and rubbed my eyes. "No, we don't pick them up, First. Nothing but trouble for the ship. If we take them to Jamaica, we have to pay agent and port fees to go in. Maybe $10,000 in all. We take them to Haiti, we have to pay their airfare back to Jamaica. Probably three or four grand total. I don't think Dickie would like either one of those options."

"But it is the law of the sea, Captain. We must pick up. . ."

"Here," I said, "we follow the law of the Caribbean, which is every Rastaman for himself."

He chewed on a lip. I went back into the wheelhouse and put the glasses away, and after a while he did the same.

"If this wind keeps up, they'll blow into Cuba in a day or so," I said. He nodded unhappily and left the bridge. When I looked back a few minutes later, the great heaving sea was as empty as the mountains of the moon.

The wind increased to Force Seven, tearing the scalps off the waves and throwing tons of water across the deck. It swirled green against the lee bulwark and shot out of the scuppers back into the sea. Several times I went down to the port deck to inspect the crack, getting splashed knee-deep in hot Caribbean ocean, but the welded repair seemed to be holding up.

We sighted the western tip of Haiti at daybreak the next morning, the mountains above Cap Dame Marie rising black into a scarlet tropical dawn. As the vessel approached the peninsula the swell fell off until the vessel was rolling along in a low chop. We steamed along the rugged coast of Haiti, through a clear green ocean shot with sunbeams. I sat at the starboard stool, squinting through my sunglasses at the rising sun. The forbidding mass of Gonave Island to the north rose bare and brown into the clear blue sky.

As I changed course to aim for the entrance to Miragoane Bay, dugout canoes with naked fishermen raced out from the nooks and crannies of the shore, paddling fiercely to put themselves in front of the ship. I finally had to get up and steer by hand to avoid the ones who had managed to put themselves in harm's way. They waved madly and held up fish.

At 1150 we arrived off the entrance to Miragoane Bay, about a mile northwest of the egg-shaped rock of Miragoane Point. We could see the rusty tin roof of the town's massive colonial church, and dots of bright paint in the bay below it, each a ship at anchor. I scanned the water for the charted buoy that marked the eastern tip of the reef, but it was gone.

Yussuf turned up the gain on the VHF and called, "Miragoane pilot, Miragoane pilot, this is the Motorvessel *Erika*." He repeated the call several times without an answer.

"Don't bother with that," I told him. "There's no pilot here."

"No pilot? With that reef across the whole bay?"

"No pilot, and the buoy on the reef is gone. But no problem. . .just stay half-a-mile off the rock and you're in 500 feet."

I took the ship off autopilot and called for Half Ahead. Yussuf went to the wheel. As we turned toward the opening in the reef Jacek came in through the port door. He was wearing bikini underwear and smoking a cigarette. "Fishing boat dead ahead," he said.

I looked up. A dugout was coming straight at us from the direction of town, a black man in ragged shorts standing in the bow and waving. "Starboard five," I said to Yussuf. He spun the wheel.

The boat altered course to match our maneuver. The man was waving a rag frantically, now close enough that I could see the hole in his toothless mouth.

I grabbed the handle and signaled "Stop Engine." The engine rumbled down into silence. The rasp of the auxiliary vibrated up through the trunk. I stepped out on the port wing and waited until we approached the canoe. The oarsman in back, an ancient black man in a plastic baseball helmet, turned the boat around and started paddling south when he realized that we were going to overshoot him.

The man in the bow shouted, "Me pilot, me pilot!" as we ghosted by. His skinny kneecaps stuck out like golfballs under the tendrils of his shorts.

I laughed. By then he was falling astern of the ship, even with the ancient oarsman's best efforts.

"Plenty danger in water now," the man yelled through cupped hands. "Port say ship must have pilot."

"Yeah, yeah," I muttered. "All right, First, let's pick him up."

The canoe caught up with the ship and both men scrambled up the pilot ladder. The old man fastened the end of the painter to a staple on the bulwark and climbed up to sit on the hatchcover. The other man bounded up to the bridge.

He was a tall man without a tooth in his head, full of a big grin and handshakes all around. He confided in Creole that the port was very dangerous now, and that he was the port pilot to steer the vessel in. He was not specific about the nature of the dangers.

When he stepped confidently toward the wheel, I nodded to Yussuf and he relinquished it. The man grabbed the topmost spoke vigorously and spun the wheel Hard-a-Port. Yussuf gasped and threw a quick glance toward the looming mass of Miragoane Point, where the pilot was apparently determined to take us. He started toward the man, but by then I had flipped the switch and had taken over steering with the knob on the console.

The pilot stopped spinning the wheel to port, gave a big grin all around, and started spinning it to starboard. He never once looked toward the rudder-angle indicator. By then I had brought the bow back on course, and with a straight face stood at the console staring toward town. I could see specks of cars coming down the hill above it.

The pilot kept up his work, spinning the wheel madly in one direction and then the other, and the vessel stayed right on course. Jacek had to go back in the chartroom to keep the pilot from hearing his stifled chortling. We drew abreast of the town, and I got tired of the game. I took the ship off autopilot and nodded to Yussuf. He shouldered the man aside and grasped the wheel.

There were half-a-dozen ships tied stern-to along the shore, discharging into Haitian lighters, and another half-dozen at anchor in the bay. I found a nice spot between a big old wreck of a cement carrier and a small Dutch freighter, and sent Jacek down to tell Manuel to go forward. We dropped the port anchor—it had the better chain, and although the bay was sheltered on two sides by mountains, it looked like it could see some wind—and Yussuf ran the yellow flag up the mast. We rode easily on the hook with the smell of land in the air.

Yussuf studied the shore with the glasses. "I don't like it, sir."

"What do you see?"

"The quay is full of people. Looks like they're fighting."

I took out the other binoculars and fiddled with the focus. The scene leaped into view. There was a narrow, ruined concrete dock, about 50 meters long, in front of a new tin warehouse. A small ship was tied stern-to at the dock, and behind it a sea of people were surging about.

I swung the glasses to the beach north of the dock, and saw a throng of men in ragged shorts unloading a rough lighter. They hoisted sacks onto their backs and trudged up through the waist-deep water to the shore, where they piled the sacks onto tarpaulins stretched out in front of a line of trucks. Men sat at tables taking tally as the sacks were passed from the tarps to the trucks. One of the trucks lurched out of a ragged breach in the wall and struggled slowly up the hill.

"Damn mess on shore," I said, watching the stevedores trying to get the sacks from the lighters to the trucks through a throng of women and children.

Yussuf was studying one of the other ships at anchor, far to the southwest near a couple of low mangrove islands. "Look at that ship, Captain," he said.

I swung my glasses around. It was a small, green-hulled British freighter of about 900 DWT, with the cargo booms splayed on deck and a tattered tarp over the fantail. A skeletal figure staggered out of the wheelhouse and waved something white at us.

"Cease firing, Captain," Yussuf laughed. "He surrenders."

"Goddamned hellhole port," I growled.

He pointed toward shore with his chin. "Looks like boat coming. I tell crew get ready for Customs."

I looked at the boat. "Customs, hell. It's full of women. It's a whore-boat."

He had already put his glasses away. He jerked them back out. "You say true, Captain. Boat full of women." He ran downstairs. The crew came on deck, and even the chief and Daniela came out of his cabin.

When I went on deck Victor was tying up the whore-boat's ragged painter. Yussuf met me with a big, childish grin. "The girls say there's no Customs, no Immigration, no nothing here. We do what we want."

I shook my head. "It's the goddamnedest thing."

The first girl came over the rail, a slim dark Dominicana wearing a red dress slit up both thighs. Her mane of glossy black hair bounced in the sun as she stepped down to the deck. The second girl was a grizzled veteran of about 35, wearing a thin tank-top over limp breasts. She climbed down the steps and hobbled along the deck.

The third girl was a pretty young thing with frizzy hair, wearing a tee-shirt and running shorts. She leaped down. The rest of the motley cargo followed, the last girl haggling with the boatman over the fare.

I decided to reconnoitre on shore. The crew came away from the main deck reluctantly to fit the outboard engine onto the rescue boat and swing it overboard for me. The clear green water boiled as I put it in gear and motored alongside the ship's side. For the first time since I'd come onboard I had a good look at the lower hull. Heavy blisters swelled under the cheap gray paint, leaking rusty water in streaks down the pitted sides. Roughly cut patches, some as big as 2 X 8 meters, were scattered along the waterline. I took a detour up the other side, found it in no better shape, and turned toward shore.

Details of the waterfront became clearer as I approached. There was a sunken barge, its deck still dry, sticking out from a point of rocky land north of the dock, and next to it was a large yellow building with bullet holes in the walls. A black-hulled ship with a British sweep in her lines, the *Porlamar* of Kings Town, was the northernmost in the line of ships discharging into boats. I tied the painter to the foot of her pilot ladder and went up.

The Filipino chief mate, a short, mustachioed man in a clean boiler suit, took me to the captain in his air-conditioned saloon. He was about 60, a blond giant with a weathered brown face and eyes the color of seawater. He pumped my hand fiercely.

"Welcome to hell, Captain!" he shouted.

"Thank you."

"Have a seat, have a seat! I have taken the liberty of opening a Beck's for you. Damned irony, what? The only beer you can buy in this shithole is a fine German beer. To your health!"

I was a little daunted until I realized that he was partly deaf. We sat down. It was a small saloon, even for a 1000-tonner, but as neat as a lady preacher's handbag. Carved grapes and vines sprawled along the mahogany moldings, and a leaded-glass door fronted the built-in liquor cabinet. Through the front windows I could see a swarm of stevedores at the bottom of the hold, sweating out the last sacks of the cargo of rice.

"You're almost done," I said.

He closed his eyes for a second, took a long swig of beer, and said, "Thank Gott for that. Bloody unbelievable, this place. Drink up, man, drink up!"

I took a sip of beer.

"Anyway, what can I tell you? Who's your charterer?"

"Jean Bonvillain."

"He's okay. Used to be big in cement, but now he's doing rice. The whole bloody country is buying rice. You got rice? About 2000 tons?"

"Sixteen hundred. She was lengthened."

"Figure a week to discharge. We came in with 900 and we've been here five days. Bloody unbelievable."

"What's with Customs and Immigration?"

He shook his head. "No such thing. The port's being run by a guy named Raoul. You'll meet him soon, don't worry. I'm leaving today, so you'll probably be seeing him for lunch. Bloody great thief he is, you know. But you'll find out. Anyway, Raoul runs the show. No cops here, no army. They got run out when Baby Doc took off. Big fire-fight over there."

He pointed to the yellow building with bullet holes in the wall. "Anyway, it's none of the ship's concern. The charterer pays them off for the cargo and everything goes along. Make sure your engineer can get oil up at any time. Two trips ago they had a big gunfight on the dock. Thirteen people killed and 22 wounded. I cut my stern lines with the fire axes and we steamed straight out over the anchors. Chief mate told me later he saw bullets hitting the water all around the ship."

The chief mate stuck his head in the saloon. "Gentleman here to see captain from *Erika*."

I stared in astonishment. "Excuse me?"

He stepped aside. Bonvillain came in looking hot and irritable. "Captain, why you no come alongside? Plenty work now." He didn't offer to shake hands.

"Mr. Bonvillain," I protested, "I do not believe there is enough water at the dock for my vessel. Besides that, the dock is not secure. I cannot. . ."

"No, no, no," he said angrily, "alongside the ba'ge, the ba'ge. You no see the ba'ge over there?"

I looked out the window. "That sunken barge? You want me to tie up to that?"

"Yes, of course. You will discharge onto the deck of the ba'ge."

I shrugged and turned to the captain. "Thank you for your hospitality, Captain, and bon voyage. Will you be coming back to Miragoane?"

He shook his head vigorously. "I hope not. I was under a three-month time charter, you see, and every trip was right here to Miragoane. Now the charter's finished, and we've got a voyage charter from Rio Haina to Guyana. I hope we never come back."

We shook hands again, and Bonvillain and I went down to the deck. He had come onboard from a big dugout, still waiting for him at the bottom of the pilot ladder.

"You tie up other side of ba'ge," Bonvillain said. "You tie up with front to shore." He climbed down into the dugout. The boatman cast off and started sculling. I got into the rescue boat, started the engine, and returned to the battered old *Erika*.

Back onboard, I told the boatman waiting for the whores to cast off, and had the inflatable hauled onboard. We upped anchor and steamed slowly toward the barge. By then, the barge's whole hatchcover was packed with Haitians.

"Yussuf," I called down to the deck, "tell the crew that no one from shore is allowed onboard without my permission."

He looked up from threading the monkey's fist through the starboard chock and nodded.

There was plenty of water depth along the mountainous shore, and we tied up without incident. I rang Finished with Engine and went on deck, where the crew were having a tough time keeping the Haitians off the ship. One of them, a husky, bearded man with gold chains around his neck, was waving a piece of paper at me. I pointed to him and motioned him across to the ship.

"Cap'n," the man said, "why you no let stevedores on ship? We go to work now."

I looked at the ragged throng. "What stevedores? Those people?"

"Some stevedores. Others. . .?" He gave a shrug.

I shook my head. "Only stevedores onboard, and only after hatches are open. And who are you? Stevedore foreman?"

"I foreman. My name Fritz. I work for Mr. Bonvillain. I unload ship." He turned around and gestured. Before my men could react, a wave of Haitians jumped across and onto the deck. "We open hatches, Captain," Fritz said. "No problem."

The Haitians fell to unchocking the tarps and removing the bands. Yussuf scurried around trying to keep track of everything, but they knew what they were doing. They started rough, throwing the hatchboards, but I told Fritz I would pay a dollar a man at the end of the day if they didn't cause any damage to my precious boards. After that they laid them on deck like their mothers were sleeping on them.

I was watching them struggling to move one of the shifting beams—the ship had greased slides instead of wheels—when Fritz came up to me. "Captain, you have big problem."

"Oh, yeah? What is that?"

He pointed to the foremast. "You no have Haitian flag. This is Haiti, you know. You must fly Haitian flag."

"Why? There's no government here."

"The Customs boss, Raoul. If ship do not have Haitian flag, must to pay $500 fine to Raoul."

"Where can I get one?"

"Maybe from shop in town." He saw something he didn't like forward and ran off shouting and waving. I looked over the throng on the barge and saw a Haitian man in a shirt and long pants. He was wearing shoes. I pointed to him and crooked my finger. He came over.

"What's your name, sir?" I asked him.

"Ronald Joanel. May I help you?"

"Do you know where to find a Haitian flag?" I pointed to the foremast.

"Yessir."

"How much?"

"About five U.S. dollars. I will bring your change and receipt."

I handed him five dollars and he made his way through the crowd and off the barge. Yussuf came up. "You gave that Haitian some money, Captain?"

"Five dollars for a flag."

He smiled sadly. "He will never come back, Captain."

I shrugged. "Maybe not. We'll see." Bonvillain appeared on the barge, followed by two men in polyester. They were arguing violently. The people on the barge made a circle around them.

Fritz came aft. "Captain, we work now to five o'clock, then we come back at nine tonight."

"For the car?"

"The car, exactly. Can you rig the boom to take it off?"

"Certainly. But how are you going to get the car off the barge?"

"The car will be unloaded into a boat on the other side. Your crew will have to be very careful."

"My crew hasn't got anything to do with this smuggling caper. We open the hatches and that's it."

"Yes, yes, Captain, okay." He hurried forward and talked to Bonvillain while the two men stood by impatiently. Finally Bonvillain waved him away and the three of them started shouting again. After 30 more minutes of Haitian deliberation they left arm-in-arm.

I looked in the hold. The stevedores were filling cargo nets with bags of rice. One of them was a tall, bony woman in an ankle length dress. I called Fritz over. "Fritz, mon umi, that's a good-looking woman you got working down there."

He looked confused. "What woman?"

I pointed. He shook his head in irritation. "That is no woman, Captain. That is stevedore."

I looked carefully. It was a man, all right, a man in a long pink dress. Fritz went back to bullying the workers. Yussuf came up. "You see the guy in the dress?" I asked him, pointing with my chin.

He nodded. "I thought it was just a goddamned ugly woman. What a country."

I went in the accommodations. Victor was busy with supper, and one of the whores, the gaunt woman in her 30's, was sitting on a stool in the corner peeling potatoes. She gave me an apprehensive smile.

Victor introduced her as Amanda, a Dominicana. She bowed her head. Her face was slightly misshapen, as if she had recovered well from a bad beating. I kidded Victor about taking advantage of women, stole a french fry from the warming dish, and went aft.

Two other girls were on the fantail, a big one and the round-hipped girl in the red dress. They smiled and winked and showed some leg, but I was more interested in watching the sea of motion on shore. A lighter was slowly approaching the beach, a rude wooden boat without a speck of paint on it, piled to the gunwales with cement, probably 10 tons altogether. Six or seven men sat high on the sacks as one man worked the sweep aft. When the boat nudged the shore in between a dozen others, stevedores came down into the water and the men on the boat started lowering sacks onto their shoulders. They trudged up the bank and laid the sacks on a fresh blue tarpaulin. A small building stood on stilts over the water between the dock and the bullet-pocked building, and from the steady stream of people, from old women to toddlers, standing in line to get in, I deduced that it was an outhouse.

Yussuf came aft with a fresh cup of coffee. "Captain, where is the teevee for the crew's mess?"

"The teevee? I don't know. It's not there?"

"The antenna wire is broken like somebody jerked it apart."

I strode into the crew's mess. Without question the teevee was gone. "Jesus fucking Christ," I said, "we're here for six hours and we've already been ripped off."

Victor was horrified, but he had seen nothing. "There have been so many people, Captain," he said nervously, "coming in and out. . ."

"It's okay, Victor. It was only a black-and-white, after all."

The two girls said they hadn't seen anyone take it, but they had only been on the fantail for a few minutes. We went forward. The Haitian idlers on deck grinned knowingly and assured us that Haiti was a terrible place for thievery. "Somebody dropped it to a boat off the fantail, Cap'n," Yussuf said. "Too many people on deck. Very hard to take a television off in the middle of the day."

"Those sneaky sons of bitches. Well, let's blow it off, Yussuf, and be glad it wasn't something more valuable. But you'd better go around the ship now and make sure every hatch and door is locked, especially the cabins, the pantry, and the wheelhouse. I guess we have to leave the forecastle open while we're working, but keep an eye on anybody going in there."

He hurried off. I told Victor to watch the stern ropes—by stooping down a little he could see them from the galley—and went up to the master's deck. I had left it locked, and all was in order.

In mid-afternoon I went down on deck. The afternoon sun poured onto the steel like lava. Down in the hold, the stevedores had stripped to their underwear. Sweat poured from their bodies. Working around the pile of sacks supporting the Montero didn't make their job any easier. Production was down. The stevedores on the barge sat quietly waiting for the next sling, their heads bound with cloth and their black faces and torsos dusted white with rice powder.

About 1630 hours the hydraulic line to the forward derrick perforated, sending a thin spurt of oil splashing against the port hatchcoaming and trickling down the deck. Manuel came up to the saloon to tell me about it, but by the time I got on the scene Jacek was already there with a piece of rubber gasket material and a couple of hose clamps. In 20 minutes another patch joined the dozen already in place, and Jacek was coming up to me wiping the sweat out of his eyes.

"Captain, you must tell stevedores. . .maybe only 20 bags at a time. Pipe no good. . .they lift 40 bags, maybe blow big hole in pipe I cannot fix."

I walked along looking at the pipe, stooping here and there to feel the back side. That was the side that couldn't be seen, so it never got painted. It was in bad shape. I could peel off long, semicircular slabs of rust half-an-inch thick. I stood up, nodded to Jacek, and went to talk to Yussuf.

"We got a problem, First," I said. "The boom is rated at three tons, but we're blowing holes in the hydraulic pipe lifting two. We're going to have to get them down to one ton."

Yussuf gave the tallyman back his book and turned. "It won't slow us down, Captain. We're waiting for the nets to fill as it is."

"I know, but if we tell the stevedores that the crane can only lift one ton, the charterer could take us two-thirds off-hire. Dickie couldn't take that for very long."

"I see. Because the charter party says three tons."

"Exactly. Now, I see that the Haitian crane driver is a little rough on the controls. Go give him a warning to go easy. Then I'll stand in the hallway and have Jacek in the engine room. The next time he jerks on the lever, I'll give Jacek the signal and he'll cut hydraulic power to the winch. You get all pissed off and tell the crane driver that he broke the hydraulic system."

He nodded. "Good plan. Okay, I'll go now."

I went back to the accommodations and watched from the hallway as Yussuf lectured the crane driver. The man bobbed his head vigorously.

Jacek was sitting with Daniela on the fantail, drinking coffee. I explained the plan, and he agreed to go down. I took a position in the door of the hallway where I could see Yussuf. I waited until the load was only a few feet off the floor—I didn't want anybody getting hurt—then I stepped into the engine-room door and signaled to Jacek. There were shouts from the hold.

I ran forward and looked down. Nobody hurt, but several bags had burst, rice streaming from them. The stevedores were fighting each other to get the spilled rice jammed into bags and bundles. I yelled at them to stop stealing cargo, with the expected effect. Fritz climbed sourly out of the hold.

Jacek came steaming up from the engine room. "Fucking stevedores ruin hydraulic pump, Captain," he shouted. "Crazy crane man know nothing about ship gear. Where you find this man, eh, Mr. Stevedore Foreman?"

Yussuf rushed over to the controls and pushed the man aside, berating him in French. The man staggered back against the men working the block-and-tackle, protesting with huge white eyes that he'd done nothing wrong.

"Fritz," I said, "your man has broken the ship's gear. No more discharging until the gear is fixed. I charge the charterer for the damage, okay?"

"Georges was doing everything regular, Captain," Fritz protested. "He is good crane man, you see already. He work plenty ships all the time, always no problem the crane."

Yussuf said, "Good crane man? I laugh, Captain. You know I tell him plenty times today go easy on control. Now he break winch."

I turned to Jacek. "Can you fix it, Chief?"

He nodded. "I fix with used spare parts, but maybe no take so much ton, eh? Must order parts from Miami."

"How much capacity, you think?"

He shrugged. "Maybe one ton."

I turned back to Fritz. "You want to try to keep working at one ton? Otherwise we'll have to wait until we can get the parts."

He spat disgustedly over the side of the ship. "We work one ton now, okay? You get new parts tomorrow?"

"Maybe. I'll call the owner. . .he'll have to get them to the airport in Miami."

Fritz leaned over the coaming and started yelling at the stevedores. They had thrown themselves down on the planks as soon as the derrick stopped. Now they stood up slowly, arching their backs and stretching their arms. The sacks started moving again, slowly at first, until one of them started to chant. The rest took it up, and the bags started flying. The boys on deck heard the chanting from the hold and started banging on 55-gallon drums and on the deck itself, keeping time with the stevedores. Even the Haitians on the barge stirred themselves and joined in. Yussuf looked down and laughed. Jacek shook his head, wiped up some of the spilled hydraulic oil, and retired to the sanity of his engine room.

I was about to head upstairs to write a Note of Protest when a Haitian jumped across from the barge. There were already so many Haitians on deck I didn't pay any attention to him, but he waved to me. I stopped.

It was the Haitian I'd sent for a flag. He proudly produced a small blue-and-red Haitian flag from a paper bag, then folded the bag carefully and stowed it in his pocket. He held out some filthy Haitian notes and a receipt, but I waved them away.

"No trouble finding it?" I asked.

"I had to go to Petit Goave."

"How far is that?"

"About an hour."

I stared. "You had to drive an hour to get this flag? How much did that cost?"

"Oh, no, Captain, I take *tap-tap*. It cost one dollar Haitian round-trip."

I pulled out a couple of U.S. dollars and handed them to him. "Many thanks. Your name's Ronald, right?"

"Ronald Joanel." He moved closer. "Captain, do you have anything to sell? Bicycles, teevees, things like that?"

"How about mattresses?"

"Mattresses? You have mattresses to sell?"

"I certainly do. Come with me." I took him to the forecastle and showed him.

"Yes, yes, Captain," he said, "I can sell the mattresses. I come back with one man, very big *homme d'affaires*, maybe buy all at once." We shook hands and he rushed off. I gave the flag to Yussuf to fly from the starboard yardarm.

I went up to the office and typed out a Note of Protest, ". . .because of the abuse your stevedore crane operator inflicted on the ship's gear by mishandling the crane controls, thereby causing damage to the ship's hydraulic pump and hydraulic piping system. . ." I stamped it with the ship's stamp and took a copy down to Fritz. He saw that it was in English and didn't try to read it.

"You have to sign one copy," I told him.

"No English. No read English."

"You have to sign it anyway, Fritz. English is the language of shipping. It's only saying that the stevedores caused the gear failure."

He signed the original reluctantly and stuffed the copy I gave him into his pocket.

At 1700 hours the stevedores knocked off, carrying their wrapped parcels of rice. I estimated that the total amount of rice they were carrying off equaled three bags, so I wrote a quick Note of Protest on a page from the tallybook and handed it to Fritz. "Three bags taken by stevedores," I explained.

He pretended not to understand. I stepped over to the nearest man, a wizened little fellow of about 50—an old man in Haiti—and took a Kraft-paper bundle from him. A kilo of rice spilled on deck when I tore it open. The man grinned sheepishly. Fritz looked angry for a second, then laughed and told the stevedores to get off the ship. The man gathered up what he could of the spilled rice and followed the others into the waiting boat. Fritz signed the note.

As I was eating supper and laughing with Yussuf and Jacek about the stevedore in the dress, Bonvillain came into the officer's mess. "Captain, I must speak to you," he said abruptly.

I made my apologies and went out in the hall with him.

"Captain, what about your crane?" he demanded. "The crane is not working?"

"No, it's the hydraulic pump. Your crane operator tore it up. We had to repair it using spare parts. I gave Fritz a note. . ."

He waved that away. "But how will you discharge my car? We must take it ashore tonight."

"No, no, Mr. Bonvillain. Your car is very important. We must take the risk. If the pump breaks, we'll use a block-and-tackle."

That pleased him. "Then have everything ready at nine o'clock. The boat will come then."

"Bring some stevedores. That's not my crew's job."

"No problem, Captain. Plenty stevedores in Miragoane." He went on deck. I heard a woman's laugh from the galley. Victor stuck his head into the hall and said, "Captain, have you seen Yussuf? He hasn't eaten supper."

"I'll check." I went up to Yussuf's door and knocked. He opened it a crack, saw me, and opened it wide. The frizzy-haired girl in the tee-shirt and running shorts was sitting on his bunk, a drink in her hand. "*Hola, Capi,*" she chirped.

"*Hola, chiquita.* Yussuf, Victor wants to know if you're going to eat supper."

He stepped out. "Captain, you know there are no restaurants in this shithole town. I want to eat supper with my girl. . .can I buy her supper onboard?" He looked at me anxiously.

I clapped his shoulder. "I wouldn't care, First, but it's Dickie's food. Tell you what. . .I'll make a note in the accounts and deduct $2.00 from your salary. Okay?"

"Thanks, Captain. Will you tell Victor. . ."

"I'll tell him. As a matter of fact, tell the crew their girlfriends can eat onboard. I'll have Victor keep a tally and I'll deduct $2.00 from wages for every meal."

He went in his cabin to dress for supper. I went up to the wheelhouse to watch the sunset. A fierce wind was building from over the mountains, cutting cat's paws in the dark water. The ship heaved at her lines like a tethered ox.

A little after dark I went out on the port wing. Cooking fires twinkled among the swirling people on shore. A thin crescent moon, sharp as a knife, rose above the mountains, followed by a lone star. The muttering of the auxiliary engines on the other ships floated across the bay, torn into whispers by the wind. Their lights danced in the choppy water.

A crowd of people appeared on the barge and climbed onboard the ship, followed by Bonvillain. He saw me on the bridge and waved me down imperiously. I went down.

"Is your crew ready to discharge the car?" he demanded.

"Yessir. Let me tell the chief to give power to the winch." I found the chief in his cabin, looking at photographs with Daniela. He got up, slipped on his clogs, and went down to the engine room in his underwear. The MWM started with a hollow knock.

Yussuf came out of his room, but I told him I would supervise the stevedores, so he went back. I watched as the Haitians pulled back the tarps and lifted off the hatchboards from above the car. The Haitian crane operator lowered the hook in place and the men in the hold threaded two ship's slings under the chassis.

There was a soft knocking of wood on wood from the port side. A big Haitian lighter came around the stern, sculled by two men standing on the afterdeck. Bonvillain exchanged some soft Creole with them as the boat glided alongside, then he came up to me. "You must put out the lights, Captain."

"What lights?"

"The deck lights. I want the ship dark to take the car out."

I looked over toward the Customs house. The upper story was shuttered and dark. The people living on the dock in front of it were settling down for the night. I went up to the bridge and shut down the lights. Within two seconds the winch was clattering and the white car came soaring up out of the hold. The ship heeled to port as the men swung it over the side. I went down.

There were two heavy logs laid across the lighter athwartships, sticking out about four feet over the sides. I came up to Bonvillain. "I thought you were going to put the car inside the boat. You're going to put it on top of those poles?"

"Is necessary," he said shortly. "The men must lift the car off the *bateau* and carry it to shore with the poles." He glanced at me. "Do not worry, Captain. We do it here in Miragoane all the time."

I looked up at the Haitian flag whipping in the night wind. "With a wind like this?"

He didn't answer. I went and got Yussuf. "You'd better come see this, First. The charterer is about to lose that Montero." He was lying in the bunk with his new girlfriend, wearing a pair of swimming trunks. He came out pulling on a shirt. Jerzy came up from the engine room to cool off, and joined us on the lee rail.

The ship was rocking in the chop. The car started swinging as the operator lowered it toward the boat. Several times he had to stop so the men on the guy ropes could line it up. At first they tried to communicate in hoarse whispers, but within minutes they were shouting in furious Creole. I went over to the barge to see if there was any reaction from shore, but all I could see were sleeping bodies amid the glowing embers of the fires.

The car was finally settled onto the logs and tied down with some ratty rope. Yussuf said, "Maybe we should give them good rope, Captain."

I waved a hand. "All is going according to plan, First. Strong rope wouldn't help them anyway."

Bonvillain ordered the boat to shove off. The two oarsmen took their positions at the transom, sculling the boat toward the stern of the ship. Still in the lee of the hull, the boat rocked easily in the wavelets.

I led Jerzy and Yussuf aft to the fantail. The big Honduran flag on the stern snapped and fluttered. Bonvillain followed us, now silent and nervous. The boat came around the stern and turned its bow into the wind.

When the first gust hit the boat, it heeled heavily to starboard and the bow yawed. The Haitians onboard shouted and the scullsmen fought to bring it back into the wind. Bonvillain jumped up on the bitts and started screaming at them, waving both arms frantically, the gold on his wrists flashing in the light from the open hallway door.

The scullsmen couldn't fight the press of the wind on the car. The bow slowly fell off to the southwest, toward the darkness and the reefs, in spite of their frantic efforts. Other men jumped up to help them, now two per oar, and for a few seconds the bow started swinging back. Then another gust hit and the boat sheered off again. Howls of dismay cut through the night. The boat drifted toward the edge of the light, the white square of the car gleaming in the darkness like an open window.

Bonvillain jumped down and grabbed me fiercely by the sleeve. "Do something, Captain, do something!"

"What?"

His hands flew into the air like birds. "Start the ship. Go after the boat. *Dépêchez, dépêchez!*"

I was still watching the boat. It was heeling to starboard under the force of the wind, now nearly broadside. The crackling of breaking wood reached us. "*Dépêchez* no good now, Mr. Bonvillain. Look."

Just as he turned the hull of the boat rolled upward, wet planks shining, and the car disappeared. A heavy splash. The boat rocked back upright, empty of car and men. It rolled wildly and drifted into the dark.

Bonvillain sent up a wail like a grieving wolf. He jumped up on the bulwark as if to throw himself into the water—Yussuf moved up to hold him back—then jumped down again, dancing in fury.

"Come on," I said to Yussuf, "we'd better get the rescue boat overboard. I hope those fellows can swim."

But before we could get the boat off the boat deck the Haitians had struggled back onboard their boat, pushing and shouting. With the car gone they were able to bring the half-swamped boat back up under the ship's counter in a few minutes, where they sat, wet and miserable, as Bonvillain cursed and spat from the fantail above them. After a while Jerzy went to the engine room and shut down the MWM, and Yussuf went back to his girlfriend. I sat on the fantail.

Bonvillain finally sent the boat away unpaid, ignoring their howls of protest, and trudged slowly off the ship without a word to me. I saw his bent figure move across the barge and down to the sleeping town.

As I was heading up to my cabin and bunk, Jerzy came out of his room with his charcoal-colored girlfriend, a busty Dominican teenager named Ysadora. He was dressed in a Tahitian print shirt and knife-pleated pants.

"Captain," Jerzy said, "you come now. We go disco. You come."

"Aw, naw, Jerzy, I don't think so. I think. . ."

He lumbered up and gave me a big hug. "Come, come, Captain, you come. We go disco."

"Jerzy, maybe you'd better not. . ."

"Disco," he roared happily. "We all go disco."

"Okay, Second," I said, "let's go disco."

I turned the ship over to Yussuf and went with them onto the barge and along the plank to shore. The power was off in town. The narrow street was packed with dark figures moving in the light from wax candles burning in the shops. A truck came around the corner from behind us, its headlights throwing the faces into high relief. We packed ourselves against the buildings to let it pass. Ysadora led us through a narrow black alley to a mud street between low cement houses, lanterns and candles lighting the interiors. A generator coughed in the distance. I could hear music.

It got louder as we walked along. The street had apparently evolved without conscious design, winding between houses so tightly packed together no car could pass between them. We picked our way from mudbank to mudbank by the flickering lights until we came to a huge tin shed without walls, lit by low-wattage red bulbs strung from pole rafters. There was a band on stage, a dozen musicians engaged in a frenetic *salsa*. The thumping of the generator lent a mindless rhythm to the music.

We moved through a crowd of neighborhood children and under the shed. Manuel and Ricardo were sitting with four German crewmen at one table, so we rustled up three chairs and joined them. A young black man swooped by and took our orders. The only kind of beer they had was Beck's.

Filipino and Hispanic crewmen from the other ships danced with their Dominican girlfriends. Loose Dominican whores moved through the crowd, teasing each other and casting bright eyes around. A number of Haitians, men and women, were also there, sweating in polyester and dancing madly.

After a while we joined our table to that of the crew of the *Brent Castle*, a British ship manned by New Zealanders. They were peach-faced boys, drunk as veterans, groping their Haitian whores with abandon. The Dominican girls eyed the Haitian whores with open distaste.

Some more Dominican girls joined us, and more tables were brought up. When the music stopped and the band stepped down for a break, several of the bandmembers came over to sit at our tables. It was a Dominican band, brought over every couple of weeks from Santo Domingo.

One of the musicians, a tall, light-skinned youth with a pencil mustache, sat next to me and asked me about my ship. He said he knew the *Erika* was in port. "Watch out for *polizontes*, Captain," he said gravely. "Plenty stowaways here." "Thank you," I said, "I will keep that in mind."

Later, after the band had quit and most of the Hispanic crewmen had gone back to their ships with their girls, one of the Haitian whores, fueled by rum and egged on by the Germans and New Zealanders, hoisted her skirt—she was wearing nothing under it—and managed, from a standing position, to urinate into a tumbler from a distance of four feet. The New Zealanders went wild. The Dominican girls crossed themselves.

CHAPTER THREE

CHRISTMAS DAY, 1987, DAWNED CLEAR AND HOT, THE SUN burning a fiery trail across the still water of the bay. I went on deck with a cup of coffee and watched the old women on shore start their breakfast fires. Several people were taking sponge-baths from five-gallon buckets of water. A line had already formed leading to the toilets.

There were half-a-dozen rough dories from the big island, Gonave, tied to the dock, their crews asleep on the gray-streaked sacks of charcoal that filled their hulls. As I watched, two more ghosted into view around Miragoane Point, ragged brown sails hanging limp from their willowy gaffs and booms. As far west as the eye could see the dark blue surface of the bay was dotted with the dugout canoes of fishermen.

Manuel appeared on deck in workclothes, his glossy black hair piled above his broad forehead. "*¿Descargamos hoy, Capitán?*"

"*No hoy, Manuel,*" I said. "*Es Navidad.*"

He started. "Christmas! I forgot it was Christmas." He ducked back into the hallway. "Hey, Victor, it's Christmas."

I heard Victor's voice storm out of the galley, "You're telling the cook it's Christmas? Can the cook forget it's Christmas, like some *huebon* AB?"

Yussuf's door was on the hook. I heard him and Sonia laughing in his cabin. I went back to the galley. Victor was mixing something red and spicy-looking in a big bowl. He grinned and kept working.

"You need anything from shore for Christmas dinner?" I asked. "Fresh vegetables? Fruit?"

"Amanda and I went to the market yesterday. I think I have everything." He paused and put the spoon down. "Captain, is it okay. . .you know, Captain, the girls here. . .they are from *La Republica Dominicana*. The Haitians hate them. They have nowhere. . ."

"You want to invite some of the girls to Christmas dinner? Sure, no problem. And all meals today are on the ship's account. You don't need to charge the crew for their girlfriends."

"Thank you, Captain, thank you."

"How about you, though?" I chuckled. "Did you charge yourself for Amanda?"

He looked shocked. "Oh, no, *Capi*! Amanda is only my friend. She is too old *para chingar*, you know. The other girls take care of her."

"Too old to fuck, eh? So what's she doing in Miragoane?"

He smiled slyly and started beating the bowl again. "She gets some work, *Capi*. She's cheap, you know. And I think Miragoane is like a home to her."

By then the town was coming alive. I could see brightly painted *tap-taps* coming down the hill by the church, filled with people in their best clothing. On the dock, no one was fighting.

"I'm going into town," I said. "Take a walk around."

Victor said, "Oh, no, *Capi*, don't go by yourself. Go with a Haitian. Very dangerous on shore here."

"It looks peaceful enough at the moment." I went up on deck and across to the barge. Ronald Joanel was sitting on the hatch. "Good morning," I said. "No work today, eh?"

He stood up hurriedly. "No work today, Captain. I came to see if you needed any help."

"Come on," I said. "I want to take a walk around town. Can you come with me?"

"Certainly." We stepped along the plank and ashore.

"I'll pay you five dollars, okay?"

"Oh, no. It will be a pleasure to walk with you and show you my town."

"Very well, then."

We filed through the narrow alley between the bullet-pocked building and a warehouse. This was the route the stevedores had to take, carrying sacks of rice from the barge to Bonvillain's warehouse.

The street was not yet full. Shops were open for business, their wooden doors propped open with barrels of flour and sugar. Rough tables on the sidewalk held lumpy candles, mosquito coils, and bottles of hair relaxer. In one storefront warehouse I saw sacks of flour stamped, "UN AID PROGRAM—NOT FOR SALE."

We came to a sad little park with some dead weeds in it, a statue of Mary in the center, her bright paint almost vanished. Ahead was the sally port by the Customs house. Two white men came out, burly blonds in short pants and tee-shirts. They looked at me. As they approached the younger one said, "What ship you from, mister?" He had a thick German accent.

"The *Erika*. I'm at the sunken barge."

The other, about 50, with green eyes and a light tan, spoke perfect British English. "Ah, the *Erika*. I understand you had a little cargo damage last night." I stared at him. He laughed easily. "I was watching from the bridge. I'm the captain on the *Weiser Trader*."

"Which ship is that?"

He turned around and pointed. I could just see the stern of his ship, one of the small ships discharging stern-to. "A thousand tons of cement. Should be finished tomorrow morning. Tried to get them to discharge today so I could get out of this bloody shithole, but they wouldn't hear of it. Starving, mind you, and won't work on Christmas."

The other man, about 20 years old, with a great soft belly that moved around under his tee-shirt like a restless panda, said, "Only 75 tons left and no work."

"Where to next?" I asked.

"Matanzas," the older man said. "Aluminum for Cartagena." He stepped forward and held out his hand. "I'm Capt. Walter Heinkel, like the airplane. This is Second Engineer Berndt Bosch, like the spark plug."

We shook hands. "Capt. Max Hardberger," I said. "Like the sandwich."

They liked that. Second Engineer Bosch said, "Like ze zandvich! Very gud!" The panda shook all over.

Captain Heinkel said, "But you are not German?"

"Nope. I'm from Louisiana."

"Well, Capt. Hardberger, enjoy your port call. Perhaps we will meet again in better surroundings."

"I hope so. We'll have to work to find worse."

The panda quivered. We shook hands again and parted. As Ronald and I walked up the street, I looked into one of the shops selling electronic junk and saw the teevee from the crew's mess sitting on top of an ancient console stereo cabinet.

"Ronald," I said, "that's the ship's teevee that was stolen yesterday."

He looked at it. "Are you sure, Captain?"

"Yes, I'm sure. You never watched teevee in the crew's mess? Look at that broken knob."

He said happily, "So you can buy it back cheap, Captain!"

"Bullshit." I took two steps into the tiny shop, picked up the teevee, and walked out. "Come on," I said, "let's go."

A black man with a morsel of food stuck to his wrinkled cheek came rushing out of a rear room. He and Ronald got into a furious argument, and within five seconds we were surrounded by a crowd of Haitians.

Ronald turned to me. "He says it is his television because he paid for it."

"I say it is my television because it was stolen from my ship yesterday. Ask him when he bought it."

The man said that he'd bought it two weeks ago in Port-au-Prince. Now the crowd was blocking the trucks on the street, and the drivers leaned on their horns.

"It is my television," I said. "I am going to prove that this man is a liar, and one who buys stolen merchandise."

Ronald translated that. The man hopped from foot to foot, spitting Creole. The crowd laughed.

Ronald said seriously, "He says he will call the police."

"Good," I said. We were right across from the police station. "Let's go see the police." The lead truck was inching forward, and the crowd was parting to let it through. I crossed in front of it with the teevee and went up the steps into the cool old building. There were some army personnel at the back of the long, empty room. They came walking toward us, big men in camouflage fatigues with sidearms.

The shopkeeper and Ronald both started shouting, but Ronald eventually won out and explained the situation. The door to the street was filled with wide-eyed heads. One of the soldiers, a muscular, middle-aged man with a streak of white hair, spoke to Ronald. He translated. "Captain, the major says you must give the television back because you cannot prove he stole it."

"Wait," I said. "Is it not against the law in Haiti to buy a thing stolen from another? That is the law in every civilized country."

Ronald translated. The major nodded and spoke.

"That is the law in Haiti, Captain," Ronald said.

"Good. Now watch this." I knew the electricity was on in town because there was an old floor fan in the back, whirring and rumbling. I went to a socket behind the front desk and plugged the teevee in. Now the people were getting pushed through the doors. They stumbled forward. Two soldiers rushed up to push them back, but the crowd had them pinned.

I raised my voice. "Ronald, tell them that when the volume control gets higher than right here, the sound gets all scratchy." I made a scratchy noise with my teeth. The Haitians gave an appreciative murmur.

Even the shopkeeper fell silent. I turned the teevee on and raised the rabbit ears. By spinning the dial, I was able to pick up a Port-au-Prince station. I slowly turned up the volume. The soldiers pushed their way in front so they could see.

It was an old Andy Griffith show, with Andy dubbed in gravelly French. When the volume knob reached the mark, the speaker started hissing and snapping. I turned it all the way up, then off.

The crowd laughed and jeered. The shopkeeper bullied forward, pleading. The major gave a little smile and shook his head. I unplugged the teevee and started out through the crowd. The former owner ran back and forth between pleading his case to the major and following his teevee, but the teevee won out. He pursued me down the steps and into the street, plucking at my arm and trying to reach for the teevee.

Ronald kept him off me. The crowd followed, heckling the shopkeeper and howling with glee. The man dropped back in despair after a couple of blocks, and Ronald and I turned into the alley to go to the ship.

After I'd returned the teevee to its place in the crew's mess, Ronald and I resumed our walk. We went up the steep hill above the town, past three cement crosses with two plaster criminals and a plaster Jesus on them. All three wore crowns of seagull droppings. From the top we could look down to a sunny green valley that led northwest to the sea, a vee of blue between the mountains. At the top of the highest peak were the ruins of an old Colonial French fort. Beyond the town the ships in the bay rode to anchor like ducks in a millpond.

Above our heads the trees rustled in the rising wind, and dust swirled up from the feet of the people walking on the road. As we were waiting for a *tap-tap* to come along to take us back to town, a middle-aged woman in a nice dress stopped at the edge of the road and squatted down. People walked past without paying any attention to her.

"Ronald," I said, "that lady's sick."

"What lady?"

I stepped over to see if I could help her. She grimaced. Ronald said something I didn't understand.

"*Avez-vous un probleme, Madame?*" I asked her. Still looking at me, she reached under her dress with her hand.

"She's making to shit, Captain," Ronald said, and at the same time I realized that she was wiping herself with her bare hand. I recoiled in horror. She stood up and wiped her hand on a piece of paper from her purse, adjusted her clothing, and marched on down the road, giving me a final uncurious look as she passed. I saw then that the verge of the road was littered with human excrement.

I agreed to go back to the ship. Ronald hailed a *tap-tap*, a Mazda pick-up truck with a huge wooden structure over the bed. This one had the legends "Sylvester Stallone" and "Rocky III" in violent colors on the roofline, and scenes from Stallone's movies painted all around the hood, cab, and body.

Ronald tried to arm an old woman out of the cab for me, but I convinced him that I could ride in the back with everyone else. The Haitians inside scrunched together pleasantly to make room for us on the wooden planks. Through the gaps in the slats I watched the steep hillside falling away on the right as the *tap-tap* threaded its way through the pedestrians.

When we got to the barge there was a volley of desperate cries coming from the dock. A number of dugout canoes hovered near the shore, the men in them yelling and gesticulating at the people on shore. I went to the end of the barge, where I could see past the outhouse, and saw a large crowd of well-dressed women standing on the dock and waving fistfuls of money at the canoemen.

"What the hell's going on there?" I asked.

"It is Christmas Day," Ronald said sadly. "They must to have some kind of meat or fish for Christmas dinner."

"They're fighting over fish?"

"There is no chicken or goat left. If they cannot buy fish, their families will have no meat for Christmas. Look." He pointed to one fisherman, holding position offshore with a paddle in one hand and a small plastic sack of fish in the other. "The fishermen are afraid of the women. They don't dare come ashore to sell their fish."

One of the women jumped or was pushed in. She grabbed the gunwale of the nearest boat and made a deal, got a bag of fish, and waded triumphantly ashore by the outhouse.

"What about your family, Ronald?" I asked. "You got any meat for Christmas dinner?"

He smiled. "I am a single man, Captain. My family went back to Bezin for Christmas, but I stayed here hoping to work tomorrow."

I clapped him on the shoulder. "Then I would like to invite you to dinner onboard. Tell Victor I said it's okay."

The shouting continued on the dock. The fishermen would pull up close, grab the money and a sack from the customer, then paddle backward a few feet, count up the money, count out the fish, and move back in to hand over the goods.

I left Ronald on the barge and went onboard to take a cup of coffee up to the bridge. A steady wind was pouring in through the open starboard door, and the wheelhouse was dark and cool. To the west the mountains tapered off blue and hazy along the coast. Across Gonave Bay was the great sere bulk of Gonave Island, rising like a ridge-backed whale across the horizon, its eastern tip hidden behind Miragoane Point.

I got up and went to the chart. The nearest point of the island was about 14 miles from Miragoane. I got the glasses and went to the window to study the island, but all I could see were brown and lifeless slopes crossed by a faint yellow tracery of paths, and trails of blue smoke from the charcoal-burners' ovens.

When I put the glasses down, I noticed that Ronald was still sitting on the hatch of the barge, his feet hanging over the coaming. "Hey, Ronald," I called, "how much you charge to go with me to Gonave?" He scrambled up and came closer to the bridge. I went out on the starboard wing. "Let's take a boat ride out to Gonave Island," I said. "I've always wanted to see what it's like."

"Gonave Island?" He looked quickly toward it. "Oh, no, Captain, I do not think you will go to Gonave Island."

"Sure I will. Come up to the boat deck."

I went down the ladder and pulled the cover off the rescue boat. In the heat, the tubes were good and taut. By the time I had the slack out of the runner on the winch, Ronald was coming up the ladder from the fantail. "Captain," he cried, wringing his hands, "you must not go to Gonave Island."

I looked at him. "Why not? This inflatable is perfectly capable of making it across. And the motor is almost new. You don't have to go if you don't. . ."

He came up close. "It is not that, Captain. The people on Gonave. . ."

"What about them?"

He didn't answer. I cranked the winch and the boat came up off the cradle.

"Captain, if you go to Gonave. . .they might eat you."

"What?" I started to grin. "Are you serious?"

He whispered, "Even other Haitians do not go to Gonave. And a *blanc*, by himself. . ."

I snorted and swung the boat over the side. His voice rose anxiously. "Mothers in Haiti tell their children, 'If you do not behave, I will send you to Gonave!'" He put a hand on the runner, as if to hold it back. I stopped cranking. "Okay, Ronald, we won't go to Gonave. How about a ride around the bay instead?"

He was agreeable to that, so we took a cruise westward, skimming past the mud-and-waddle huts that lined the southern shore. On the way back, Ronald said, "Captain, you want to see a ship that sank two weeks ago?"

"Sure. Where is it?"

"By those islands." He pointed toward a group of low mangrove islands south of the abandoned freighter. "It ran aground during a storm, and the owner never came. The crew lived onboard for a while, then they went ashore. Then another storm came and washed it back into deep water, where it sank."

I pointed the bow toward the islands. In a few minutes I could see the long, pale shape of the sunken ship, barely under water, through the blue of the waves. I cut power and we drifted up to it.

The ship was flat on its starboard side, with its port side about two feet under. The port running light was still sitting in its box, sparkling red in the sun. The masts and booms gleamed yellow in the depths. I came in close, until the boat's prop was running just above the bulwarks. The water was so clear it looked like we were floating on a cushion of air.

On the way back, I ran us under the abandoned freighter's counter. Her name, *God Only One*, was scrawled in sloping letters on her bustle stern. The old man didn't come out.

Yussuf and Sonia were on the *Erika*'s fantail, making *coco loco* with a bottle of Barbancourt rum and a pile of coconuts. I took a tall, cold glass of the milky mixture. The musician from the disco who had warned me about stowaways joined us a few minutes later. Sonia said that he was a friend of hers from Santo Domingo named Humberto. He was wearing a polyester shirt and long pants. He gave me a limp hand to shake.

We had Christmas dinner on tables set up on the No. 2 hatchcover, a festive affair lubricated by Portuguese wine and slop-chest beer. Later, as I was reading a book in my saloon, there was a knock on my door. It was Humberto. I put the book down. "*¿Sí, señor?*" I said.

He stepped in. "*Disculpeme, Capitán.* I have a question for you. I would like a job onboard your ship."

I opened my mouth, but he held up his hand. "No, no, *Capitán*. I am not a seaman. I just want a job to Miami." He reached in his pocket and pulled out a fat wad of U.S. hundreds. "Two thousand dollars to sign on the ship."

I shook my head. "Sorry. I can't do that."

He smiled. "I understand. But $2500. . ."

"It's not a matter of how much. I won't smuggle you into the U.S."

"No, no, *Capitán*, it is not smuggling. I will jump off before you go into port. No one will ever know."

I stood up. "*Mira*, Humberto. I'm not that kind of captain. And don't get any ideas about stowing away, either. I kill stowaways." I made a neck-breaking gesture with both hands.

He backed up. "Oh, no, *Capitán*, oh no, that is not my way. You see that I have asked you civilly. If you say no, then it is no. . ." He retreated to the companionway and downstairs. I returned to my reading.

At midnight I put the book away and took a walk around the ship. Manuel was talking to Victor and Humberto on the fantail. I went upstairs and turned in.

Something woke me. I couldn't tell what it was, but I got out of bed and looked on deck. The ship was dark and quiet. Manuel was sitting in a lawn chair in front of the house with a machete across his lap. He moved a little, and I saw that he was awake. There was a faint clank from the engine room. Another.

I slipped down the companionway and whispered into Jacek's cabin. He murmured something in Polish to Daniela and got dressed. Yussuf's door was on the hook as well. He opened it a crack. I pointed down to the engine room and made a catching motion with one hand around the other wrist. He grinned and slipped the hook. He was already wearing sweat pants. I drew him out on deck, into the fresh night air. I quieted Manuel with a finger to my lips. He got up and came over.

"There's a thief in the engine room," I whispered to them. "He's down there now. Yussuf and Jacek and I will go down and catch him. Now listen. . .I'm going to act like I want to kill him. Yussuf, you try to keep me from doing it. Try to persuade me not to. We'll talk in French. I think my French is up to it."

Yussuf chuckled. "Very good, very good."

"We're not going to hurt the guy. We're going to let him escape. Manuel, you stand by the door to the engine room, and when he comes out, pretend you're trying to chop him up with the machete. But don't hurt him, whatever you do. Okay?"

We went across to the engine-room door. It was open, light flooding out. We stood silently. Another clank of metal on metal, far below in the bowels of the ship. Jacek's brows drew together angrily. He started to step through, but I held him back and went first.

I could see the man's shadow cast forward from under the day tank, dancing on the floor plates. He was in the shop area of the lower deck. I got to the bottom of the ladder to the second deck, level with the main engine heads, when Jacek or Yussuf made a small noise above me. A head stuck out from under the bottom of the tank. It was a Haitian, his eyes wide in fright. He ducked back under the tank, but by then Yussuf and Jacek and I were charging down the ladders, yelling and cursing.

He jumped down into the shaft alley, holding his hands up in front of his face, jabbering in Creole. He had piled up all the chief's hand tools, even the big wrenches, into a piece of tarpaulin on the workbench, and was in the process of wrapping it up when we came in. I jumped down into the shaft alley with him and grabbed his tee-shirt, but it tore loose in my hands, showing his naked, sweaty chest. He was a gaunt man with close-cropped hair, about 20, with a misshapen jaw. He worked it furiously, clasping his hands together and begging for mercy.

I got a hand around his ripped collar and pulled him toward me. He fell forward with his feet tangled in the frames. Yussuf got down on his knees from the lower deck and took the man's other arm. We pulled and pushed and got him up on the floorplates. He struggled to his feet, but I jumped up and shoved him forward. He fell against the trunk of the main engine and slid down between two of the crankcase doors.

I turned to Yussuf. *"Aidez moi lancer le voleur dans la mer."*

The thief pulled himself up to his knees, begging for his life.

Yussuf said, in French, "Please, *Capitain*, don't kill him. Let's just beat him up."

"No," I said, "I want to kill him."

Jacek came down the steps with a couple of junk auxiliary cylinder heads and a length of chain. When the man saw that he turned gray. *"Seulement un 'tit chose,"* he whispered.

"We've got to take him up on deck to kill him," I went on. "I don't want to get blood all over down here." I pulled the man to his feet and shoved him ahead of me up the ladder.

He gained strength as we went up. I kept my hand on his collar until we got to the middle of the ladder to the main deck, then I let go and pretended to stumble. The man bolted up and out the door.

Manuel's voice roared, *"¡Alto, ladron, alto!"* There was the snick of a blade against the steel bulkhead, a despairing wail from the Haitian, and a wild laugh from Manuel.

More whacking sounds, followed by a splash. By then I was out the door myself, with Yussuf and Jacek behind me. We ran to the port bulwark and looked overboard. Luminous rings showed where the thief had gone in, but he was still underwater. For a long minute nothing moved, then he breached at the edge of darkness, a black dot in the black water, ringed by faint green light. We could hear him whuffing and blubbering as he struck off for shore.

"Come back," Yussuf called in French, "Come back, *voleur*, and we will kill you."

"You can bet it'll be all over town tomorrow," I told the crew. "He'll be telling all his thieving buddies how he narrowly escaped death on the *Erika*."

Daniela got up and got dressed, and we all went up to the master's saloon for some Customs scotch. A few hours later the donkey engines and main generators on the other ships started up. I could hear the clatter of hatchboards. The stevedores arrived on the sunken barge to be counted onboard.

Fritz limped up to me. "I heard about that thief you caught last night." He held his tally pad out like he was going to write me a ticket. "You are lucky you did not hurt the man."

"Oh, yeah? He's even luckier."

"You would have gone to jail if you had hurt that man. There is law in this country. . .he must have a trial before he is punished."

I was already walking away. "Yeah, yeah," I muttered.

About 10 minutes after discharging started the hydraulic line broke again. This time no one noticed until most of our hydraulic oil had been pumped into Miragoane Bay, leaving a nice long slick out to westward as far as the eye could see. Yussuf came and got me, and I went down to take a look. Jacek was already there with gasket material and hose clamps, but he had a grim look. "We have no more hydraulic oil, Captain. I used the rest of the spare oil the last time the pipe broke." He cast me an apprehensive glance. "I forgot to tell you."

"Don't worry. I'll blame it on the stevedores." I found Fritz on the barge eating from a plate of lumpy rice. "Fritz, your crane operator did it again. He broke the hydraulic system. Now we lose all our hydraulic oil. Where can I get some more?"

He stirred around in the rice, probably looking for a piece of chicken, but soon gave up. "Po'-au-Pranz have hydraulic oil. You get it there."

"I need to talk to the ship's agent. Who's the agent here? I haven't seen the agent once since we got here."

"No agent. Mr. Bonvillain is agent."

"Well, tell him he needs to get us a drum of AW 68 as soon as possible."

"Mr. Bonvillain is in Po'-au-Pranz."

I called Yussuf over. "Have them keep humping the rice forward. Make piles around where the derrick can lift from, so we don't have to move them. Fill as many nets as you can while we're waiting. I'm going to try to get some more oil."

Before I left I called around to the other ships in harbor, but none of them had any spare AW 68. I took the next lighter ashore, sitting with the boatmen on top of the bags, and gave a stevedore five *gourdes* to carry me piggyback up to dry land. I saw Georges, the crane operator, on the street, and he led me to the telephone office, marked by a wrenched door of planks propped open with a coral rock. Inside the dim room was a telephone on a shelf. A woman sat behind a heavy mesh cage, eating something glutinous on a metal plate.

"*Téléphone aux Etats Unis?*" I asked.

"*Pas de téléphone,*" she said, around a mouthful.

"*J'ai l'argent.*" I pulled out a fistful of *gourdes*.

She waved a finger in the air and swallowed. "*Pas de téléphone. Il est hors de service.*"

"*Quand il sera bon?*"

The question seemed to make no sense to her. Neither could she answer when I asked how long it had been out of service. On my way back to the ship I saw

Ronald, hurrying along with a small bag in his hand. I asked him about the telephone.

"Oh, no, Captain, the telephone never work here. Maybe long time ago, I don't know. For telephone you go to Petit Goave."

"Then why is the office open? Oh, never mind. How far is Petit Goave? An hour, you said?"

"Yessir. I am sorry, Captain, but I must go to Bezin with medicine for my mother now. I can come back this afternoon and go with you to Petit Goave."

"Hell, don't worry about it. But where are the mattress buyers?"

"I bring them tonight, Captain. They must to come from Port-au-Prince." He saw a *tap-tap* heading for Bezin, shook my hand hurriedly, and ran to jump into the back.

I caught a *tap-tap* going east and endured an hour's ride over the mountains to Petit Goave, at a fare of 50 cents. The telephone office was dark and narrow, with a row of wooden booths on one side. It was stifling hot. A small fan behind the desk pointed at the young woman crouched there. She waved me toward the booths.

The operator connected me with Shell Oil in Port-au-Prince, but they wouldn't deliver without prior payment, except through an agent. The other two oil companies said the same thing. I tried calling Dickie, but there was no answer. Finally I called the cargo broker, who called the charterer's brother in Miami, who called someone in Port-au-Prince, who went to Shell with cash, paid for the oil, and arranged to have it delivered by pick-up truck to Miragoane.

Back at the ship, the stevedores had knocked off for lunch, and were crouched on the starboard side in the narrow shadow of the barge's hatchcoaming, eating the cooked rice they'd brought. Yussuf met me in the hallway.

"There are two Haitians waiting for you in your saloon, Captain. The stevedore foreman says that one of them is the port director and the other is his bodyguard."

I nodded. "All right. I'll go up."

I had left my windows closed and locked, but Yussuf had opened them and turned on the fans. Raoul, the infamous port director, was a short, heavy-set man, coal-black, with a roll of muscle around the back of his neck like a Junker. His bodyguard was a big brute with a ridged forehead and an Uzi.

Raoul gestured for me to sit down in my own saloon. They were behind the table, so I sat in one of the chairs.

"Is this your first time to Miragoane, Captain?" he asked.

"Yes, it is. In the old days I used to go into Port-au-Prince, but never into Miragoane. I used to use the church roof here for a landmark, though."

He smiled tolerantly. "So you know Miragoane is an official port now, Captain. I am the port director."

It wasn't a question. I waited.

"You are a professional captain," he went on. "You know your ship cannot discharge cargo after Custom House is closed."

"You are right. I am a professional captain. What are you talking about?"

He licked his lips and looked at my mini-fridge. Reluctantly, I said, "May I offer you gentlemen a drink?"

The port director said Coke for both of them. I served them cold cans with no glasses. They didn't mind. "What about the night before last, Captain?" Raoul said, smacking his lips after a long gulp. "Did you discharge cargo that night?"

"Of course not. The stevedores quit at five o'clock."

He continued to look at me. The bodyguard played idly with the auto switch on his Uzi. Victor appeared in the door with plates of food for all three of us, with glasses of ice for the drinks and folded napkins. He winked at me as he put my plate down.

The conversation was interrupted while the Haitians dug into the rice and beans with spiced chicken and chopped peppercorns, a Victor specialty. When the port director finally wiped his chin and placed his fork decisively by the side of his plate, he said, "Captain, I understand you are on a six-month time charter to Mr. Bonvillain. Is that true?"

I hesitated. "As far as I know. I'm just the captain."

He nodded. "Then you will be coming to Miragoane many times. You may want to do business in Miragoane, eh? Many captains make good money this way. My brother deals in *pepe*. . .I will have him come to see you before you leave."

"Many thanks," I said. "I would be glad to speak with him."

He paused delicately. "But, frankly, I have a problem, Captain. I came personally because I would like to help Mr. Bonvillain. I know he would not want his cargo or the ship he chartered to get into trouble."

I waited, all ears now.

"Captain," he continued, "you did not clear Customs on entering the country. This is a very serious offense."

"Raoul," I burst out, "there is no Customs here. I flew the quarantine flag for three hours and nobody came out."

He drew back. "You flew the qua'ntine flag? Captain, you have disease onboard?"

I laughed. "No, the Q-flag. So Customs will come out and clear me into the country. Is that not true? Is there Customs here?"

"Well," he puffed, "I am Customs here. Under the new government, I have Customs authority."

"All right," I said, "very well. But that is something you must take up with the charterer. Have you talked to Mr. Bonvillain?"

He gave me a hard look. "Captain, two nights ago you allowed a car to be imported into Haiti without duty. You allowed your ship to be used for smuggling. I have authority to arrest you and seize the ship."

"Now you're making yourself understood. What is the fine for not clearing in?"

His eyes narrowed. "One thousand dollars." Then he added experimentally, "U.S."

I shook my head quickly. "Oh, no, that's too high. This is only a small ship. Why, the fine should not be over 200. . .300 dollars."

His brow knotted. He looked at his henchman. I stood up. "Director, you know that I will be here many times. I'll be able to get whatever you need when we go back to Freeport. . .refrigerator, air conditioner, whatever. I think a $500 fine is about right for this little ship."

He finally agreed to $500. I asked them to step down to the officer's mess while I got the money, which they did. I got it out of the ship's safe and took it down. The port director took the money without comment and slipped it in his pocket. It was hot in the mess, and they bolted as soon as the money changed hands. I went upstairs to log the incident, type a Note of Protest, and make the proper entry in the ship's accounts.

Ronald appeared in the saloon door and said that he had two men from Port-au-Prince downstairs who wanted to buy mattresses. I went with him to the fantail, where two gold-bedecked men sat waiting. They were both wearing flowered shirts and triple-pleated pants with tight little cuffs over nylon socks and low-cut loafers. They stood up as I stepped over the coaming.

One was very short with frog-eyes. The other was a gangly youngster with rubbery lips. They both spoke fair English. After a few minutes to assure me that we were going to be lifelong friends, and that I would become a rich man trading in Haiti if I just stuck with them, they let me take them forward to the forecastle.

They leaned the mattresses this way and that, talking in Creole between themselves. They lifted and prodded and poked the mattresses, fingered the coverings, and examined the labels upside-down. It was hot in the forecastle, so I went on deck. There was not much the stevedores could do until we got more hydraulic oil, as they had already filled the area where the derrick could pick from, but they had nowhere better to go, so they lounged around in the shade of the bulwarks.

The Haitian buyers came out and asked me how much I wanted for all the mattresses.

"There's 40 mattresses. I'll take. . .four grand U.S. for all of them."

They were shocked and outraged. "Oh, no," the tall one cried, "you'll never get that. Why, new mattresses in Port-au-Prince are selling for 80 dollars."

"Those are cheap Mexican mattresses," I told them. "These are the finest U.S. manufacture. Look at the label. . .made in Houston. How about that?"

They were impressed. They went back in and spent the rest of the lunch hour reinspecting them. Then they emerged, soaked in sweat and dabbing at their streaming faces with their rayon shirttails. "Three thousand is all we can offer," Frog-Eyes said.

I shook my head and started to lock the door. The tall one tried to stop me. "Oh, no, no, Captain, we will come to agreement. We can pay $3200."

After another half-hour of haggling we agreed on $3500 for all of the mattresses. We shook hands over Cokes in the saloon, and they promised to be back that evening with the money and a truck.

The hydraulic oil arrived shortly after 1500 hours. I knew it had arrived when Ricardo came to tell me that there were two men swimming in the water by the ship with a drum of oil. I went down to the fantail.

There was a yellow-and-red drum of Shell AW-68 floating in the water under the counter. Two naked Haitians were dogpaddling around it. After consultation with Jacek, I had them maneuver it around to the port side, where Yussuf and Manuel lowered the boat-davit runner with a nylon sling on it. The Haitians choked the sling around the barrel, kicking and diving to keep it in place, and Manuel winched it up on the boat deck. The swimmers wanted me to pay them for their labors, but I gave them the empty drum instead, which suited them just fine. They swam off toward the dock herding it ahead of them.

By 1545 hours, the boom was lifting cargo again. I was sitting on the hatchcoaming, staring idly into the hold, when there was a stir among the stevedores. I heard them giggling, then a suppressed laugh. I looked up.

The stevedores were staring toward the top of the accommodations. I turned around and looked, but for a moment the sun's glare blinded me. When I got my eyes shielded and peered again, I saw Daniela sitting on the monkey island—the roof of the wheelhouse—in a bikini bottom and no top, her blonde hair blowing wild in the wind. Her great, milky breasts and crimson nipples gleamed in the sun. Haitians are no strangers to the sight of women's breasts, but those stevedores had never seen ones like that before.

Just before dark Ronald returned with the mattress buyers. They were hot and tired from their drive, and probably wanted me to invite them up to the saloon for a cold Coke, but I kept them on deck.

The first problem was that they had not been able to raise the whole $3500. Froggie said that he had some buyers right there in Miragoane, and that if I would give him all the mattresses, he would be back in a few minutes with the rest of the money.

I said that that was a fine idea, but it would be just as convenient for the buyers in Miragoane to come to the ship. That way Froggie would be able to pay for all of them before leaving the ship, and the buyers could arrange their own transportation for the mattresses.

That possibility did not seem to have occurred to him. He hmmed and hawed and said he would see what he could do. He left Rubber-Lips on deck and went down off the barge long enough to get to the end of the alley, then came back. "Captain, I have talked to another buyer, and he has given me the rest of the money."

"Excellent. Let's count the money and you can arrange to get them off the ship."

His bulging eyes regarded me carefully. "We must load them into little boats, Captain."

"*You* must load them in little boats, my friend. Now, the money."

He was offended. "Do not worry, Captain. You are dealing now with a real *homme d'affaires*. A real businessman."

"The money," I said. "Show me the money or get off the ship."

Finally he produced a pile of wadded-up U.S. dollars and counted them out on the hatchcover. They totaled $3274. He gathered the bills together and presented them to me proudly.

"That's not $3500," I pointed out.

"Oh, Captain, it's only a little bit," he said. "I will have the rest for you tonight."

"Tell you what. You're three mattresses short. I'll let you have 37 mattresses for what you've got."

A big Haitian lighter came around the stern and pulled up to the pilot ladder. Froggie quickly agreed to take the 37 mattresses and handed me the money. The ragged Haitians in the boat scrambled onboard and started carryng the mattresses from the forecastle to the gunwale. They lowered them with ropes down to the boat, where the crew stacked them carefully on plastic sheeting laid over the peeled poles that served as floor timbers.

I was standing on deck when the last mattress came out of the forecastle. I went over and looked in, and saw that there were no mattresses left. I spun around in the doorway. Froggie was climbing over the bulwark for the pilot ladder. I ran for him.

When he saw me coming he wavered between jumping and coming back, and decided to come back. "Why, Captain, what is the problem?"

"Three mattresses, goddamn it. You took all of them." The last mattress was going over the side. I grabbed it and pulled it away from the Haitians. They crowded around me, jabbering and plucking at me. Froggie was in the middle of them, but I couldn't hear what he was saying.

Manuel and I got the mattress back inside the forecastle and shut the door, then I walked toward the Haitians at a slow, terrible pace. They fell away and left Froggie standing alone by the pilot ladder. "*Monsieur*," I told him, "if you do not tell the boat to send two mattresses back, I will kill you."

He tried to laugh if off, but the laugh got stuck in his throat and came out a gargle. I kept coming. He backed against the ladder, his eyes bulging and blinking. I picked up a piece of jagged dunnage and kept walking at the same slow pace.

"Okay, okay, Captain," he said, pulling dollars out of his pocket. "I pay for the two mattresses in the boat, okay?"

I shook my head. "Not okay. Put two back. You had your fucking chance."

He whined and pleaded, but finally gave the boat instructions to send two mattresses up. When they came on deck the stevedores cheerfully carried them into the forecastle. Froggie shook my hand and promised to buy all the mattresses I could bring next time. He tried to give me his card, but I wouldn't take it, which seemed to distress him greatly. He got in the boat and it sculled away toward the houses on the south side of the bay.

We were discharging the next morning when another ship came in, about 800 tons deadweight. She was an old Dutch or German ship, with swinging derricks on a mast amidships. I could see her coming in from the west at dawn, and by midmorning she was off Miragoane Point. When I put the glasses on her I saw that she was listing heavily to starboard.

I called Yussuf up to the bridge and handed him the glasses. "My God," he said, "she is about to turn over. She must be listing 15 degrees."

"More. Maybe 20."

He whistled softly. "She is in plenty trouble. Full of cargo, too."

The ship turned into the bay and steamed toward the anchorage, showing the bare rusty metal of her port bottom. She dropped anchor with a faint rattle and swung into the wind.

I called the vessel on VHF. "Vessel that just entered Miragoane harbor, this is the *Erika*. Do you need assistance? Over."

After several calls, the ship answered. "This is the *Santo Filipe*," a Hispanic voice said, an old man. "We are okay. We have some water in the hold, but we will fix problem now."

"Is there anything we can do to help, over?"

"No, Captain, nothing. Maybe charterer here in Miragoane now, come on board, say what to do. Thank you, Captain."

After a while the ship put its boat in the water, and the captain came up to my port side. He was an arthritic old Mexican with a mane of white hair. He said that they had been running on their tanktops for months, as the Dominican owner had no money to patch the hull, but that the tanktops were good and hadn't leaked.

Then the tanktop over No. 3 starboard had sprung a leak. The ballast pump was keeping up with it for the moment, but he wanted to know if I had any diving equipment onboard. His men had tried to reach the hole by free-diving from the ship's boat, but they couldn't stay under long enough to find it.

I said we didn't have anything like that, and he went on into town after asking if he could leave his boat tied to the *Erika*.

Later, I heard that he hired an AB named Johnson from the *Bahia Mar* who could hold his breath for two minutes, to take down a gob of underwater epoxy and press it into the hole. It must have stopped the leak, because that evening the ship was on an even keel, and a few days later it started discharging. A third of the cargo of bagged rice had gotten wet, and the odor of the rotting bags had damaged the rest. The story went around that the cargo was declared a total loss, salvaged by the crew, and sold ashore for a staggering sum.

Right at noon the port director showed up. I told him that the electricity was not working in my saloon, and that he would be more comfortable in the officer's mess. He condescended to take his lunch there, and I didn't see any more of him that day.

I had just finished lunch in the saloon when there was a knock on the office door. Manuel brought in a big old wreck of a man, a barrel-chested, spider-legged *blanc* with a tiny Haitian woman in tow. "How d'you do, mate?" the man boomed, gripping my hand. "I'm Pete Fields. This is my wife Denise." The little Haitian woman, maybe 20 years old, ducked her head and smiled sheepishly.

He sat down in one of the chairs with a groan and stuck his worn jogging shoes straight out in front of him. "Bad pins, mate. That's what you get from a life at sea. Mind if I sit down?"

"Not at all. Madame?" I gestured toward one of the other chairs, but she sat on the floor in front of Pete.

"I used to be in the shipping business myself," he said. "Retired to Haiti here. I run a consulting business now."

"I see."

"I just stopped by to see if there was anything you needed. Stores, groceries, repairs. . ."

"I think we're okay."

"The wife can do the crew laundry." There was a note of desperation in his voice that made it sound as if he were offering her for other services as well.

"We have a Dominicana who does our laundry."

"You do, eh? Gotta watch those Dominican whores. They'll steal you blind, take my word for it."

I convinced him that there was nothing he could do for the ship and that the ship's cook didn't need his wife to stay and help with the cooking. He got up.

"I say," he said, close to me, as if it meant anything that the girl could hear, "I'm waiting for some money from the U. K. It was wired yesterday, don't you know, so should be in Port-au-Prince now. Could you spot me a hundred U.S. to get to Port-au-Prince and pick it up?"

"I'm sorry, but I don't have any personal money. I'd have to use ship's money, and then I'd have to justify it to the owner."

He was staring hungrily into my eyes. "I could leave the wife, you know, as a guarantee. . ."

I laughed shortly. "I don't think so."

He turned toward the door. The little Haitian woman sprang up to help him down the companionway, going first so he could crush her if he fell. They went out and I did not see them again.

Two days later the stevedores reached the engine-room bulkhead. Bags were still piled against the sides and in the corners of the hold. The stevedores formed a long line along the length of the floor, tossing the bags from man to man until they reached the derrick. I was lollygagging on the gunwale when I saw Bonvillain step up on the plank to the barge.

"Mr. Bonvillain," I called to him, "I'm very glad to see you."

He looked surprised. "I am glad to see you too, Captain. But I must talk to you. . .the ship must work overtime tonight."

"I thought there was no overtime here."

"No, no, I have special permission. We must work overtime tonight."

I shrugged my shoulders. "That's okay with the ship. It's in the charter party."

"How long you think it will take to finish discharging?"

"If we work all night, maybe by noon tomorrow."

He frowned. "Can you finish by eight a.m.?"

"I don't think so. Maybe by putting extra men in the hold. The problem is working the cargo forward to the derrick."

"Okay, I put how many? Ten extra men? Twenty?"

"Make it 20."

"Okay, I'll do that. The next shift will come onboard at five."

He started to hurry away, but I said, "There's something else."

"What's that."

"The port director came yesterday and charged me $500 for not clearing in."

"Oh, he's crazy," Bonvillain said, still moving toward the plank.

"He's not so crazy. He's $500 richer. I entered it in the log. Dickie will expect you to repay the ship that amount."

He glared at me. "That is the ship's problem. That has nothing to do with the charterer."

"Oh, yes it does." I pointed a finger at him. "The charter party says, 'One safe berth, one safe port.' The fact that the port director comes onboard and extorts money from the ship means that this is not a safe port. If you want the ship to stay here under those conditions, you'll have to pay the illegal costs."

He stalked off the barge without replying. I went up to the chartroom and turned on the SSB after making sure there was no one on the monkey island. It was a big old Skanti TRP, and took a while to warm up. After I found a good bandwidth at 4 Mhz, I waited until there was a break in the cruise ship traffic and called Whiskey Oscar Mike.

Several vessels were calling, but the operator chose me. "Go ahead, *Erika*." It was the same operator who'd taken many of my calls since we left Mobile. He sounded like a cultivated young man. I gave my position and he tuned the station's antenna, then passed me to the High Seas Operator. Dickie answered on the first ring.

"We're down to a couple of shifts on the offloading," I said. "How's the charter hire payment?"

"What do you mean, Captain?" His voice pulsed with the atmosphere.

"Are you owed any charter money? We're almost out of cargo."

"Yeah, it's due today. His brother in Miami called yesterday and said he was sending a wire transfer, but my bank hasn't gotten it yet."

"Don't hold your breath. They're trying to get the ship offloaded in a hurry. Probably so they won't have to pay to reposition."

"But, Captain, I've got a six-month charter party. If they don't pay, they lose the ship."

I snorted. "They don't care about that. And they don't care about the charter party. I recommend I close the hatches until they pay. Otherwise they'll drop you now and you'll have to steam back to the States on your own nickel."

He thought about it. "But how will you stop them from discharging?"

"Leave that to me."

"Okay, Captain, do what you think best. I'll be waiting here. Let me know what happens."

We hung up and I went down to the engine room. Jacek was filing on a part at the workbench. I explained what I wanted and he nodded. I went up and watched the cargo operations until the derrick was just about to lift the load, then stepped into the engine room and signaled Jacek. He cut power to the hydraulic pump and the runner went slack. When I went on deck the crane operator waved to me and pointed to the controls. Fritz was hurrying over.

"Hydraulic pump broken," I told him.

"But, but," he stammered, "Georges didn't do anything. He didn't even pick the load up. . ."

I nodded. "I know. It's the ship's fault. I'll sign a note."

"You, you always blame crane man. . ." He blinked. "It's the ship's fault?"

"Yeah. I said I'd sign a note."

The stevedores collapsed onto sacks, arms outstretched, sucking in the overheated air through gaping mouths. Fritz hurried off to fetch Bonvillain, who arrived a few minutes later like a storm cloud.

"What is the problem, Captain?"

"Hydraulic pump. It just went out."

"You must fix it. We must finish discharging tonight."

"Sorry. Chief engineer says it will take him all night to fix it. He has to machine a part onboard. Very difficult.'

He spat in frustration. "You must fix it, Captain. You must fix it."

"We'll do our best, Mr. Bonvillain," I said blandly, "but you'd better count on tomorrow morning, not tonight."

He stomped off and Fritz discharged the stevedores. Ronald came onboard and talked to Fritz in Creole for a few minutes, then turned to me. "Captain, did you know Fritz is getting married Saturday?"

"No," I said. "Is that true, Fritz?"

He nodded tiredly, wiping his face. "It's true, Captain."

"Then I've got a wedding present for you. Come on." I took him to the forecastle. "Pick out one of those mattresses for a wedding present."

Fritz looked at me suspiciously. "You're giving me a bed, Captain?"

"Sure. Many happy years to you and your wife."

He grinned suddenly. "You have made me very happy, Captain. We do not have a bed, you know. I bought some ca'pet so we would have something to sleep on."

"Well, now you have a bed. Name your first child Max after me. I will have contributed to his creation."

He laughed loud and long, then he and Ronald carried the mattress over to the barge, where one of the stevedores helped him carry it down to the alley.

"He's very happy, Captain," Ronald said when he came back. "You have given Fritz a good wedding present."

When Bonvillain came onboard the next morning he said, "Captain, is the pump fixed?"

"Why, yessir, it is, but we have another problem."

"What is that?"

"The charter hire is overdue."

He clapped his hands in anger. "The charter has been paid. You must open the hatches."

"I just talked to Dickie. He said he was supposed to get paid yesterday, but the money was never transferred."

He dismissed that with a wave. "The money just got held up at the bank. Open the hatches. I will take care of this with Dickie."

"No can do. Not until Dickie tells me to."

His lips curled into a snarl. "Captain, you must open the hatches. It is illegal to keep my cargo onboard."

"Wrong. Look at the charter party."

"Charter party? What charter party? This is Haiti, Captain. We don't have charter parties."

"So?"

"So I could have you arrested and taken off the ship." He changed tone abruptly. "But that won't be necessary. All you have to do is call Dickie and he will tell you to open the hatches."

"Okay," I agreed, "Let's go upstairs and call him."

Halfway up the stairs he changed his mind. "How about this? I will give you one day's charter hire onboard, and you can start discharging."

"How about this?" I said, still going up. "We call Dickie and you give me what he says you owe."

He didn't like that. He grumbled all the way up to the bridge. He was still grumbling when I made connection with WOM, but he put on a brave tone for the microphone.

"Dickie," he gushed, "Dickie, why is your captain causing all this problem for me? You know the crane have plenty problem, and now we are very behind schedule. Yes, I know that, Dickie, but I have many losses on this cargo, because crane does not work. . .yes, yes, I understand, but if I can pay for two days. . ."

He finally agreed to pay for seven days' charter hire. He handed the phone to me. Dickie said, "Captain, Mr. Bonvillain will pay you in cash in Miragoane. I need you to take the money to Port-au-Prince today. I'll come down on the three-o'clock flight and pick it up. I need the money tomorrow, and Mr. Bonvillain says he doesn't have enough money in the bank to wire it to me. Can you do that?"

"Sure," I said. "I'll leave Yussuf in charge."

We hung up. Bonvillain and I went on deck. "Don't forget the $500 I gave to Raoul," I told him.

He opened and shut his mouth a couple of times, then made a strangled noise and went off to get the money. Ronald came onboard as he was leaving.

"Captain," Ronald said, "there will be a big strike today. Maybe plenty problem on the highway."

"What kind of problem?"

"You know, when Haitians strike, they close up all roads with blockade, what you call roadblock. Maybe dangerous to go to Port-au-Prince today."

"What's this strike about?"

"General Namphy says all the small ports in Haiti must to close up. Ships only can come in to Port-au-Prince and Cap Haitian."

"So the government can get its share of the pie, is that right?"

"That's right."

"Well, I've got to go anyway. The owner's already on his way to the airport."

"I will go with you up to the highway, to make sure it is safe."

"Thanks, Ronald. Good idea."

When Bonvillain got back, he counted out $9877, mostly in 20's and 50's. I gave him a receipt and he huffed out without shaking my hand. I put $500 in the ship's safe and the rest in a small overnight bag. As I was about to leave the ship Yussuf and Sonia came up. Sonia said, "*Capi*, I have a friend who needs to go back to Santo Domingo. She's catching the plane this afternoon. Can she ride with you in the *tap-tap?*"

"Sure," I said, "but I'm leaving now."

Her friend was on the *Dieu Qui Sauve*. Yussuf called the ship on VHF, and the girl met me at the dock. She was a heavy-set girl with café-au-lait skin, about 25, with lingering acne and a scar across the bridge of her nose.

I found a *tap-tap* that agreed to let us have the entire back of the truck for $20 U.S. as long as he could take passengers in the front, and we set off. Without having to drop off and pick up passengers, we left town quickly and headed up the mountain.

The mood was jumpy at Ville de Rousseau, the mountain town where the road to Miragoane meets the highway between Port-au-Prince and Les Cayes. We stopped for gasoline, but there was none to be had. *Tap-taps* waiting for a gas truck to arrive clogged the road. Two white Mazda trucks with their beds full of armed men in blue work clothes came roaring up from the direction of Les Cayes. The *tap-taps* jerked out of the way of the Mazdas, scattering the old ladies tending cooking pots on the shoulder of the road. The flying squad went past honking their horns and disappeared.

I called Ronald over. "How long until the gas gets here?"

"I don't know, Captain. Madame Sarah say the truck come soon."

"Who?"

He pointed to a big woman standing on the curb with a carpetbag clutched in her meaty hands. "She hired the truck and bought the gas. She will sell the gas when the truck comes. We call lady like that 'Madame Sarah.'" He looked around. "I will ask the *tap-taps* coming from Port-au-Prince what is happening on the road." He went off.

A tank-truck with a faded Texaco star on the side came grinding up the hill from the direction of Port-au-Prince, the cab full of men. They piled out and started selling fuel directly from the truck, taking *gourdes* by the bucketsful from the *tap-tap* drivers coming from Les Cayes. They said there was no fuel on the southern coast.

Then it was our turn. A big Haitian in a sweaty guayaberra shirt motioned the driver forward. The dusty street under the truck was wet with spilled gasoline, but the Haitians walking along smoked their cigarettes with abandon. Ronald climbed up into the back of the *tap-tap*. "Captain, I don't think you should go to Port-au-Prince today."

"Why not? Because of this strike or whatever?"

"The strike. Is very bad. *Tap-taps* trying to go to Les Cayes say the roadblock is on the road. Maybe better tomorrow."

"Shit." I looked through the slats. The driver and several others were watching the flowmeter on the truck with intense interest.

"I've got to go," I said. "The owner is already at the Miami airport. The road to Port-au-Prince is open, right?"

He shrugged. "As far as I know. The Macouts just went in that direction." He pointed at the approaching vehicles. "And *tap-taps* are still coming from Port-au-Prince."

The fuel man stopped the nozzle and held a can under it. The valve was bad, and fuel leaked from it in a steady drip. The driver paid the Madame Sarah and got in the cab.

Ronald hesitated. "Okay, Captain," he said, "God bless you." He climbed out.

We pulled away with several *tap-taps* right behind us and went down the hill. The roadside was full of people carrying sticks and machetes. They yelled and waved their sticks at the *tap-tap*, but they didn't seem hostile, and the driver waved back to them as we went along. My buttocks started hurting. I was sitting on the edge of the wooden seat. I sat back and tried to relax.

We went about three kilometers, then the driver hit the brakes. We were coming up on a low concrete bridge over a creek. There was a hasty roadblock set up in front of it, mostly stones and branches, stretching across both shoulders to the low thornbushes that covered the hillsides. The driver looked back quickly, past me to the traffic behind him. There was a crowd of people on the left side of the road ahead, struggling with a boulder the size of a footlocker.

"Holy shit," I said, jerking my shirttails out of my pants. The Dominicana tore her eyes from the roadblock ahead to stare at me as I unzipped my pants, opened the bag, and started stuffing U.S. bills into my underwear.

The driver tried to head for a gap on the left side, where the *tap-tap* might have made it through, but at that moment the bushes erupted with people. The Dominicana cried out and clutched her purse to her throat. I gave up on the money transfer, zipped my pants, closed the bag, and sat down. The driver skidded to a stop and threw the *tap-tap* in reverse, but by then the cars and other *tap-taps* behind us had jammed the narrow road. We were trapped.

The *tap-tap* was surrounded in an instant by black faces. The driver had his window almost closed, and he was pleading with them through the gap. Faces peered in through the slats at the girl and me, and ragged men and women filled the open rear door. I could hear faintly, as if coming from a long way away, the Haitian women crying in the cab of the truck.

Something hit me in the back. I half-turned and saw the end of a branch sticking through the slats. The Haitians laughed and the stick jabbed me again. I jerked forward on my knees—there was no room to stand—and saw sticks coming through the other side, hitting the Dominicana. She was crying, green eyepaint and mascara running down her face.

One of the women at the back reached in for my bag. I jerked it away. Luckily the gaps in the slats on the sides weren't wide enough to reach through. The Dominicana slid off the seat into my arms. I could feel her heart pumping like a piston. Another Haitian reached in and got a hold on my wrist. I tried to jerk free, but I wasn't strong enough. His face was close to mine. He was laughing. The faces around him were laughing. Something hit me on the cheek, hard enough to stun me. I was getting dragged out of the truck.

A face towered above the rest, a bearded face. I knew that face for an instant, then it disappeared. The hands fled from my wrists, and the people at the back parted. The face was Fritz's, the stevedore foreman. He was wearing his white hardhat and carrying a cudgel. He shouted at the others. They drew back from the sides of the *tap-tap*.

"Captain, you should not be on the road today," he said sternly. "We are closing the road because the government has closed the port."

"I noticed," I said. "Thanks for saving my ass."

He laughed. "You can go on now. Be careful, Captain." The crowd had moved on to the *tap-taps* behind us, but their mood was suddenly playful, rocking the vehicles without further violence. The driver inched forward as the Haitians got out of the way, and in a few moments we were on the other side of the roadblock and rumbling over the bridge. Naked Haitians bathed and washed clothes in the creek, staring up open-mouthed at the madness on the road.

I fell back against the slats. The girl climbed up on her seat, eyes closed, still crying. I had the bag clutched between my legs. When I forced them apart and let it drop to the truck bed, my knees shook. I let my breath out and rested my sweaty forearms on my thighs. The *tap-tap* continued until we were several turns away from the roadblock, then the driver stopped and came back. He was a little old man with a ball of white hair on his head and tufts of white hair growing out of his nostrils.

"*Tres mal, tres mal*," he cried. "You very lucky, not so, not so? When 'Aytien get stick in hand, *tres mal*. Very sorry this happen. *Ah, mes enfants!*"

He got back in and we continued to Port-au-Prince without further incident. He let us out at the main *tap-tap* area, where the girl and I caught an auto taxi to the airport. She had repaired most of the damage to her make-up, but she sat without speaking as we inched through the anarchy of Port-au-Prince traffic.

At the airport, I said goodbye to the Dominicana and went to the other side of the building to wait for Dickie. The American Airlines jet landed a few minutes later. He got off the plane and walked across the tarmac.

He came through Customs looking out of place in his clean white shirt and khaki pants. We shook hands and went upstairs to the airport restaurant. Neither of us had eaten, so we ordered Creole chicken and I had a Beck's. Dickie ordered two Cokes and drank the first in two gulps. I told him about the incident at the bridge.

He was shaken. "Jesus, Max, it's not safe for the crew and the ship to be in this country." He looked around the restaurant, as if the hordes might break out of the kitchen at any moment.

"It's bad," I agreed, "but the *Erika* just hasn't got any other trade."

"I'm finding that out. I got another charter, but it's rice to Haiti again."

"That's all right. Where to where?"

"Lake Charles to Miragoane."

I laughed. "The crew'll like that. They've all got girlfriends in Miragoane. Yussuf's got himself a real cutie."

Dickie nodded. "I could tell Yussuf's a lady-killer. He working out okay as chief mate?"

"Yeah, he's good. Knows the sea. Smart and responsible. I don't know if I've ever had better."

He opened the other Coke. "So, you've got the money from Bonvillain?"

"In the bag." I pushed it over with my foot. "$9377 even."

"You counted it? Okay, fine. I'll recount it in Miami, but I'm sure it's okay. This will come in handy. I got debts up the ass."

"What about Lake Charles? Who's the agent?"

"I don't know yet. Call me about three days out and I'll give the full details. You're going up some river to a lumber dock, I understand. It's not in the port of Lake Charles."

The loudspeaker announced the first call for the flight back to Miami. Dickie and I parted company at the security checkpoint. He shook my hand again and said, "Captain, you're doing a hell of a job. I sure appreciate it."

"*Es parte de la profesion*," I said.

The trip back to Miragoane was uneventful. I got onboard just before dark. An evening wind was blowing, and the ships were dancing on their stern lines under the press of it. There was a party on the fantail of one of the ships, colored lights strung along the boat deck, bouncing and swaying in the wind. I stood on the barge for a few minutes, watching the party, then went onboard the *Erika*.

The next morning, as the stevedores were sweeping up the last grains of rice in the hold and securing them in paper bundles to take ashore, I took a turn on deck and saw a familiar white ship turning the corner to come into the bay. I went up to the bridge and got the glasses. There was no mistaking the high sides and small mast house forward of the accommodations.

"Hey," I shouted down to Yussuf, "see that ship? I used to own her."

He looked. "That strange-looking ship? What is it?"

"Converted gas carrier. Used to be the *Marion P. Billups*. She was converted to cargo a few years ago. Some friends and I bought her on credit in the Miami River, but we couldn't come up with the money to finish the project, so we lost her."

The ship steamed south to the anchorage and turned into the wind, her main engine sending puffs of black smoke skyward. The anchor chain clattered faintly. Her new name was hand-painted in sloppy, sloping letters on the bow, *Queen of the Sea*.

"What kind of damn name is that?" I growled to myself, but it didn't make me feel any better.

The stevedores left the *Erika* at 1600 hours. I found the chief in the mess and gave orders to get oil up.

"Yes sir," he said. "Thank God we are leaving this shithole."

I sent word ashore for Ronald, and when he appeared I took him to the forecastle. "There's two mattresses for you to sell. Here's another 100 dollars. Will that be enough to pay for your help?"

"That's enough, Captain. Thank you, thank you." He went off to get help carrying them home.

Yussuf was in his cabin with his girlfriend. "Come on, First," I said. "We've got to do the stowaway search."

"Coming, sir." He led the girl out on deck, carrying her bag for her. She was crying. He kissed her and watched as she climbed down to the barge.

He and I started in the forecastle, checking the paint locker and under the piles of cordage. We went into the hold and looked around, but it was empty and there was nowhere for anyone to hide.

We searched the engine room and worked our way through the spare cabins. As I was climbing the stairs to the boat deck, the engine-room telegraph rang on the bridge, signaling that the main engine had oil pressure up.

On the way to the bridge I checked the boat deck. I looked behind the welding machine and between the oil-drum pontoons of the little painting raft. When I opened the door of the SOLAS room, an exterior closet just big enough to hold the 12 batteries required for emergency radio power, a tall, spindly Haitian was crouched on top of the batteries like a spider. He jumped out and knocked me over. I hit my head on the rescue-boat davit and slid to the deck.

He was a cream-colored man with matted hair and a crooked leg. He jumped over me, limped aft, and climbed over the railing. I shouted, but before I could get to my feet he dove into the water. I ran to the side. He was already pulling for shore with a steady stroke. The Haitians on the barge who'd come to see the ship off started hooting and laughing.

We finished searching the ship, then I ordered the lines cast off and we backed slowly away from the barge. There was movement in the crowd, and Ronald appeared at the end, waving. I sounded five short blasts of the horn, the heavy notes bouncing between the mountains. He was still there waving as I ordered Half Ahead and we drew away from the town.

Within minutes the houses shrank to pink and blue dots under the great red roof of the church, and a few minutes after that we crossed the break in the reef. I turned on the autopilot, set a westward course to take us clear of Rocheblave Bank, and went out on the port wing. Yussuf was already there, watching the coastal mountains slip by.

"Glad to be at sea again, First?"

"Always, Captain."

"Going to miss your girlfriend?"

He shrugged. "She'll be here when we get back. She already *cambio* to other ship, I think."

It was almost 1800, so I took the first watch. The sun was low in the western sky, streaming in so bright I could hardly see the radar screen. Haitian fishing boats were heading landward under their patchwork sails, their crews too tired to chase us. Just before sunset I turned the ship north into the Windward Passage.

By midnight of December 31, we had started up the Old Bahama Channel with the mountains of Cuba sullen and brown to the southwest. After Yussuf relieved me, I went down to the pantry and got a bottle of Portuguese wine.

"I know this violates the rules of watchkeeping, First," I told Yussuf as I stepped into the wheelhouse with the bottle and two glasses, "but we must drink one toast to the New Year."

He was wiping the windows. He put down the rag and checked his watch. "Ah," he said, "it is the New Year in three minutes."

"That's right." I poured our drinks and handed him a glass. "Happy New Year, Yussuf. Calm seas and pretty girls!"

He laughed with pleasure. "Happy New Year, Cap'n."

The next morning we neared the narrows between Cayo Confites on the Cuban coast and Cayo Lobos on the Bahamas Bank, only 11 miles across. I was watching two radar echoes ahead, both steaming to pass me to the south by a couple of miles, when a Hispanic voice on the radio cut in, "All ships in the Bahama Channel within 12 miles of Cayo Confites, this is Charlie Lima Golf, Vessel Traffic Control. All ships must report their position, name, and cargo."

"What the hell is this?" I muttered to myself as I turned up the volume.

The radio crackled. "Charlie Lima Golf, this is the *Copenhagen*. What are you again?"

"*Copenhagen*, this is Vessel Traffic System. Please report the name of your ship."

There was a pause. "I just did," the ship replied.

"What is your cargo?"

This time I could hear laughter on the cruise ship's bridge. "Humans," the radio operator said. "Our cargo is humans. This is a cruise ship."

A British accent cut in without identifying itself. "What is this bloody Charlie Oscar Golf business? Anybody out there know?"

"Ship calling Charlie Lima Golf, please identify yourself."

The only reply CLG got was, "Bloody hell!"

The Vessel Traffic System, if that's what it was, kept calling as long as we were in range. We passed Cayo Lobos and reached international water again without talking to them, although other ships did give the requested information and there seemed to be no reaction.

We passed Key West at night, brightly lit, with the headlights of traffic on the Stock Island Bridge flickering out over the water. The southern tip of America fell behind as we fought our way westward against a three-knot current. We passed the Dry Tortugas the next morning, the old fort clearly visible on the horizon.

We had a routine passage across the Gulf, broken only by an engine stoppage of two hours for the engineers to bleed the injectors. We arrived off the Lake Charles seabuoy at 2200 hours on January 5, 1988. The pilot station instructed me to anchor until dawn, then steam for the mouth of the Calcasieu River, where the pilot boat would meet us. We pulled off the fairway near some three-legged drilling rigs and dropped anchor. I filled in the Garbage Log and told the chief to enter five tons of oily water pumped ashore in Miragoane into the Oil Record Book. With my documentation ready, I went to bed.

We hoisted anchor at 0600 the next morning, the men working in a cold drizzle under low, sodden skies. I called the pilot boat and was advised that she was passing Cameron at that time. I conned from the radar while Yussuf took the ship past the seabuoy toward the marshy coast ahead.

The pilot boat approached on the starboard side and the pilot climbed up. He was a big man with a fuzzy beard and a broad, smooth forehead. His expression was somber. One of the Lake Charles pilots had been killed during the night, crushed between the pilot boat and a ship's side, smeared into jelly when the vessels rolled together.

We passed Cameron, a collection of low oilfield docks on the right, and continued up the channel. Shrimp boats and supply boats, their windshield wipers working steadily in the thickening rain, passed us heading seaward. After several hours we turned a bend and entered Lake Charles, a small, round lake between the port on the west and the town on the east. The pilot gave Yussuf orders to steer for the interstate bridge to the north.

"I understand we're going to some lumber dock?" I said to the pilot.

"Yeah. I never took a ship there before. I don't think any ships have gone that far upriver since I started doing this 10 years ago. Anyway, I drove over to the dock this morning to make sure it's safe. There's a barge there to tie up to, but the riverbank is unimproved."

"Great," I said. "How far from civilization is it?"

"Oh, it's right in town. The river doubles back to the south."

We passed under the interstate bridge, under the unfamiliar rumble of tires on roadbed, and through the open railroad swing bridge. There were workers on the western embankment laying concrete riprap. The river wound north between cypress-covered banks with expensive homes peeking through the trees. The bridge of the ship was higher than the trees, and we could see the horizon in every direction.

The river turned east. We steamed along at Dead Slow, the engine puffing quietly, the pilot keeping the ship in the unseen channel. The river got narrow and turned south. The ship hugged the western bank, where a string of run-down camps clung to the marshy verge. Delighted children came pouring out of the houses to run along the riverbank far below, jerking their arms up and down, oblivious to the cold rain. The pilot stepped over to the horn lever and gave them two long blasts that seemed to get swallowed up in the clouds scraping by overhead.

We turned to port and saw the barge dead ahead, on the south bank of the river, below a couple of dilapidated sheds and a nice brick office building. Saplings and man-sized shrubs were growing in the corners of the oyster-shell parking lot. An army of uniforms waited on the high bank for the ship to dock.

The barge was a standard 200' X 40' deck barge. Two men were waiting on it, but they weren't professional lineshandlers. By some deft commands, the pilot got the ship turned around to point downriver. At one point, with the ship perpendicular to the river, I looked aft and saw that the ship's fantail was actually overhanging the low marsh of the north bank.

We had to run Dead Slow Astern against the current for a spell, while the men on the barge learned how to throw the monkey's fist back, but we finally made All-Fast. There was a long, decrepit pier sticking out into the river, and the barge was nosed up against it. The pier did not quite reach the ship, so I told Yussuf to run the gangway down to the barge. The pilot had me sign the chit and went to a waiting car.

It took an hour to clear Customs and Immigration. The Customs inspectors brought their battery-powered drills, but they didn't use them anywhere I could find later. USDA found two coconuts behind a box in the pantry, but didn't fine us.

When the vessel was cleared in, and all hands given I-95 landing passes except the Poles, I went on deck and down to the barge. There was a beefy man of about 60 standing at the foot of the gangway, one of the amateur lineshandlers, about to come onboard. He held out his hand. "Carleton Pitt," he said. "Are you the captain?"

"Yes, I am. Max Hardberger."

We shook. "The rice starts arriving tomorrow morning," he said. "I talked to Dickie Vance. He says he'll be here about three p.m. today."

"Oh, yeah? Good."

"And your crane will be here about two o'clock."

"My crane?"

"Dickie bought a cherry-picker for the ship. He said you're going to mount it between the hatches."

I looked at the midbridge and nodded. "Sure. Might have to do some welding."

Pitt touched my arm. "This charterer, Garot, you know him?"

"Garot who?"

"Jacques Garot. He's the charterer. I've never met him, but he's coming tomorrow. He's a Haitian."

"Of course."

He shook his head. "Well, I've heard. . .you never heard of him?"

"No, but that doesn't mean anything. I'm just the captain."

"Right, right. Well, Captain, I'm the agent as well, so if there's anything I can do to help you or the crew, let me know."

I frowned. "You're the agent? And you also own the dock?"

"Well, I'm just renting the dock."

"I need you to sign off the chief engineer's wife. She's from Poland and she's flying home. She sailed with us for two voyages."

His face got blank. "Sign her off?"

"Yeah, sign her off. So she can go home. You *are* the agent, aren't you?"

"Well, my wife just started the agency. We're just getting our feet wet." He gave me a painful smile.

"Well, you'd better sign her off properly or you'll risk losing your bond." I started toward the bow to take a look at the draft marks. "And the ship better not get charged for lineshandlers."

He laughed weakly. I turned around. "I'm serious. I won't authorize the payment. You made my engineer start and stop the main at least five times because you couldn't throw the monkey's fist back."

"Ah, the line-holders I hired didn't show up, so Buddy and I had to do it. We're sorry about that. The ship. . .won't be charged."

He went up to the pier. Yussuf came down to the barge. "That's the agent and dockowner," I muttered to him, jerking a thumb at Pitt's back as he walked across the parking lot. "He's a fucking snake, take my word for it."

He looked shocked. "Captain, you just met him."

I nodded. "I'll bet you a case of Beck's in Miragoane that he's a fucking snake, and I won't collect unless you totally agree. Deal?"

He shook my hand. "Deal, Captain. But the Moslem way is to let a man prove he is not your friend."

I grunted. "The Moslem way is to get fucked, then." I shut my mouth. "Oh, hell, Yussuf, I didn't mean that."

He laughed. "I know what you mean, Captain."

About 1400 a short, squat man in a cowboy hat and pointy-toed boots arrived and said that he was going to deliver a cherry-picker. There wasn't much I could say about that, so I agreed he could do it. He clomped off and drove away. I went up to the office building and found Pitt engaged in a sulfurous argument on the phone, so incensed that he made a number of indiscreet remarks in front of me. When he got off the phone, red-faced and panting, I said, "That cherry-picker's on its way. How're we going to get it on the ship?"

He took a deep breath and worked a halfhearted smile onto his face. "I'm renting a big crane to load the rice. It should be here any minute."

"How's it going to load the cherry-picker? From the bank? You can't put a big crane on the barge."

He thought for a moment. "No, not on the barge. It will load from the bank."

"Well, that's okay for the rice, but that cherry-picker's got to weigh 15 tons. I don't think a crane's going to be able to swing it out to the ship."

"Oh, yes," he said, moving me toward the door. "Don't worry, Captain, it's a big one."

I let him ease me out and went back to the ship. An hour later the crane came up the street on a flat-bed trailer, another truck behind it carrying the boom in two sections. They swung wide on the narrow street and managed to get into the parking lot. After some consultation with Pitt, the crane men started setting up on the high bank across from the middle of the barge, using timbers from the barge under the outriggers. I stayed on the ship and didn't interfere.

Dickie came onboard in the late afternoon. His flight had been delayed. He was wearing a light herringbone sweater and canvas pants. He had a fresh haircut and maybe a manicure and pedicure. After some preliminary chitchat I told him that the shore crane was never going to be able to load the cherry-picker on the ship's deck from that distance. We went out on deck and looked across the barge to the crane.

"Oh, yeah," he said. "Look at that boom. It must be 100 feet long. It'll reach."

"It won't hold 15 tons at that distance," I said patiently. "It might be able to land the cherry-picker on the barge, but then how do we get it from the barge to the ship?"

"Ship's gear?"

"Oh, no. It's got barely three-ton capacity, if that." I looked at the heavy rail-road timbers that lined the deck of the barge. "I've got an idea, though. If we can get it to the barge, we can drive it on its own wheels up a ramp over the bulwark and onto the midbridge. The bulwark and the midbridge are about the same height."

That seemed like a good plan to him. When the cherry-picker arrived a few minutes later, the cowboy drove it off the flatbed and into place under the boom of the shore crane. It took a while to get a crane driver from the crane company, but he finally arrived and took a long look at the riverbank and the barge. He was an older man with a square diamond stud in his left ear and a tattoo of a teardrop at the corner of his right eye. I went up to stand by him at the edge of the parking lot, where the clam shells were falling down the muddy slope in heavy clumps from the erosion of the bank.

"What you think?" I asked him. "I'm the captain of the ship."

He spat a glop of chewing tobacco on the ground. "I dunno. I might could get it over to the barge, but no way I can put it on the ship."

"That's what I figured."

"Let's check the GVW on the cherry-picker."

We looked for it, but the data plate was missing, along with a number of other parts of varying importance.

"Well," the crane driver said, "might as well give it a try. Who's the boss of this here operation?"

I pointed to Dickie, standing at the door of the office talking to Pitt. "He's the ship owner."

The crane-driver went over and talked to Dickie and Pitt for a while, then went to the crane. "Long as you guys agree Lake Charles Heavy Lift don't have no liability for nothin'," he called back to them. "That agreed?"

"Yeah," Dickie said, "that's agreed."

With Yussuf and Manuel helping, the driver got the cherry-picker slung properly. He lifted it up and the engine hardly noticed the load. He swung it toward the edge of the bank with Yussuf and Manuel holding the guy-ropes, stopped, and let it stabilize. He eased it out over the narrow strip of water and stopped again. I was standing behind the crane.

One of the rear outriggers started to lift off its wooden pad. I yelled at the driver, but at that moment a piece of the river bank slid out from under the front outriggers, and the crane took a sharp lurch forward. The cherry-picker bounced heavily on the runner.

One of the timbers sprang out from under the left front outrigger and sailed into the water. The crane nosed forward. The driver let off the brake with a screech and the cherry-picker dropped like an anchor into the Calcasieu River, coming to rest with the cab half submerged, pitched forward with the tip of the boom dug into the mud bank.

The driver leaped down from the cab and collapsed on the ground. "Jesus," he whispered, "I almost bought it there." He gathered himself up, lit a cigarette, smoked the first inch in two breaths, and walked over to look down at the cherry-picker.

Pitt and Dickie were on the other side of the crane by then. Pitt was cursing furiously. I heard him say, "Fucking crane-driver!" But when the driver walked around to his side there was no more of that.

The driver smoked a second cigarette, got back in the cab, raised the outriggers, and backed the crane onto firmer ground. I got the crew to carry some more timbers up from the barge, and we shored up the bank to the point that the driver agreed to try to get the cherry-picker out. He pulled the crane forward, put down the outriggers, and got the cherry-picker back on dry ground, muddy water pouring from the cab. There were heavy oil trails weaving downriver, but they were soon gone.

Dickie hired the people who sold him the cherry-picker to come get it and take it back to their shop for repair. After it was gone he came up to the saloon for a Coke. "So tell me about Miragoane," he said. "What was it like?"

"It's a hell-hole."

"At least the day rate is good. Garot is paying me $1700 a day."

"That's good. As far as I'm concerned, it's worth the hassle. The only other work this little ship could get would be down in the lower islands, around Venezuela, and that trade has its own difficulties."

He finished the Coke. "At least the ship's coming back to the States every trip. The crew likes that, right?"

"Yeah, and it's good for the ship. We can resupply and repair here."

Dickie had a motel room near the interstate bridge, and after supper onboard he retired to it. I walked to the nearest convenience store and called my wife.

The next morning, the fat boy who'd helped Pitt handle the lines arrived shipside at 0630 in a beat-up '78 Mustang. "Ah'm heah fuh de woman what's goin' to N'Awleens," he declared, from the dock.

"Are you taking her to New Orleans?" I asked.

"Naw, Ah'm takin' her to the bus station."

I went ashore. "Let me see her travel papers."

He handed the bundle to me. The travel arrangements approved by INS clearly stated that the agent had to take her to the New Orleans airport and accompany her to the gate. Not only that, but they stated that she was not allowed out of the transit lounge at the Cincinnati stop-over. "Oh, shit," I said, and went to talk to Jacek. I found him stuffing the last things into Daniela's suitcase.

"Jacek, I've got bad news," I said. "INS won't let Daniela go see her sister in Cincinnati."

"What? Let me see."

I showed him the papers. She questioned him sharply in Polish. When he told her what the papers said, she started crying.

Jacek turned to me. "Twelve years she no see her sister." He stretched his hands out to me. "Captain, why? We are not criminals. We are not even Communists. Why cannot Daniela go see her sister?"

I went ashore with a heavy heart and called INS, but they wouldn't budge. I didn't tell them about the bus ride. When I got back to the ship I could hear Daniela crying in the officer's mess. Jacek was trying to calm her without success. When I went in she started shouting at me. I stared.

"She's thinks it's your fault," Jacek said apologetically. "She thinks it's because you put her on the crew list."

"I had to," I said. "She came onboard on a crewman's visa."

He translated that, but it didn't help. She glared at me, her face swollen, her eyes red and hot. I stepped out on the fantail, where Jerzy was smoking a cigarette. He smiled sympathetically. Daniela shouted again, and something she said bothered Jerzy. He tossed away the cigarette and stood up. He spoke in Polish and tried to take my arm.

I heard a rattle in the galley. Daniela came out the starboard door with a butcher knife in her hand, sobbing hysterically. Jerzy jerked me bodily off the deck and got me into the hallway. She followed, carving the air with the knife.

I yelled, and Jerzy let go of me. I fell to the deck under a high swing of the knife that would have decapitated me. She was still coming. I ran through the galley and along the hallway to the companionway, sprang up it, and slammed the door to the office behind me.

I could hear Daniela coming up the companionway. The knife stabbed into the door. She stabbed the door again and again, sobbing. The stabbing got slower, and finally stopped, and there was only sobbing. Jacek came up and led her downstairs. When I opened the door, the knife was still stuck in it.

I stayed in the saloon while she and Jacek got her luggage and went ashore. The boy was waiting on the bank with his engine running. Jacek went up to the parking lot with her. He wasn't supposed to be ashore at all, but this wasn't the time to point it out.

They hugged, Daniela got in the back seat of the car, and the boy drove her off. Jacek took a long time coming back to the ship.

No rice arrived that day. Dickie and I went driving around until we found a steel loading ramp at an oilfield dock that we could rent for $300 a day, and we got a truck to deliver it to the lumber dock. The cherry-picker arrived from the repair shop and the same crane driver came out to handle the ramp. He put it between the shore and the barge, and I drove the cherry-picker down. My crew stacked baulks of timber between the bulwarks and the midbridge. The crane man put the ramp between the barge and the ship, and I backed the cherry-picker up the ramp, across the timbers, and onto the midbridge. I put down the outriggers, Jerzy welded them to the deck, and the crew secured the rig with chains and binders.

I was watching Manuel and Ricardo secure the boom when there was a shout from the stern of the ship. I went through the accommodations. Victor was holding a piece of light rope with a three-foot alligator on the other end. It was up on its legs and had its tail in the air.

"Victor," I said, "that thing is going to bite someone. Throw it back in the water."

He gave the line to Jerzy and went into the galley. "We're going to eat it for supper, Captain," he said, coming out with a two-foot carving knife. "*Caimano muy delicioso.*"

"*Sí,*" I said, "*y muy prohibitado tambien.*"

Word of the capture had spread, and the rest of the ship's crew now crowded onto the fantail. At that moment I heard a vehicle pull into the parking lot. It was a white van, coming to a stop at the head of the pier. For a dreadful moment I thought it was the Coast Guard, but when two elderly gentlemen and three well-dressed women got out with plastic bags in their hands, I realized it was a visit from the local seamen's mission.

"Get this alligator over the side," I told the crew. "The seamen's mission is here." I looked around for a stick to get the alligator to bite, so I could swing it overboard, but it was too late.

"Hello," one of the ladies said from the pier, "hello the ship! We're from the Baptist Seamen's Mission."

I put down the stick and turned around. "Oh, hello. I'm the captain. As you can see, the crew doesn't know that you can't catch alligators here. I'm trying to throw it back safely."

"Oh, don't do it yet," she said. "Harry, Harry, come on. They've caught an alligator."

"I'll be," one of the old gentlemen said, hurrying along the pier. "A big one?"

They came down to the barge and up the gangway. The old guys came down the boarding steps in a sprightly way and shook the crew's hands. They were dressed in western shirts with string ties, and said they were Baptist preachers. One of the women was middle-aged and the other two were wizened little things, apparently the wives of the preachers, but none was introduced.

The middle-aged woman, a big friendly blonde with calves like bowling pins, said she wanted to see the alligator, so we went back to the fantail. With all seven crewmen there, and five visitors not including the alligator himself, the fantail was crowded.

Victor, at last convinced we could not eat his prize, reached for the rope, and Jerzy stepped across to hand it to him. The alligator sprang. It launched itself at Jerzy's kneecap, but he already had weight on the leg, so all he could do was snap his kneecap back. The animal's snout shot past his knee with half-an-inch to spare. Even then it tried to twist in midair and get a tooth in him, but missed.

Victor grabbed the rope and jerked the alligator's head to the left, but he pulled too hard, and the animal went skidding across the deck toward one of the older ladies, snapping and writhing.

She squeaked and tried to lift both her legs up off the deck at once, the tip of the creature's snout only inches from her feet. When that didn't work, she tried getting them up one at a time, very rapidly.

Victor got the alligator reined in again, I grabbed the tail, and together we swung him overboard. He slipped out of the noose as soon as he hit the water, showed us a shiny yellow belly, and slid to the bottom.

I looked around at the assembly. The crew were shamefaced at having brought danger to people of God, but the ladies were breathless and bright-eyed, and the gentlemen thought it was pretty exciting too. Jerzy sat on a bitt and looked fondly at his kneecap.

In mid-afternoon the skies opened up and a heavy rain started to fall. It rained for six days without let-up. After the second day, with the forecast the same, I left my number with Yussuf and went to New Orleans. Every morning he called with the same information. Still raining, no loading.

On the seventh day the rain stopped. I took a bus back to Lake Charles and went onboard at 2200 hours. At 0700 the next morning the first truckload of rice pulled up, and at 0800 a motley collection of stevedores arrived in a battered school bus.

Yussuf and I were on the wing of the bridge. "What the hell is that?" I said. "Don't tell me they're using prisoners to load the ship."

Yussuf groaned. "Not prisoners again."

They weren't prisoners, but day laborers Pitt had hired from some derelict labor pool. Some were old men, some were winos, and some were both. They filed off the bus carrying their hardhats and stood bewildered on the bank while Pitt talked to their foreman, a puffy-faced man in red coveralls.

The crane driver arrived and cranked it up, the stevedores picked their way across the gangway, and the first pallet of rice swung into the air.

It took all morning to get the stevedores going, but after they'd sweated some of the alcohol out of their systems, and learned what we were up to, they got a rhythm going and the pallets started disappearing into the hold.

In mid-afternoon I caught a ride to the airport with Dickie and rented a car. He had a reservation for the 5:10 flight to New Orleans, connecting with a direct flight to Chicago. We parted at the Avis counter.

I went driving around until I found a huge carpet store on the edge of town, near a warren of lower-class neighborhoods. According to a sign facing the interstate, the store invited customers to "TRADE IN YOUR OLD CARPET ON NEW WEARFREE CARPET," and to take advantage of the store's "EASY PAY FINANCE TERMS."

The owner was a pockmarked Lebanese in a sharkskin suit. When I told him I had a ship, he immediately offered to come himself to fit it for new carpet. "Well," I said, "what I had in mind was getting some free carpet."

He bent his oiled head closer. "Excuse me?"

"You got any used carpet you can't sell? Let me have it to take to Haiti."

"You want used carpet? You want to buy used carpet? Come, come."

He grasped my elbow firmly and led me out the back of the store. Across the rear alley was another building, a windowless tin warehouse, and inside was a mountain of carpet rolls reaching almost to the ceiling. Although it was a cool, cloudy day outside, the air in the warehouse was hot and dank.

"I don't want to buy carpet," I said, "I want free carpet. Any carpet you can't sell I'll haul away for you."

He didn't like that idea, and made several other proposals, concluding with one that I pick through the carpet in the warehouse and pay him $20.00 for each roll I took.

"Naw," I said, "I don't have any money. I'm just a ship captain."

As we were walking back to the store, he said, "You have a truck to pick carpet up, right?"

"I can get one."

"And you will come and pick up the carpet?"

"Yeah, if it's free."

He stopped and poked me in the chest with a short, dark finger. "You take all the carpet in the warehouse, you can have it free. But you must take it all."

I estimated how much there was. "Okay," I said dubiously, "I think I can do that."

"You take it all, okay?" He opened the store's rear door, chuckling. "I give trade-in for old carpet, but what can I do with it? This is America. Nobody buys used carpet in America. I have to pay for the warehouse to keep it, or I have to pay the garbage company to haul it off." He shut the door behind us and whispered in my ear, "You take it all!"

With some mental reservations, I went off to find a Hertz truck-rental outfit.

When I got back to the dock, Pitt came to the door to call me into the office. He introduced me to Jacques Garot, the charterer. He was a short, handsome Creole of about 50, wide in the shoulder and narrow in the hip, dressed in a tan double-breasted suit and low-cut Italian loafers showing an inch of brown silk sock.

He offered me a limp hand to shake. He did not smile. "Captain," he said.

I looked at Pitt. "So, we finish about noon tomorrow?"

Pitt nodded. "Looks like it, Captain."

"Mr. Garot, have you ordered bunkers yet?"

"You do not have enough bunkers, Captain?"

"Of course not. I gave Mr. Pitt my bunker figures when we arrived. You didn't get them?"

"No, nothing. I have made no arrangements for bunkers."

"Well, we can't sail without bunkers. I recommend a minimum of 50 tons."

"Fifty tons? For one trip?"

"There is no fuel in Haiti, as you know. She burns 2.5 a day, times six days down, that's 15 tons, and 15 back, plus reserve, plus fuel for the crane and the generators."

Garot swiveled his head toward Pitt without moving his body, like an iguana. "Can you make arrangements for the fuel?"

Pitt said, "Sure, but I'd like you to make your own arrangements for payment." He laughed nervously.

"We'll discuss that later, Carleton," Garot said. He stood up and held a hand out to me. "Nice to meet you, Captain. I know we will enjoy working together."

"It is a pleasure to serve," I said unctuously. I looked at Pitt. "You might want to take care of that fuel order this afternoon. It sometimes takes a while for the truck to get shipside, and we don't want to be held up."

"Sure," he said with forced enthusiasm, "I'll take care of it."

I went back to the ship, gathered the deck crew, and left the chief in charge. We got to the carpet store as it was closing, and the Arab opened the warehouse. Night fell, dark and starry, but we worked on until we filled the truck.

We labored until 2200 hours to stow the carpet in the forecastle. After it was full, we piled the rest of the rolls on the barge, with dunnage under them and a tarp on top.

The last bag of rice went into the hold the next day at 1345 hours. The stevedores filed off and we closed the hatch as a light rain began to fall. I piled the crew into the truck. It took two more trips, but finally the only rolls left in the warehouse were about four dozen against the back wall that had mildewed into a gummy mass. I showed them to the Arab and he kindly agreed that I didn't have to take them. He seemed surprised that I had actually taken the rest, and wanted to know when the ship would be back to pick up another consignment.

When we got to the dock with the second load it was almost dark. A night wind was tearing through the tops of the willow trees along the river. Pitt came out of the office wearing a raincoat, although the rain had stopped, and met me at the head of the pier. The lights of the ship's house were behind him, and I couldn't see his face.

"The pilot won't take the ship downriver," he said flatly.

"Why is that?"

"All this rain. He says the current's too fast under the railroad bridge."

We could hear the rush and tumble of the swollen river as it tore against the riverbank. "I can believe it," I said.

"It's a very big problem, Captain. I have to move that barge tomorrow morning."

"You can't move the barge until the ship's gone," I said. "There's nowhere for the ship to tie up to."

"You can tie up to the trees on the bank."

I shook my head. "I can't let the ship get that close to an unimproved bank. Stumps, machinery, concrete. . .who knows what's down there?"

He pressed his lips together and gave me a hard stare. "Well," he said, turning toward the office, "we'll see."

"And we'll have to take on bunkers before we leave."

"That's the fucking charterer's problem," he said over his shoulder. "And that barge has got to go first thing in the morning, Captain."

I let him go and went onboard. All the lights were lit, and the generator was thumping cheerfully down in the engine room. I joined Yussuf and the AB's in loading the rolls of carpet onto the top of the rice in No. 1 hold. Then we had beers on the fantail and turned in.

Dawn broke clear and cold. The gusty night wind had settled into a stiff, steady blow out of the northwest. I opened my saloon windows, breathed in the sharp, sweet air, and said out loud, "This'll blow us all the way to Haiti."

I got dressed, got a cup of coffee, and went out on the wet deck. The cherry-picker was still a surprise, after two months onboard without it. There was a tug parked ahead of the ship, its bow nosed into the southern bank. It was a small one, about 800 horsepower, freshly painted red and white. I went up to the point of the bow, stood on the step, and called over, "Ahoy the tug!"

A round little man stepped out, his cheeks full of breakfast. He maneuvered carefully past the wheelhouse and came up on the steep forward deck.

"Are you here for the barge?" I called.

"Yeah. How come you're tied up to it?"

"Because I just loaded here."

He swallowed the last of his food. "That there barge belongs to MARAD. You're not supposed to be using it. It was just bein' stored here."

"I'm not using it. The charterer was using it."

He looked it over. "Where's the rest of the timbers? They was on the deck when I brung it over."

I pointed. "They're up on the bank. They were using them under the shore crane."

He shook his head sadly. "I gotta report all this. MARAD ain't gonna be too happy, I kin tell you." He went aft. "Them's the go'ment, you know. You kin't fuck wit' the go'ment."

"Carleton Pitt," I called, "that's the guy. He's the one leasing this dock."

"Yeah, that's the guy. He's gittin' paid by the go'ment to keep this barge here. An' he's using it to load a ship. Lordy, lordy."

At that moment Carleton's white LTD wheeled into the yard, the front end bouncing on bad shocks. He jumped out and bounded down to the barge.

"It's all taken care of," he called to the tug captain as he came up. "Don't worry about it, Captain. We're going to move the ship out in the river so you can pull the barge out."

I climbed down from the step and went over to the side of the bow, where I was almost directly over his head. "We're going to do what?"

He backed up so he could look at me. "Captain, I need you to cast off from the barge and move into the middle of the river. I've got some men coming to take your ropes, so we'll . . ."

"Mr. Pitt, the ship can't do that. Not without a pilot or tugs."

He stalked aft, like he was heading for the gangway with a purpose. I slid down the ladder and went aft to meet him. He stopped short. "Captain, you are going to cast off your ropes and move the ship away from the barge. I'm sorry to have to put it like that, but there ain't no other option."

"Sorry, sir, but I can't do that. If you want to order the pilot, fine, but we'll have to keep going. I can't tie up again with the barge gone."

He spun around and yelled up to the office, "Bubba! Bubba! Come down here!" He turned back to me. "Captain, we're going to cut your ropes. I recommend you tell your engineer to start the engine, or whatever you gotta do."

"I'll show you what I gotta do." I turned toward the accommodations. Yussuf was watching from the hallway, coffee cup and cigarette in hand. "Yussuf," I called, "get the whole crew on deck as soon as possible."

"Yessir," He disappeared.

Pitt stamped on the steel deck of the barge so hard it rang like a gong. "I'll fucking show you. I'll go get my .45."

I laughed. "Thanks for the warning." I started running for the accommodations. "Yussuf," I yelled, "keep the crew inside. He's going for his gun."

I heard the tugboat captain's voice. "What the fuck's goin' on here?"

I ran up to the office and unlocked the safe. It took 30 seconds to load the ship's .38. I ran downstairs. Jacek was standing in the hallway in his underwear, his hair sticking straight up.

"Get oil up, Chief," I told him.

He stared blankly at the pistol. "Yessir. Trouble onboard?"

I peered around the edge of the door to the dock. Pitt wasn't on the barge anymore. "The asshole that owns the dock might try to cut the lines. Get ready in case he does."

"You're going to shoot him, Captain?"

I looked down at the pistol. "I don't know. I might."

He pushed his feet into his clogs and hurried downstairs. I went up to the bridge and got on the VHF. "Lake Charles Coast Guard, this is the Motorvessel *Erika*."

"*Erika*, go to 68."

I met them on 68. "I'm at the old lumber dock on the Calcasieu. I'm a 1600-ton freighter. The dockowner is threatening to cut my dock lines. I have no pilot onboard."

"Stand by, Captain."

Another voice came on. "What is the problem, Captain?"

I told him.

"Captain, do not cast off your dock lines without a pilot onboard."

"Roger that," I said patiently. "Please be advised that the dockowner has threatened me with a firearm."

That got their attention. We signed off and I went out to the wing of the bridge. Pitt was nowhere to be seen, but his car was still in the parking lot. The captain was in the wheelhouse of the tug, talking on the VHF. In a few minutes I heard a siren coming, and two police cars wheeled into the yard.

One policeman went into the office and two others came out on the pier. I went down to meet them. One was a black woman and the other a tall white man with a sickly complexion. I told them what had happened.

"He told you he had a pistol?" the woman asked.

"He said he was going to get his .45. I don't know what else that would mean."

"Did you see the pistol?"

"I haven't seen him since then. I think he's up in the office."

They went away, and five minutes later a Coast Guard van pulled up. Two Guardsmen in gob caps came down to the barge, one of them carrying a shotgun. I met them on the barge. The heavy-set one with the shotgun did the talking. "There won't be any cutting of dock lines, Captain," he said. "I can promise you that. You can go aboard if you like, and we'll check with you later."

I went up to the wing of the bridge. The policemen came out with Pitt and went to his car. He bent down and got a pistol out from under the seat. One of them wrote something on a piece of paper, handed it to him, and took the pistol. They went to the barge and talked to the Coasties, then got back in their patrol cars and left.

The Coastie with the shotgun put it in the van and came to the end of the pier. "The dockowner says the pilot's on his way now," he called. "The tugboat says he'll wait for the ship to sail to move the barge. You have any more problems with that guy, give us a call."

"All right," I said. "Thanks."

Pitt had ducked back inside the office. The chief rang Engine Ready. Yussuf came into the wheelhouse, checked the oil in the steering pedestal, checked the radars, and wiped the windows. Manuel and Ricardo were walking forward.

A brown Corvette nosed into the yard. The pilot got out of the passenger seat, a tall man in a baseball cap. Manuel brought him up to the wheelhouse.

"Captain?" the pilot said.

"Yessir. We're ready to single up, but I have to tell you that we do not have enough bunkers to sail."

"What do you mean?"

I gave him a brief rundown of the morning's festivities. "We obviously have to leave, but we have to go to a fuel dock. Is there one between here and Cameron?"

"There's one in Cameron. Is that where you want to go?"

"I don't know. I'll try to get the owner on VHF after we leave and get instructions."

He put his bag down and leaned out the window to look down at the rusty deck and patched tarpaulins. "You ought to do some maintenance on this ship, Captain," he said gruffly.

I made a show of looking at my watch. "Pilot's late, First."

Yussuf stared at me. The man said, "I *am* the pilot."

"Is that so? I thought you were the surveyor."

He reddened and shut his mouth.

"Anyway," I said, "let's get underway."

We singled up, dropped bow and stern lines at the same time, and pulled out into the river. It was high, three or four feet higher than it had been when we came in, and the ship towered over the cypress trees. The lumber dock dropped out of sight astern.

"How's the current through the railroad bridge, Pilot?" I asked, but the man still had his nose out of joint about the surveyor crack, so he didn't say anything. "Must be okay," I went on, "because that's where we're heading."

He barked a rudder angle at Yussuf and ignored me. We were steaming at Dead Slow, but the current carried us at an alarming speed past the camps, now flooded out and deserted, water washing through their doors. We couldn't reduce rpm's without losing steering-way, but the pilot guided Yussuf expertly along the channel. The houses fell behind, and on both sides of the river brown water stretched away into the cypresses.

We came out of the narrow channel and turned south. The interstate bridge was visible above the tops of the trees. When we rounded the last bend I could see muddy water thrashing against the riprap of the embankment below the railroad tracks.

We approached the narrow passage rapidly. The pilot glanced at the telegraph to make sure it was on Dead Slow. The bow started swinging to starboard. He said quickly, "Port five, quartermaster."

Yussuf swung from midships to port five.

"Port 10," the pilot called. We were bearing down on the embankment, where workers in yellow slicker suits were crawling over the riprap. I could see their faces.

I glanced at Yussuf. He was gripping the wheel tightly, his eyes on the pilot's face. The bow was finally swinging to port. The current had us now, coming around the bend of the river. It had caught the stern, and as the bow swung into the slower water on the inside of the bend the ship started a slow, terrible spin to port.

"Starboard five," the pilot said. "Starboard 10!"

Yussuf spun the wheel, eyes on the rudder-angle indicator.

"We're not going to make it," I said calmly. Now the workers were scrambling to get out of our way. One of them lost his footing and fell between two boulders.

"Hard-a-Port," I said to Yussuf quietly. "Let the ship keep coming around. Steam back upriver and we'll drop anchor."

The pilot whipped around from the window. "Starboard 10, quartermaster!"

It was too late to try to get upriver anyway. The pilot was right. "Okay," I said to Yussuf. "Starboard 10."

The bow was coming around to starboard, slowly, slowly. We were bearing down on the narrow opening between the swing bridge and the embankment. The bow was passing in front of the bridge.

We hung on and waited for impact, but the bow had cleared it. "Midships," the pilot ordered in a hoarse voice, but Yussuf was ahead of him, already spinning the wheel back. The ship shot through. The men on the embankment were shouting at us, but I couldn't hear what they were saying.

As the ship drew away from the bridge, the current slowed and the rudder began to bite again. All three of us started breathing.

Nobody spoke as the ship steamed under the interstate bridge and across the lake. On the other side, in the river again, the pilot ordered Half Ahead. The ship headed for open water like a horse for the stable.

I managed to get Dickie through the VHF Marine Operator, and he told me that Garot had made arrangements for the ship to take on bunkers in Cameron. When we got to the small oilfield town at the edge of the marsh, the current in the river was running so high we had to go downriver and turn back upstream to approach the dock. The pilot was five seconds late in calling for Stop Engine. The ship crashed into a steel dolphin.

"Good thing that dolphin's filled with cement," the pilot said, after we'd made fast. "Otherwise you'd own it right now."

I didn't trust myself to reply. I threw the pilot ladder over the port side myself and went down to the dock. I walked aft along the low mudbank. There was a dent in the stern of the ship at the turn of the buttocks, about a meter wide and 20 centimeters deep. Bright scars in the paint showed where the top of the pipe had dug into the plating.

The pilot came down the ladder and called over to me, "I'm going to wait in the office. Let me know when you're ready." He picked his way across the muddy verge toward the small office trailer. "The ship's going to have to pay my waiting time, too."

"And well worth it," I called back. He cocked his head and thought about that. The bearded Cajun boy who'd taken our lines passed the hose up the ship's side to the chief. When we had taken on 50 tons, and the fuel hose was pulled off the ship and coiled on its drum, the pilot came out of the office and headed for the ladder. I stopped him.

"You're not allowed onboard," I said. "You're a danger to the ship."

His eyes bulged in the weak light. "What the fuck you talking 'bout, Cap?"

"I can't let you onboard. You almost wrecked my ship at the railroad bridge, and then you caused damage to the vessel in docking."

"Hey, buddy," he said, sticking out his chest and leaning into me, "shit happens. That was just the current. As far as the railroad bridge goes, there was no damage, was there? I had the vessel under control at all times."

I laughed shortly and went up the ladder. Yussuf and Manuel were waiting on deck. I told them to pull it up. "You can't sail without a pilot," the pilot yelled up. "That's illegal."

"We dropped the pilot off at the fuel dock," I said. "I'll put it in the log."

"The fuck! I'm calling the Coast Guard."

The dock boy had witnessed all this with some consternation, but he finally threw the lines clear and the crew pulled them in. I spun the bow around in the wide channel and pointed it at the Gulf of Mexico. When I looked back the pilot was steaming toward the office trailer with the dock boy in tow.

I listened on Channel 16, but nobody called us. Fifteen minutes later, at the seabuoy, I aimed the vessel southeast and turned on the autopilot. Yussuf stayed on the bridge while we waited for the Coast Guard, but they never came. An hour later we were in international water, steaming at 11 knots toward Haiti with the wind and sea at our back.

CHAPTER FOUR

THE SHIP PLUNGED EASTWARD FOR THREE DAYS, AND ON THE fourth dawn we passed between Key West and Havana under a clearing sky. The wind filled to the south and got warm and full of the smell of Cuban dirt and flowers.

I kept well off Cuba until we reached the narrows between Cayo Lobos and Cayo Confites. We passed the Cayo Lobos lighthouse, rising into the sky from the island hidden below the horizon, and listened to the mysterious Charlie Lima Golf ordering ships to report. Some did and some didn't, and nothing seemed to happen either way. I did note that CLG appeared to have a radar now, and was calling ships by position, but I kept to the Bahamas side of the straits and CLG either didn't see me or ignored me.

A giant cruise ship came barreling up from the southeast, gleaming white in the noonday sun, the bone in her teeth. I kept my course—she could drive around my little stinkpot in circles—and the giant ship shot past us. I called up the crew, and they gathered on the port rail to stare.

She was the *Sovereign of the Seas*, half ship and half space-cruiser. Her bridge was a giant glass disk half-way up a raked, faired mast that tore a hole in the sky. I talked to her watch officer on VHF, and he said that she was returning to Miami from her maiden voyage. Within minutes she had shot off to the northwest toward Cayo Lobos, leaving a wide flat wake and a thin trail of black smoke. CLG didn't say anything to her that I heard.

In mid-afternoon, alone on the deep blue again, with the tops of the mountains of Cuba sticking out of the southern horizon like dirty teeth, I heard a distress call on the radio. I turned it up and sent a reply in the blind. "Ship calling Mayday, ship calling Mayday, this is the *Erika*. Call again, please."

"*Orca, Orca, Orca*, this is the *Pano*."

We went to 13—he didn't have many channels—and he said, "*Orca*, main engine stop. Can you help me?"

His voice kept drifting in and out. He was off the Cuban coast and drifting south. No wonder he sounded excited.

I woke Yussuf and got Jacek from the engine room. "Ship in trouble," I told them. "Take her off the tailshaft, Chief."

Yussuf came up to the bridge with me. We were getting closer, and now the VHF could reach the ship easily. "*Pano*," I called, "what is your situation?"

"I have chief engineer on bridge now. He say oil pump break, engine shut himself down *automatico*. Back-up oil pump no work long time. He say he fix main pump maybe five, six hour."

"What is your position?" I asked. He didn't know. The water depths in the area were too great for anchoring more than 12 miles offshore. I fiddled with the radar for a while—it was an old Verft 48-mile unit, but its actual range was about 24 miles—and finally picked up the ship, off the starboard bow at 20 miles.

I rang for maximum rpm and altered course to the vessel while Yussuf worked out her position. She was 15 miles from the nearest point of Cuban soil, Punto Banes. We were about 19 miles from the 12-mile limit ourselves.

"*Pano*," I called, "this is the *Erika*. Repeat *Erika*. Be advised that you are 15 miles NNE of Punto Banes. You are outside Cuban waters at this moment. My ETA to your position is one hour and 45 minutes. What is your drift rate, over?"

He answered in Spanish, but I told him to stick to English. He got the hint. At any rate, he didn't know how fast he was drifting, which made sense since he hadn't known his position until I told him. A few minutes later Yussuf worked out his drift from the radar. He pulled the canvas curtain aside. "It's going to be tight, Captain."

"Just make sure you keep us out of Cuban water," I said. "At least 13 or 14 miles offshore. Maybe you'd better get a line ready aft. We don't want to wait around for the *Pano* to get it together."

"Yessir." He went out and down.

"*Erika, Erika*, this is the *Pano*! There is a Cuban gunboat coming out from shore! He is coming right at us!"

"Roger, *Pano*," I said. "Be advised you are drifting southwest at one knot. You are still 15 miles off the coast. My ETA now is one hour and 25 minutes. Can you start your engine? Ask the chief engineer to start the engine. Try to make some distance to the north."

After a few minutes he came back. "Chief say main engine get damage if he start. He no start."

"Is he on the bridge?"

"Negative. Chief in engine room."

"Tell him to start the engine anyway. It's worth damaging the engine."

Silence. "I no can start engine, Captain," he wailed. "I lose job if order chief start engine."

I held my voice steady. "*Pano, Pano*, you lose ship if you go into Cuban waters. Then you lose job for sure."

"Captain," he cried, "Gunboat almost here. They are aiming a machine gun at me."

"Captain," I said, "if you have any men on deck, tell them to get below. Tell your men to get below."

There was a hissing when the Cubans found our channel. "*Motonave Pano*," a gravelly voice said in Spanish, "you are in Cuban waters. Your vessel is under arrest. Tell your crew to come on deck."

"Ah, Christ," I muttered. I still couldn't make visual contact, although at this point we were only about 12 miles away. There was a whitish haze over the surface that blurred the horizon and made the ocean the color of stainless-steel. "Cuban Coast Guard cutter," I said in Spanish, "this is the MV *Erika*. Be advised that the MV *Pano* is three miles outside of Cuban territorial waters."

"*Motonave Erika*," the voice said, "what is your position?"

"I am 12 miles northwest of the *Pano*. We are coming to her assistance. Be advised that we will remain in international waters at all times."

"*Motonave Erika*, advise yourself that the *Motonave Pano* is now in Cuban waters, 12 miles from the reef. If you enter Cuban waters, you will be boarded and seized as well."

I stepped to the chartroom and checked the chart. There was a submerged reef offshore, but no islands marked, so it didn't count.

The radio barked, "*Erika, Erika*, this is *Pano*. We have main engine started. We are making a turn to the north. . .Chief engineer say we can run maybe 15 minutes at half-speed. . ."

There was a chat-chat-chat-chat-chat sound in the loudspeaker. It was a machine gun, and close to the ship. If you ever hear a machine gun over the radio, you won't forget it. At that moment I saw her dead ahead, a tiny blue dot on the dull sea, but I still couldn't see the gunboat.

The captain lapsed into frantic Spanish. "They are shooting across my bows. Hurry, *Erika*. . .now they are shooting over the deck." I could hear the machine gun again, stuttering in long bursts. The captain cried in Spanish, "I surrender, I surrender. Stop shooting, stop shooting!"

"Stop your engine," the Cuban commander ordered. "Put the pilot ladder over the starboard side. Bring all your men on deck."

I turned the autopilot back toward the northeast. The ship heeled with the sudden turn, and Yussuf came running in from the wing. "What's happening?" He grabbed the glasses and swung them. "There's the ship, Captain. Why are you turning away?"

"They're done for, First," I said grimly. "They got the engine started, but the Cubans started shooting, so they had to give up." I went back to the chart table and started marking positions and times. "They're still 14 miles offshore, but the Cuban boat says they're 12 miles from the reef." I looked at him through the window. "They're the gunboat, so they get to make the measurement."

"What's going to happen to the crew?"

"Oh, they'll get sent home. The Cubans just want the ship."

There were no more radio communications between the *Pano* and the Cubans, so I assumed the boarding and seizure were successfully accomplished. I called Whiskey Oscar Mike, had them connect me to Miami Coast Guard, and reported the incident. When we got 25 miles offshore I turned back on course for Cape Tiburon, the easternmost point of Cuba.

We rounded the point the next day, and had a rough eight hours fighting a heavy wind and swell out of the northeast, coming directly onto the ship's port side and washing across the deck. About 1300 hours I left the bridge in the hands of Iron Mike and went down into the hold. I started crawling over the sacks with a flashlight. There was a slice of hot air about three feet thick between the top bags and the hatchcovers, and that was what I crawled through. I could smell wet rice.

Most of the damage was confined to the port side, where water was working its way under the tarp and through the boards. The welded repair on the port deck seemed to be holding.

I woke Yussuf. "We've got cargo damage, First. I need you to see what you can do to tighten up the tarps in a couple of places where the cargo is getting wet. Then check back with me."

He nodded sleepily and started getting dressed. I went back to the bridge. It was a clear, cool day, with high, wispy clouds racing across the bow of the vessel. The deck was awash, green water running to the lee scuppers. I made a Note of Sea Protest in the log, but didn't mention damaged bags.

Yussuf came up to report that the crew had gotten all the leaks stopped, but it looked like there might be several hundred damaged bags. I nodded.

"Isn't that very bad for the ship?" he asked.

"Of course. When we get out of this damned sea, we'll slow down, open up the hatches, and see what we've got."

A few hours later we were in the lee of Cap Mole, the westernmost point of Haiti's northern peninsula, and the seas died down. The wind continued a steady blow that tore whitecaps from the low swells and threw them against the side of the ship, but no more solid water came on deck.

It was late afternoon. I left Jacek on the bridge to watch for traffic and went down with the deck crew. We got the tarps rolled back and opened some boards.

There weren't as many wet bags as we had thought. "Listen, guys," I said, "a lot of these bags have only a little saltwater on them. We can sell these bags ashore."

Yussuf laughed. "You are a Greek captain for sure. Even Haitians will not eat rotten rice."

"Case of Beck's?" I pointed to a bag I had balanced on the hatch coaming, about to throw it over the side. "Look, only this area of the bag is wet. Most of the rice in this bag is still dry."

Manuel nodded. "*El Capitán tiene razon.* Many times we save rice, corn, flour, all kinds of food from damaged bags that the charterer leaves on the ship." He gave a toothy grin. "One time, we saved over 20 bags of coffee that had mildew spots on them. The captain made us take them out of the hold, just like today. He said we could sell them and keep the money. We all went together to a Chinese grocery store near the port and sold them for $100 a bag. We had a party onboard that night."

"Well, unfortunately," I said, "whatever we get for them is the ship's money, but I can give some advances out of it."

We finally threw 40 bags overboard and stacked 82 on deck as salvageable. There was a clean tarp over the rescue boat, so we spread it bottom-up on the deck and started going through the rice. I rummaged around in the forecastle and found a roll of plastic sacks left over from some long-forgotten cargo. We rebagged the rice, throwing the wet clumps overboard, and carried the sacks of dry rice aft to the steering flat to stow under the spares.

When I got back on the bridge Jacek was sitting on the starboard stool smoking and drinking a Schaefer beer, happy as an oyster. I checked the chart. He had already marked the vessel's position and had made a slight deviation to the east on the autopilot.

"Jacek," I said, "I didn't know you could navigate."

He shrugged and took a sip. "I was third mate on tankers. Polish license, Now I work in engine room. Who cares? Work is work."

"Speaking of work, I hate to bring this up, but isn't it your watch, Chief?"

"Yes, my watch," he said indignantly. "But you say I stay on bridge. I send Jerzy to engine room. . ."

"It's not that, Chief. You're drinking a beer."

He looked at the can. "Oh, sorry, Captain. It so hot, you know." He got up and moved toward the door. "One beer no problem me, Captain."

"It's okay, Jacek. Thanks for helping out."

He stopped at the wing and said, "I detain on board, Captain. I work hard, keep good engine room. One beer no problem."

"I know, Chief. Don't worry about it."

He went down the steps and away. I climbed up in the chair and stuck my tired legs out through the open window. The sun was almost in the ocean on the starboard side, lighting the underbelly of a low cloud layer with a hot red glow. On the southern horizon, the jagged spine of the great island, Gonave, was rising out of the fiery sea.

We steamed past Gonave during the night, and when I went on the bridge at 0600 we had turned into Gonave Bay. Just east of Rocheblave Light, marking a submerged reef south of the island, were two old shipwrecks, their ribs showing rust-red through great holes in their sides. Both were still upright and pointed east, frozen in a ghostly race toward the sun, now rising huge and red above the black mountains of Gonave.

All morning we slid along the southern peninsula, marking our progress from point to rocky point without bothering with the satnav. Just before noon I sighted the red roof of the Miragoane church through the glasses. It was still Yussuf's watch, and he was catching the log up in the chartroom. "I can see the church," I called to him. "Wait. . .I can see a boat. It's the whore-boat."

He laughed. "I don't believe that, Captain."

"Lots of ships in harbor. Looks busy."

I called for Half Ahead. We pulled up around the end of the reef and turned south with the great rock of Miragoane Point looming on the port side. The water here, only half-a-mile from shore and marked at 300 fathoms on the chart, was as dark a blue as the open ocean. Fishing boats appeared ahead. I took the ship off autopilot. Yussuf started for the wheel, but I waved him away and took it.

We went past the point north of town and into the anchorage. It was full of ships, maybe a dozen. Strangely, there were no ships tied stern-to at the shore, and as we chugged southward I could see that the dock area, which had been teeming with people before, was now empty.

I turned into the wind off the mangrove islands, not far from the abandoned freighter, and dropped three shackles of chain in eight fathoms. Arrows of sunlight pierced the blue water far below the ship as I walked forward to check the windlass. It was a hot, windy day, and the ship bobbed in the waves as she hunted back and forth for an easy place to lie. From the bow I could see a narrow streak of color in the water between us and the islands. It was the sunken ship Ronald and I had visited in the rescue boat.

Back on the bridge, I got on the radio and called blind, "What is the situation in the port?"

A Middle European voice answered without identifying itself. "Bloody awful, Captain. Army is in control of the port, it looks like. Not so sure, actually, since they had a small battle yesterday. All the ships that were discharging have gone out to anchor, as you can see."

"Have any ships been attacked?"

"No problems like that, Captain. It's all on shore."

"Okay, roger that."

We were too far away to tell much with the glasses, but I could see soldiers on the roof of the old army building. I thought I heard gunfire a couple of hours later, but I wasn't sure.

When I went down to the deck about 1600, the crew were lounging about with their good clothes on. "What are you guys doing?" I asked them. "Waiting for the girls?"

That's exactly what they were doing. Yussuf was dressed in a pair of black slacks and a white shirt, wearing street shoes. Jacek was wearing a pair of long pants and stylish half-boots. Victor was on deck too, but in his apron.

"You, Jacek?" I said. "What would Daniela think about this?"

He snorted. I looked toward shore, but there was no boat putting out toward us. "They're not going to come all the way out here," I said. "It's too far to scull one of those boats."

"They'll come, Captain, they'll come," Yussuf said. "They know we're here." He said, in Spanish, to Victor, "You think the girls know we're here?"

Victor laughed. "Of course they know. They all live in the old man's hotel on the top of the mountain. They can see the ships coming many miles away. They have contests to see who can identify a ship first."

"Well, I'm sorry we're so far away, fellows. Tell you what, you can take the rescue boat in if you want."

Jacek pointed. "Boat coming now, Captain."

He was right. There was a boat pulling out from between two of the anchored freighters, and there were no other ships between us, so it had to be coming here. It was full of people, but they didn't look like gaily dressed whores.

I went up to the bridge and used the glasses. The boat was full of soldiers with weapons. "Get back to the officer's mess, men," I called down to the deck. "That boat is full of soldiers."

They fled into the accommodations. Yussuf came up to the bridge. "What do you think, Captain?"

"Maybe they got some law in this port now. Better run up the Q flag. I should have done it anyway."

He got the flag from the cabinet and went outside. The boat had the wind and waves behind it, and finally it pulled up to the starboard side. The old oarsman tied it off. I went down on deck. There were six unfamiliar soldiers in khaki uniforms and three civilians, one with a medical bag. The soldiers slung their M-16's over their backs and climbed up the pilot ladder first, followed by the civilians. Manuel dropped a rope for the medical bag.

The Haitians gathered on deck at the foot of the steps. I stepped forward and held out my hand to a middle-aged man with a gold-braided cap. "I'm the captain," I said. "Welcome onboard."

None of them could speak a word of English, but with Yussuf translating I was given to understand that they represented the government of Haiti, and they were there to clear the ship into the country.

I took them up to the saloon and handed them Cokes from the refrigerator. The heat in the saloon was tolerable. One of the soldiers was carrying a U.S. baseball grenade in his hand. He put it on the table, and when the ship rocked it made a half-roll and fell off the table. The pin was in, so there was no danger. The soldier picked it up with a grin and put it back on the table.

The major in the gold braid wanted the crew's passports. I handed them over in proper order and brought the crew up one by one. He had a hard time with Yussuf's passport—being Arabic, it read from back to front—and finally gave up on it.

Every man had to be inspected by the doctor, who looked down their throats with a single greasy spatula, listened to their hearts with a battered stethoscope, and peered into their eyes intently before finding them healthy enough to enter Haiti. Then the cabins were searched, and quite thoroughly.

The major came back up to the saloon with Yussuf and asked for the "cargo papers."

"Tell him the charterer has that. Mr. Jacques Garot."

Yussuf translated. The man was standing imperiously in the doorway, but when Yussuf said the name, he jumped and backed away. He said a few words and hurried down the companionway.

"What'd he say?" I asked Yussuf.

"He said he didn't know Mr. Garot was our charterer, and not to worry about the cargo papers."

"Well," I said, "It's nice Garot has some pull around here. I hope he doesn't use it on us."

I went on deck. The civilians were already in the boat. The last soldier was stepping over the gunwale, his rifle strapped to his back. He was wearing broken black penny loafers without socks. By the time they finished disembarking, the whore-boat was putting out from shore. The crew assembled once more on deck.

It was more or less the same accumulation of Dominicanas, missing a few and with a few new ones. The first one aboard was Yussuf's girl, Sonia, with the round-hipped one, Altagracia, behind her. Amanda came up, not doing very well on the ladder even after years of practice. One of the new ones was a tall, slim, black-skinned beauty with straight hair falling to her waist. A young Hispanic man came up behind them, slender and well-dressed. He saw me looking at him and introduced himself as Tomas, a friend of Victor's. I welcomed him onboard.

The boatman was the same old gentleman, wearing the same blue baseball helmet. I got a can of beer from my fridge and threw it to him. He gave me a toothless salute. When I went up to the bridge again there was a ship calling me, one of the Haitian-owned freighters anchored close in, the *Dieu Kapab Express*. I answered. A Haitian voice said, "This is Jean Renet. I work for the charterer of your *batiment*. I am *chef* of the operations in Miragoane."

"Congratulations," I said into the mike. We were still on 16, since that seemed to be the custom in Miragoane. "What is the situation on shore? Be advised that we have cleared Customs and Immigration."

"Of course you clear Customs. I send them to you and pay for boat. Okay, Captain, bring your ship in and put the ropes behind to the shore. Put the ropes to the iron in the port."

"Why are there no ships tied to the shore now?"

"Em, Captain, *petit* problem today with army, but all is okay, I promise. All ships come back today, and tomorrow we discharge your cargo."

I could see two ships already moving, preparing to anchor stern-to. I talked to both, letting them know I was going to be dropping both anchors and backing up to the north of the port area. They were going to be south of me, all three of us in a row. The *Gitan Express* put out only one anchor, but it was because she only had one anchor. The other ship, the *Dieu Kapab Express*, was still adjusting her shore lines with the stern capstan as I steamed in.

Using the ship's natural tendency to back to port, and a few Half Aheads with rudder Hard-a-Port to correct to starboard, I backed the ship into the space between Bonvillain's barge and the *Gitan Express*. There were several Haitian boats below our counter, fighting each other to take our stern lines, and I finally had to go aft and point to the two boats I wanted before the others would back off. The chosen boats struggled shoreward with their cargoes of hawser.

Even with my crew paying out through the chocks, it took both boats a quarter-hour to get our lines ashore, and meanwhile I had to keep kicking the engine to maintain position. There was a moment when I thought I was going to get blown into the barge—the chief was a little slow on giving me Half Ahead—but I got power in time and swung the stern back in line.

With one line looped over a huge I-beam jutting out of the ground and the other tied around a tree at the back of the port, the crew made the lines fast and I was able to signal "Finished with Engine."

I went down and got the lunch Cookie had left for me on the back of the stove. The civilian throng was gone from the dock. There were tents pitched on the level ground. Soldiers loitered about. The sally port to the street had a new gate made of steel plate. The windows of the port director's office were open, and I could see soldiers milling about behind them.

Two machine-gun emplacements had been constructed on the flat concrete roof of the pockmarked army building, circular stacks of white sandbags with wooden timbers supporting tin roofs. The building had a fresh coat of yellow point, and a new Haitian flag flew from a short mast above it.

Someone on shore was trying to get my attention. It was a man in civilian clothing, waving his hand. A gold watch glittered on his wrist. He was yelling, but the wind carried his words off into the hills. I ignored him and went upstairs.

Half-an-hour later the same man came storming into the saloon. I was doing ship's accounts at the long table, as close as I could get to the DC fan without getting whacked, but I stood up to receive him. He was my size and age, wearing enough gold chain to sink a rowboat. "Captain," he said, without shaking hands, "did you not see me on the dock?"

"I saw someone on the dock. It may have been you."

"Why did you not send your boat for me?"

I leaned across the table. "Who the hell *are* you?"

He drew back as if slapped. "I am Jean Renet. I work for Mr. Garot."

I sat down and picked up my pen again. "How was I to know that? Now, how may I help you?"

He clapped his hands in Gallic frustration, then sat down abruptly and adjusted his pants. "Captain, we should not start our relationship in such a manner. Forget it. . .I got a boat to bring me out. Now, Captain, is your crane good?"

"It seems to be. We just put it on."

"Excellent." He rooted in his faux-alligator handbag and pulled out an envelope. "Captain, you must sign these papers."

I took the envelope and extracted the forms. Bills of Lading for 7,500 bags of rice. I threw them on the table. "I can't sign those."

"Why not?"

"Because I don't sign false Bills of Lading."

He picked them up and thrust them at me again. "This is nothing. It is a formality. You know Haiti. . .with the army in control of the port, everything must be done differently. You are an experienced captain. You know how these things are."

"Mr. Renet, I know exactly how they are. And I'm telling you now I will not sign false Bills of Lading. I suggest we go up to the bridge and call Mr. Garot if that is a problem."

He stood. "Very well. Let us go up."

I took him to the bridge and called down to Yussuf, who was directing the AB's in rigging down the lashings. He had unhooked the longwire antenna so it wouldn't foul the boom, and we had to wait for him to get it hooked up again. Jacek had the cowl up on the crane engine. I stood at the window while Jean stamped his feet behind me and made annoyed sounds with his teeth.

With the antenna strung, I powered up and got WOM clearly on several band-widths, but they were full of cruise ship traffic, for it was that time of day. I tried several times, but the cruise ship operators got in ahead of me each time. I finally got a callback on 8 Mhz, from the same operator with the cultivated voice. "That's *Erika* with a 'k,' right?" he said.

When he got his antenna tuned and connected me to AT&T, I handed the microphone to Jean. He knew how to use it, and made a collect call to a Miami number. I picked up the radio log and started filling in the call, noting carefully the number he called.

He talked in Creole for several minutes, then handed the mike to me. "This is the master," I said. "Go ahead."

"Capt. Hardberger?" Garot's voice was heavy with menace, even from 800 miles away, "I need you to sign those Bills of Lading. I will be down in Miragoane on Tuesday, and I will make sure then that you are taken care of."

"I'm taken care of now. I've got Social Security. But I'm still not signing any false Bills of Lading."

Jean winced when I said that. Garot started blustering over the airwaves that I was misinterpreting, that it was all very legal, that Haiti was different, etc. Finally he had me hand the mike back to Jean.

After they got through with some more Creole, I took the mike and closed the call down. Jean said, as I led him out of the chartroom, "So Captain, you do not have to sign the Bills of Lading. I will take care of it. The major is a close friend of mine."

"Lucky you."

He ignored that. "The major is very strong here now, with more than 100 soldiers in Miragoane."

We went down to the main deck together, where he finally shook my hand. "You will be ready to start at eight o'clock in the morning, then?"

"Sure. Tell the boats to come up on the port side, because I want to do some work on the starboard side."

"What kind of work?"

"Chipping and painting."

"Very well."

We parted as friends. I looked over the side as he climbed down and saw that he had hired Papa to bring him out, so I went in the galley and got a plate of food at the back of the stove and put it in a bag for the old man. Papa touched his helmet gratefully, stowed the bag under the thwarts, and sculled Jean off to the dock. Even though Jean was a close friend of the major's, none of the soldiers paid any attention to him except the guard at the gate, who made him open his handbag.

When I went back to the fantail, three Dominicanas and Humberto were sitting there. One of the girls, a hawk-faced thing, thin as a mangrove pole, was eating a plate of ship's food. Humberto was drinking a Schaefer's. The tall girl with the straight hair got up and offered me her chair, but I shook my head and sat on the bulwark. She gave me a big smile to show me she had all her teeth. Victor introduced her as Lucerna, from Rio Haina. I led him forward. "Who's paying for that skinny girl to eat, Victor?"

"I am, Captain." He held out his account book, which he kept in his back pocket. I glanced at it. He had meticulously noted a $2.00 charge against each crewman who let a guest eat onboard, and the guest's name. I saw that he was paying for several meals.

"Victor, which of these girls is your girlfriend? You can't feed them all."

He chuckled. "I do not have a girlfriend in this port. The cook does not have time for a girlfriend. Luz—the girl eating—she has not eaten today, so I offered her some food."

He put a hand on my arm. "Captain, you see that the girls do not take the crew's plates from the back of the stove. Only the Haitians do that. These girls have a hard life here. I don't mind spending a little money to help them."

I shook my head. "You have a family at home, Victor. You need to save your money for them. I don't mind the girls onboard as long as they don't steal things, but I can't have them eating unless they're with a crewman. As a girlfriend, I mean."

"I had a friend eat onboard at lunch. A Dominicano."

"The guy in the nice clothes? That's fine. I was talking about the girls."

Just before supper a boat pulled up and Yussuf hauled a case of Beck's Beer up with a rope. I was sitting in front of the house. He put it at my feet. "Captain, I am paying you what I owe you. That damned Carleton Pitt is a snake."

"Then I am a wise Moslem, Yussuf. I could be the Ayatollah."

At 2200 hours Yussuf and I worked out a watch schedule for ourselves and the AB's. I took the 0200 to 0600 watch. Before going up to my cabin I took a walk around the ship and made sure all the lockers, the forecastle, and the pantries were locked. A canoe came up to the pilot ladder and a short, powerful man with grizzled hair climbed onboard. He carried a heavy cudgel and a machete in a net bag. The boat wafted away into the darkness.

The man introduced himself in Creole as Kokimo, the watchman for the cargo. He had tiny black eyes under a low, bony forehead, a map of badly healed scars on his cheeks, and a massive, primordial jaw. I got him a folding chair to sit on in front of the house, and he settled in with the machete and knobbed stick across his knees.

Manuel woke me up at 0145. I got dressed in the hot, damp cabin and went down on deck. Kokimo was asleep on a piece of cardboard he'd found somewhere, curled up on deck with his hands under his cheek. I fixed myself a cup of coffee in the galley. As I stepped across to the officer's mess I saw that the door to the reefer room had a broken hasp hanging from the frame. The padlock was gone.

I opened the door and walked in. Trails of icy mist swirled in the frigid air. There were some boxes of vegetables left, but all the frozen meat had been taken. There was no point in waking Victor, so I closed the door and walked aft to the fantail. The port slept quietly, with a dozing sentry on guard by the gate and another sentry sleeping in a chair on top of the army building. I went forward and looked over both sides, but there were no boats around.

I nodded grimly to myself, got a folding chair from the fantail, and took it up on the boat deck just below the floodlights. With the lights illuminating the fantail, I was invisible from aft. I sat there for the rest of the night, but there were no more incidents, and toward dawn I dozed off.

Roused by a cup of coffee at 0600, I sent a boy in a canoe ashore to look for Ronald. A few minutes later Victor came on deck. "Captain, may I buy an octopus for $1.00?"

"Sure. But what about the stolen meat? Did you know the reefer room was broken into during the night?"

"What?" he said. "I did not know, captain. Oh, *que lástima*. What will we do for meat?"

"We'll have to buy some here," I said. "Let's go see that octopus." We went aft. There was a boat under the counter, one of its crew holding position with a hand on a staple. In the stern of the canoe was a big, bluish octopus in a wire basket. The boy in the back lifted the basket to show me the creature. It threw a tentacle out of the basket and around the gunwale, but the boy popped it free and pushed it back in.

I wadded a dollar into a ball and threw it down. Victor lowered a bucket, hauled the octopus up, and grabbed it by the throat. By then Jerzy and Jacek were on the fantail, crowding forward, and when Victor pulled the octopus out of the bucket, it whipped a tentacle around Jerzy's thick forearm.

Jerzy got a frozen expression and tried to jerk his arm away, but the animal held tight. He lurched back, pulling the octopus out of Victor's grasp. It threw the rest of its tentacles around Jerzy's legs, the sack of its body hanging down to the deck, its great liquid eye staring up blankly. Jerzy came out of his spell and started dancing frantically, howling in Polish, but Jacek was laughing too hard to do anything.

Victor grabbed the animal by the neck again. The tentacles around Jerzy's legs didn't have much of a grip on his pants, but it took a concerted pull to get his arm free. When the tentacle came off, its suction cups popping, it left three concentric rows of red circles on his forearm.

Jerzy stared at his arm in horror, then he started to laugh. He had to go all around the ship to show everybody, even the Haitians in the boats, the red circles on his arm.

Ronald arrived a few minutes later. "Ronald," I said, "I need to get some chipping and painting done. Can I hire Haitians to do that?"

"Yes, of course, Captain."

"How much?"

"Five dollars U.S. a day."

"Okay, I want you to find me 20 Haitians at five dollars each. I'll pay you eight dollars a day to ramrod them. Okay?"

He grinned. "Okay, Captain. I do that."

"I want everybody onboard by eight o'clock tomorrow morning."

"Yes, Captain."

"And there is another thing. I have some rice to sell. About 50 bags. Most of it is okay, but some might be wet. Can you sell it?"

"Certainly, Captain!"

"But you cannot tell a single person that it came from this ship, or there will be big trouble."

He smiled. "I am used to this business, Captain. We must to discharge the rice very late at night so no one will see." He slid down the pilot ladder and into the boat.

Discharging continued without interruption throughout the day. At 1700 hours the stevedores and lighters went home. Jacek started the harbor generator and the ship got quiet. A party was getting underway on the deck of the *Gitan Express*, and music and laughter floated over the water. Ricardo and Manuel went across in a Haitian canoe, wearing their shore clothes.

Just before dark, a dugout canoe approached the pilot ladder and a ragged old Hispanic man came on deck. I was sitting in a chair in front of the house. He limped up and said, "¿*Capitán?*"

"¿*Sí?*"

"*Capi*, I am an old seaman on the *God Only One*." He pointed toward the abandoned wreck in the bay. "The owner is a *puta* Haitian who left us to starve. Now everybody has gotten off except me, but I have no family in Peru to send me money to get home."

"That is very bad, sir," I said. "That is every seaman's nightmare."

"Yes, *Capitán*, I am stranded in this filthy country. Can you give me some money for a ticket home? I promise on my father's honor that I will work and send the money to you."

I got up. "I'm very sorry, but I have no money to give you. However, I can give you some food. Wait for me here." I went back to the pantry and filled a small bag with canned meat and vegetables.

When I handed the old man the bag, he looked in it. "I have not had fresh meat for a week. Can you give me some fresh meat?"

I shook my head shortly. "We're low on meat ourselves." I steered him toward the boarding ladder. "Good luck, old man. *Vaya con Dios.*"

He climbed over the side and the boy paddled him back to the *God Only One*, now a shadowy black hulk in the fading light.

At 2200 hours, when we started the night watchkeeping schedule, I took the first watch and sat on the bridge listening to the BBC. About midnight, I was resting my head on my hands with my eyes half-closed when I saw movement on the deck, well forward. I stood up and squinted.

A Haitian had just sprung over the bulwarks on the port side. He was crouched down by the bitts, hidden from the forward mastlight by the forecastle. I could see his face clearly when he stuck his head up to peer at the doorways. He couldn't see me behind the lights on the brow of the wheelhouse.

I went out on the wing of the bridge. The Haitian came creeping aft on the port deck, keeping below the level of the hatchcover. He was wearing nothing but a pair of ragged shorts.

I slipped down to the port hallway and waited. The music from the party next door and the rising night wind masked any noise he might have made. I was about to stick my head out to see what had become of him when he appeared right in front of me, gliding along the hallway, his eyes as white as headlights.

"Argh!" I shouted, and grabbed him, but he was as greasy and smelly as a pig, and within a second he'd slipped from my grasp. He ran on deck and dived into the water. I jumped up and followed, and got a glimpse of his head making a phosphorescent bow wave as he swam away.

I ran forward and saw his canoe tied to the starboard anchor chain, hidden from the light by the bulk of the ship. Yussuf came up on the starboard deck with Kokimo right behind him. "What happened, Captain? I heard somebody yell."

"There's a fucking thief in the water. There's his canoe. I caught him sneaking into the accommodations."

Yussuf leaned over to look at the canoe. I went to the other side, but couldn't see the Haitian. "I'm going to get that canoe," I said. "I want this fucking town to know what happens when you steal from the *Erika*." I took my clothes off and laid them on the hatchcover. "Get some big nuts or shackles. You can throw them at the guy if he tries to attack me." I jumped into the ocean.

The water was as warm as mother's milk. I broke the surface and looked around, but still couldn't see the Haitian. A few long strokes put me alongside the canoe. I pulled myself into it and started untying the painter, a piece of rotted cord, when I heard a heavy breath behind me. The Haitian's head was coming around the bow.

I jerked the cord free from the chain. The Haitian cried out when he saw me, but by then I was paddling toward the pilot ladder. There was nothing on the hull for him to hang onto, and he was clearly afraid to follow me aft, so he swam out to the anchor chain and started calling plaintively in Creole.

I tied the boat to the pilot ladder on the port side and went on deck. Yussuf met me. "What are you going to do with the man's boat, Captain?"

"I'm going to burn it."

"Captain, you can't do that."

"Watch me." I went to the boat deck and got the can of gasoline for the outboard motor. The Haitian started crying and waving his free hand, holding himself up waistdeep in the water. I poured about a gallon into the canoe. The ancient wood soaked up the gasoline instantly. By then the party on the *Gitan Express* had gathered at the starboard gunwale to watch.

"Captain," Yussuf said, from behind me, "he says he has three children. He says he cannot live without his boat."

"Tough shit. Hand me your lighter." I soaked the end of a broken board in gasoline, cast off the canoe, and lit the board. The man made some last desperate pleas. When the canoe had drifted four or five feet from the hull, I tossed the board into it.

The fumes in the bottom of the canoe erupted in a fireball that rolled skyward with a heavy "Whoomp!" The partygoers on the *Gitan Express* cheered. The burning canoe looked like a crack in the shell of the earth. It drifted to the northeast and came to rest against the broken concrete behind an old warehouse, snapping and crackling like a forest fire.

Several soldiers on the roof of the army building came to the edge to watch the canoe burn, and some men went up on Bonvillain's barge to see what the excitement was about. The thief was still on the anchor chain, now silent, watching the flames consume his canoe. The party on the *Gitan Express* resumed, the Haitians drifted away, and finally the thief, with a small despairing cry, slipped from the chain and swam off into the darkness.

At 0100 a big launch came sculling up to the starboard side with Ronald and a small gang of stevedores. "You're still awake, Captain?" he called when he saw me on deck.

"We had a little excitement onboard," I said.

He led the men up the pilot ladder. I told him about the thief and the canoe.

"Maybe you get problem, Captain. Maybe the man go to Justice Court."

"I'll worry about that later. You ready to get that rice?"

There were 48 bags in the steering flat, roughly 50 kilos each. Ronald estimated that he would get about $25 per bag. We found a few bags that stank of mildew where we hadn't cleaned out all the wet clumps, but he insisted that he could sell them anyway. The cargo went into the lighter and it struck off for Bezin across the bay, Ronald standing on the bow like Washington crossing the Potomac.

About 0200 Jacek came back from shore, sitting upright on the thwarts of a little launch. He handed the boy a lump of *gourdes* and came unsteadily up the pilot ladder, dirty and disheveled. He said he'd been at the disco and had fallen down. He went off to his cabin and put the door on the latch. The next time I went by I could hear him snoring through the crack.

Manuel came back drunk and jolly from the party on the *Gitan Express*, but he loudly insisted on taking his watch, so I went upstairs and collapsed into my bunk.

Victor woke me with a cup of coffee at 0700, and even then I had a hard time getting up. I put on a fresh outfit of damp clothing and went downstairs. The sun was above the mountains, and the boats were alongside. The stevedore foreman was a short, powerful man named Roger. He had a voice like a gravel pit and a somber manner, and the stevedores did what he said.

A boat full of Haitians pulled up to the starboard pilot ladder and tied off. Ronald was standing in the bow with a weathered notebook. He came up the ladder, but when the others started to follow, I motioned them to stand by. They looked up with happy grins. "*Cinq dolar Americain chaque homme*," I called to them, holding up five fingers.

"*Oui, Capitain, oui*," they shouted.

"Okay." I turned to Yussuf. "Put Manuel and Ricardo in charge of eight men each. Send two to the engine room. You know what needs to be done. Put half of 'em on chipping the starboard side and use the other half for general work."

I had Ronald count the men aboard, noting each man's name as he came over the bulwark. They were mostly from Ronald's home village across the bay, Bezin. Some only had one name.

Jean came out in Papa's boat and climbed up the pilot ladder. He shook hands perfunctorily. "Who are these people?" he said, pointing at the workers.

"I hired them. We're going to chip and paint the starboard side of the ship."

"All right, Captain. Tell me, does your cook have breakfast? I left P'-au-Prince without eating."

"Certainly. I'll show you back."

I took him aft. When I looked out the door, I saw a launch pulling toward the ship with a soldier standing in the bow. I went on deck to meet him. He put a piece of paper in his mouth and climbed up the ladder. He was a young man with a wide freckled face and a dirty uniform. The chipped handle of a .38 Police Positive stuck out of a worn leather holster.

"*Capitain?*"

"*Oui.*"

He handed me the paper. It was a dingy photocopy of a legal document of some kind. I called Ronald over. "What is this bullshit?"

He glanced at it and said apologetically. "It is from the Justice Court. You have to go to the Court because of the *bateau* you burned last night."

"And this. . ." I read the name, ". . .this Anse Larriere, that's the thief?"

He nodded.

"So now he's suing me for the canoe?"

He nodded again.

"It says I have to go at two o'clock today. Is that right?"

"Yessir."

"Okay, fine. I'll go. Can you come with me?"

"Of course."

I nodded toward the soldier. "Why is he bringing this? This isn't army business."

He shrugged. "No police in town now. They all ran away. Anse hired this soldier to bring paper to you."

"To scare me, eh?" I crumpled the paper up and put it in my shirt pocket. "*Merci*," I said to the soldier. He bowed stiffly and went back down to the launch. "And how much do you think he's going to want?" I asked Ronald.

"It says 5000 *gourdes* on the paper."

"Jesus. How much is that in money?"

"Em. . .800 U.S. dollars."

"What the fuck! What if I don't pay? What can they do?"

"They can stop the ship from leaving. Sometimes ships catch boat between them and smash it up. Justice Court make the ships pay or the port director does not allow the ships to leave."

"How's he do that? There's no patrol boat in this shithole. What if I just up anchor?"

He shrugged. "I do not know, Captain."

"Well, we'll go to the Justice Court and see what happens."

A few minutes later a boat full of soldiers came alongside and poured up the pilot ladder like army ants. Most of them carried pistols, but a couple carried M-1 carbines and one man had an Uzi. Another had his belt festooned with antique U.S. pineapple grenades. The squat black major came last. Jean came bustling out of the accommodations with egg on his chin. He and the major went over to the side and started talking earnestly, heads together. I nudged Yussuf and pointed to them. "Watch 'em start fighting."

It took less than a minute before Jean was gesticulating and the major was poking him in the chest with a forefinger. They moved aft together, locked in argument, and went into the accommodations.

The crane engine died abruptly, a load still hanging in the air over the boat. The crane driver set the brake and got out. After a few minutes Jacek came up from the engine room with a handful of tools. He staggered a little getting up on the hatchboards. I went and joined him by the side of the crane. He stank of rum.

"Jacek, you haven't been drinking already, have you?"

He gave me a sour, red-eyed look. "Too bloody hot in engine room." He turned his back to me and opened the cowl.

The major came out of the accommodations, striding purposefully along the deck. He motioned to the soldiers where they were squatting in the shade of the bulwark. They jumped up with their weapons at ready.

He barked a couple of sentences to the other officers. Jean rushed out calling to him in Creole. The major ignored him. Some of the stevedores came out of the hold. Jean told them to go back down and keep working. One of the officers grabbed Jean's sleeve. Jean tried to jerk away, but another soldier stepped up with his hand on his pistol. Jean made a disgusted wave to the men in the hold to come out.

I eased over to Ronald. "What's going on?"

"The major say the cargo is too much for the cargo papers," he whispered. "He say ship must to stop discharging until there is an investigation."

I groaned. "An investigation? Is this a fucking joke?"

The major got in the boat, followed by the officers and most of the men. Two soldiers with carbines stayed behind. The stevedores started getting into the lighters. The lighter that had been under the hook pulled off toward shore half-full.

Jean came up and explained that it was nothing, a minor problem, and that we would start again at 1300 hours. He didn't seem to have noticed that the crane was broken, and I didn't point it out. He left the ship in one of the lighters. When it got to shore, he called a stevedore to carry him on his back up to dry land. He jumped down and handed the man some money before going out through the sally port.

With the discharging stopped, I was able to put all hands on the chipping. The Haitians hammered furiously. Blisters and slab rust flew off the old hull in clouds.

I went aft at noon to have lunch. Amanda, Sonia, and the other girls were eating on the fantail, laughing and chatting in Spanish. Victor asked me when we would be getting some meat to replace the stolen provisions.

I turned to Amanda. "*Señora*," I began. Being a whore, she had to be a *Señora* even if she never married, since "*Señorita*" carries the presumption of virginity. "Where can I buy some. . ."—I wanted to say "plucked chicken" because I didn't want Victor gutting and plucking chickens onboard—". . .some *pollos desnudos?*"

All I could think of for "plucked chickens" was "naked chickens."

"*¡Pollos desnudos!*" cried Amanda. The girls looked at each other and burst out laughing. "*¡Pollos desnudos!*" Amanda repeated. "The captain wants naked chickens!"

She knew what I meant, so I gave Victor some U.S. money and told him to go with her after lunch to buy enough chickens to last until we reached the next port. We took the same boat in and parted company at the sally port. A young man in uniform was on guard at the gate, wearing plastic bath slippers on his horny feet.

Ronald met me at the sally port and took me to the Justice Court, a hole-in-the-wall next to a warehouse at the north point of town. Behind the courtroom, through an open passageway, I could see hundreds of cases of Coca-Cola and Beck's Beer. The courtroom itself was a bare concrete cubicle with a desk at one end and two chairs in front of it. Benches lined the wall on either side of the front door.

The room was packed. An old man in a shapeless suit and a narrow gray tie sat behind the desk. Two Haitian women in bright clothes sat in front of him. On the benches were a dozen Haitians watching the fun. A soldier with an ancient bolt-action Enfield lounged in the rear doorway.

There was a stir when I came in. The thief was sitting at the end of a bench. He gave me a ferocious grin.

It took half-an-hour for the judge to dispense with the women. They left together, still shouting at each other and waving their arms in the air.

The judge motioned me forward. I sat in one of the chairs and the thief sat in the other. Ronald stood behind me to translate.

The judge asked the thief some questions. The man responded with a detailed reenactment of the fiendish crime, complete with anguished histrionics as he showed how he had pleaded from the anchor chain for his family's livelihood. The crowd liked it, and laughed and clapped when he was finished. He sat down proudly.

The judge asked me something sternly. I told my story through Ronald. The judge then spoke to me. Ronald whispered in my ear, "He says that if the man stole something, that is a problem for the police. He says you burned the man's *bateau*, so you must pay for it."

"How much?"

"Five thousand *gourdes*."

I nodded and stood up. "Tell him," I said loudly, "that my ship is territory of Honduras, and this court has no power over my ship. Tell him I will not pay for a thief's boat."

I started for the door, but the judge said something to the soldier, who jumped up and came across the room with the long muzzle of his rifle narrowly missing people's heads. Ronald called to me to stop.

I stopped. Ronald said that the judge had ordered the soldier to take me to jail if I didn't pay. He whispered in English, "Tell the judge that you will go back to the ship and get the money, and then stay on the ship. Don't tell the judge you won't pay."

"Fuck that. Tell the judge I'm ready to go to jail. Tell him this will be an international incident. Maybe he will go to jail in Port-au-Prince."

The judge didn't like the part about going to jail in Port-au-Prince. He ordered the soldier to take me off. We walked together, Ronald trailing along unhappily, down the street to the old police building where I'd reclaimed my teevee.

The soldier explained the situation to an older man, some sort of non-com. The man studied me gravely and shook his head. Ronald saw his chance and started talking. The soldier joined in, and soon I was being retried at the police station.

Finally the non-com shooed us all out and the soldier went back to the Justice Court. Ronald guided me toward the port. "The sergeant doesn't want to put you in jail," he explained. "He says they can't take care of *blanc* ship captain in jail."

"So what now?"

"I don't know. Probably the ship cannot sail."

"Son of a bitch." I kicked the ground. "No fucking agent in this port, either. Well, we'll see about this bullshit." I stopped in the street. Ronald had to come back to me. "Listen," I said, "how well you know Kokimo?"

"The watchman? He's from Bezin. . .he's my cousin."

"Good." I lowered my voice and we started walking again. "I want you to give Kokimo 50 dollars to go visit Anse le Voleur. I don't want him to hurt him. I just want him to tell Anse that if he doesn't drop this bullshit lawsuit, I'll have his fucking legs broken. You think he'll do it?"

Ronald laughed. "You are becoming a Haitian, Captain." He got serious. "Kokimo will do it, but I must be very careful to tell him not to hurt the man."

I slipped him 50 dollars and went through the gate into the port. Several of the other ships were still discharging, and sacks of rice and cement were coming up the beach on the backs of the stevedores. I threaded my way through the dust-caked men to flag down a launch.

At 1500 hours the stevedores arrived onboard with Roger, who told me that the Customs problem had been resolved. I got some of my Haitians off the paint raft and had the hatches opened up, and at 1524 the first bags of the shift dropped into a boat. I watched for a while from the deck, then went up to the bridge.

To the south, the *Gitan Express* was discharging drums of Shell motor oil by lowering the drums into the water, where the straps were loosened and the drums were swum ashore, barely afloat, by naked Haitians. At the shoreline, the drums were rolled out of the water with sharpened poles and up to the backs of trucks. I was studying the old ship's classic German lines when Jean arrived. I waited patiently as he made his way to the bridge.

"Captain," he said, "we have plenty problem. You know duty on rice in Haiti is $5.00 U.S. per bag. The major says I have to pay duty on every bag that goes ashore." He wrung his hands. "Mr. Garot will be very unhappy. The army has put tallyman on the deck."

"Just don't get my ship seized," I warned him.

He had me shut down the crane while we strung up the longwire. I duly logged the downtime to charterer's account. We had no trouble getting WOM on the 12 Mhz bandwidth, and he called Garot in Miami. They talked in Creole, Jean making wild, exculpatory gestures at the blank face of the Skanti while he pleaded for understanding.

Finally, he handed me the microphone. Garot's voice came out of the tinny speaker. "Captain, why you do not accept the figure of 7,500 bags?"

I pressed the button and laughed into the microphone. "Mr. Garot, this is a time charter, so I cannot sign for any number of bags."

I could hear him gnash his teeth. "Captain, Jean has Bills of Lading for you to sign. I am ordering you to sign them. That is all." He hung up. I signaled Yussuf to lower the longwire. Jean said, "It is very bad to make Mr. Garot angry. This is a bad time in Haiti to make a man like Mr. Garot angry."

I turned. His face was in shadow, framed by the white-hot light outside. "Is that a threat?"

After a long moment he moved closer to the window. His expression was placatory. "No, no, Captain, of course not. You just do not understand what is happening here. You do not know how Haiti works."

"I know all too well. It doesn't."

He finally gave up and took his unsigned B/L's ashore. A half-hour later six soldiers came up alongside and spoke to the soldiers onboard. The soldiers on deck immediately turned around and started shouting at Roger. Roger started shouting back, the stevedores poured out of the hold, and pandemonium erupted.

I went downstairs to calm things down, but as soon as I stepped out of the accommodations there was a long burst of automatic fire from the boat alongside. Everyone on deck threw himself flat.

I looked over the side. One of the soldiers in the boat was shouting to the stevedores, holding his weapon on his hip. They picked themselves up slowly, and the soldiers on deck started herding them toward the pilot ladder. They moved docilely at first, but got louder and angrier as they got down in the boats. There were well over a hundred of them, and when the boats were filled with people they stayed tied up alongside, arguing fiercely with the soldiers in the launch.

The soldiers probably realized that there were more Haitians around them than they had bullets in their guns. Their boatman cast off suddenly and sculled away. The Haitians started laughing and catcalling. The soldiers stood stiffly in the bottom of the boat as it rounded the bow. A steady wind was blowing out of the west, across Gonave Bay, and when it hit the bow of the little doughdish the boat took a sudden heave that made the soldiers forget their dignity and grab for the gunwales. More howls of laughter from the stevedores.

The soldiers had cleared the deck of all the stevedores except Roger. They tried to make me send my workers ashore, but Ronald managed to convince them that the cargo problem didn't have anything to do with ship maintenance, so we were allowed to continue chipping and painting. At 1700 hours, as soon as the workers were paid, Ronald went ashore to get the carpet buyers.

A few minutes later, Victor left for fresh vegetables with Amanda and a couple of other Dominicanas, carrying empty garbage bags. "Get plenty of coconuts," I called down as their launch passed under the counter. "*Coco loco*, you know!"

Amanda pointed at me. "*¡Capitán Loco!*"

The other girls laughed and joined in. "*¡Capitán Loco, Capitán Loco!*"

After they left I went up to the saloon. Jacek came in. "Permission to go ashore, Captain?" he asked. He was dressed in a flower-print shirt and long pants. The black stubble on his lantern jaw had been freshly scraped, but his eyes were wet and red, and when I went up to him there was rum on his breath.

"Jacek," I said, "of course you can go ashore, but you'd better be careful, eh? This is Haiti, you know."

"No problem, Captain," he said seriously. "I will be with friends."

"Tomorrow is a work day. You're a good chief, but duty is duty."

He looked offended. "I will be back for my watch at midnight, Captain. You see how I keep the engine room."

"I do," I said. "I appreciate it."

He gave me an exaggerated salute and went downstairs. I looked out my window and saw the boat waiting for him, full of seamen from the other ships, dark men with hair slicked sideways, pieces of Kraft paper spread on the thwarts under their good pants. When I went on the boat deck I could hear music from the disco floating up to the empty evening sky, past Jesus and his fellow-sufferers outlined starkly above the ridge of the mountain.

A boat delivered Kokimo onboard. He stowed his cudgel and machete carefully under his chair and came up to me at the gunwale. In broken English and Creole, he explained that he had tried to avoid violence, but the thief had been insolent, and it had been necessary to give him a few "*coups a tête*." He did not believe that I would be hearing from Anse le Voleur again. I thanked him and he took his position in front of the house.

I felt the ship tug uneasily under me. A stiff wind had been blowing all day, out of the west, which was unusual. Now there was lightning playing around the western mountains, and the wind had gotten a cold edge to it. I walked forward and checked the anchor chains and chocks, making sure there were crowbars across the hawse-holes. The ship was heaving against the starboard anchor with the port chain dropping straight down into the dark water. We were the most windward ship, but the ships to leeward of us were successively exposed at their bows because the line of ships tended toward the southeast.

At 2315 a sharp gust came roaring out of the western blackness and hit all the ships at once. The *Erika*, heavy with cargo, lurched slowly southward under its weight. I was in the galley fixing a sandwich at the time. I ran forward and looked at the other ships. The stern of the *Gitan Express* had swung to the south as her slack starboard hawser—the captain had not crossed them—came up bar-taut, shaking water out of its thick body like a dog. It was fastened to a ruined pillar at the water's edge, which looked secure enough. I couldn't see where her other line was fastened.

I checked our shore lines. With crossed lines, our stern had only swung half as far, so there was still good clearance. The wind cut across the bay with the smell of rain in it. A Haitian launch a few hundred meters ahead of the *Gitan Express*, full of crewmen going to the ships at anchor, was caught in the gust and spun completely around. The boatman sculled hard for the lee of the *Erika*, the boat leaping in the sudden, hard chop.

I could hear loose tin on the roofs in town start banging, and a hoarse voice yelling in Spanish from one of the ships.

Yussuf appeared on deck in his jogging pants, with Jerzy and Ricardo behind him. "Look how much the *Gitan Express* is swinging," I said. "Shit, here comes the rain."

A scattering of drops hammered on the deck like shot. The rigging of the forward derrick set up a low, mournful whistling, and the Haitian flag at the yardarm snapped like electricity.

A sheet of rain loomed in the ship's deck lights, off the starboard bow, rushing toward us out of the night. The whistling of the rigging shot up in pitch like a bosun's pipe. The bow rounded to starboard on the scope of the anchor chain. The rain swept between the *Erika* and the *Gitan Express*.

We retreated to the port hallway, under the cover of the overhang, as rainwater sluiced across the deck and poured aft. The ship had a slight port list, and the water whirlpooled in the port scuppers. I went aft and checked our stern lines again. The captain of the *Gitan Express* was on the dock, his shore clothes drenched, waving frantically to the Haitian boat that had tied itself to our pilot ladder. The Haitian flapped his arms and yelled that he didn't dare try to come get him, but neither could hear the other.

I went forward. "The captain of the *Gitan Express* is trapped on shore," I told the crew. "He was at the disco, and now the boat won't pick him up."

We watched the rain blowing straight across the deck. "The Haitian is smart," Yussuf said. "How could he scull the boat in this?"

Then the *Gitan Express*'s anchor gave way. One moment her lights were shining on the port side of the *Erika*, then for a sickening second it looked like the *Erika* was swinging wildly to starboard as the other ship's lights fell off.

"Oh, my God!" Yussuf said.

"Oh shit," I said. "The *Gitan Express* is dragging anchor."

"*Puta madre*," Victor said.

I stuck my head out into the rain. The bow of the *Gitan Express* hit the midsection of the *Dieu Kapab Express*, next to it. A lone figure on the *Gitan Express* was working his way forward on the port side, wearing a yellow slicker suit plastered to his body by the wind.

There was a screech as the *Gitan Express* ground heavily along the starboard side of the *Dieu Kapab Express*. I went up to the bridge with Yussuf, Victor, and Jerzy behind me. We could see through the rain-distorted windows that the weight of the *Gitan Express* had almost pushed the *Dieu Kapab Express* against the next ship, which I believe was the *Tondo*, a Guyanese half-shelter-decker. The crew of the *Tondo*, bare-chested and drenched, were frantically hanging out truck-tire fenders.

By then, the crews of several ships were standing on the dock. I could see the captain of the *Gitan Express* cringe every time his ship hit the *Dieu Kapab Express*. The lone crewman onboard was still trying to hang a tire over the port side, but it was a futile gesture. We could see his small yellow figure in the mastlight, circled by driving rain.

The starboard stern line of the *Dieu Kapab Express* parted. I could hear the crack from the wheelhouse. "There she goes," I said calmly. The ship started to wheel, still anchored, as the bow of the *Gitan Express* plunged and gouged its way aft along its side. Then the *Dieu Kapab Express* swung free of the *Gitan Express* to hit the *Tondo* port stern to starboard stern, hard enough to throw the *Dieu Kapab Express*'s port life raft in the water. We could see little of what was happening at the time, but the life raft was recovered the next day by a Haitian and sold back to the ship.

The rain fled away toward the eastern mountains, leaving a windy drizzle that tapered off to a hot, wet calm. Even in the dark the wet decks steamed. With the wind and rain gone, the air was full of Spanish curses and frantic calls to boat-men. Haitians went sculling up to the dock and took off the crews.

The water turned oily and sluggish. The *Gitan Express* was firmly aground, the bow almost touching the back wall of the Hotel de Ville. The crew climbed onboard in stunned silence. The captains of the *Dieu Kapab Express* and the *Tondo*, one Honduran and the other Guyanese, screamed threats at each other while the crew of the *Dieu Kapab Express* worked to get another line ashore. Since the *Erika*'s lines had held nicely, we all turned in except Ricardo, who was on watch.

There was a light breeze blowing at dawn. The boats must have gotten the word that we were going to work, for they were lined up at the ship's side. I could see from the wheelhouse the damage to the *Dieu Kapab Express*'s side, starting with a heavy dent in the bulwarks midships and continuing aft in a series of bright gashes. There was a great dent in the starboard corner of the house where the bow of the *Gitan Express* had swung against it before clearing the ship.

The *Gitan Express* was still aground, listing to starboard. The crew were on deck, discharging bags of cement into boats. They must have started during the night. A few minutes later the boats cleared away and her main engine started. The captain managed to get her bow swung around to starboard enough to go to Dead Slow Ahead without hitting the *Dieu Kapab Express*. She went out to an-chor.

Jean was onboard at 0800, claiming that the problem with the army was fixed, and at 0822 the first slingload went overboard. Ronald and his two carpet buyers came onboard at 0900. They were from Port-au-Prince, a tall, soft-looking egg of a man and a sharp-faced little ferret with a rodent's habit of sniffing the air for danger. I took them into the forecastle with a couple of workers to move the rolls around. The air in the closed compartment had taken on the odors of stale beer and vomit. The Haitians looked through the carpet so long that Ronald and I left them and went on deck. Ronald pulled a fat roll of U.S. dollars out of his pocket. "The money for the rice, Captain."

"You sold it all?"

"Yessir." He handed me the money. I counted it. Over a thousand U.S. dollars.

"You were able to sell the wet bags?"

"My brother took them up to the mountains. They paid about 180 *gourdes* each for the wet bags, about $15. But I was able to get more for the good rice. About $25 a bag."

"Excellent. But how much do I give you for your cut?"

"Oh, no, Captain. I already took $150. The rest is yours."

"Ah hah." I put the money away. "Many thanks, Ronald."

After an hour in the forecastle the two buyers had selected 20 dozen rolls. Ronald brought them to me on the fantail, hot and irritable, their shirts plastered to their flabby chests. They offered me 1400 *gourdes* a dozen, about $120.00.

"Twenty dozen rolls?" I said. "Shit, I thought these were big time buyers. Hell, I've got 100 dozen rolls to sell. Okay, 1400 *gourdes* a dozen, but they've got to come back tonight when the port office is closed. Tell them to bring a boat around to the starboard side right after dark."

They didn't want to wait, but when I mentioned that it was to avoid problems with the army, they agreed to come back and left.

We were discharging at nearly 30 tons an hour—pretty good for a crane and a swinging derrick—when a bag slipped out of the net as it was being swung and fell into the hold. I was standing at the coaming, watching operations, and saw the bag fall. Before I could open my mouth the bag landed on one of the stevedores and broke his leg. The bone snapped like a pencil. The man screamed and fell to the floor, writhing in agony.

The other stevedores gathered around him, staring. "Ronald!" I yelled. He came running up. "There's a man hurt in the hold. Tell them to hold him down so he doesn't do more damage to his leg."

He went to the coaming and started yelling. I called to Yussuf and Manuel to get the litter out of the ship's hospital, then went down the stevedore ladder.

The man was still throwing himself around, howling. His left leg was sticking out at a right angle, the skin and flesh twisted around the break. I knelt down and held his leg so I could look at it. There was a wound on the inside of the calf, about six inches below the knee, with torn flesh and gristle visible, but I couldn't see a bone-end. The man flopped like a fish when I straightened his leg. It was as limp as a raw steak.

The litter finally arrived and the crane operator lowered it with the cargo hook. We loaded the man and strapped him in. The crane lifted him out of the hold and over the side. I went topside in time to see the litter lowered into an empty lighter. The men in the boat held the litter secure as the boatman sculled it toward shore.

I called Ronald over. "How close is the nearest hospital?"

"Em, P'-au-Prince."

"What, there isn't anything closer? The drive to Port-au-Prince will kill the guy."

"That's all, Captain. There is, em, a *clinique* in Petit Goave, but the doctor comes on Wednesday and Saturday. Now only nurse there."

"Well, hell, if I'd known that I'd have given him a shot of painkiller for the trip."

When I turned around Manuel was coming up to me with a broken hasp and lock in his hand. "*¡Capi, mira!*" he cried. It was the lock to his cabin. During the excitement someone had broken the lock on his door and had stolen $175, his stereo, his little black-and-white teevee, and his shore shoes.

This coming on top of everything else, I went berserk for a few minutes. I went down and tore open all the stevedore bundles in the hold—holding the pitiful caches of pilfered rice they planned to take home for supper—and looked around the rest of the ship to see if the items were secreted somewhere, but of course I never found them.

"Don't worry, Manuel," I finally told him, "I'll use ship's money to replace your things. It wasn't your fault your cabin was broken into."

Boiling with fury, I went looking for Ronald. I found him on deck. "Ronald, does a *houngan* live around here?"

He started. "A *houngan*? A witch doctor? Why do you want a witch doctor?"

"I want him to put the powder on this ship. How much will that cost me?"

He laughed nervously. "There is a *houngan* who lives up on the mountain, Captain." He pointed to a collection of huts pasted against the skyline. "He is a very powerful man."

"Yeah, I bet. How much would he charge me to come down and put the powder on this ship?"

Ronald drew back. "That is very dangerous, Captain."

I laughed. "Save it for the tourists. How much?"

He thought. "Fifty U.S. dollars."

"Good deal. Here's some money for the *tap-tap*. Go get him, but make sure you bring him back before five o'clock. He's no good to me if the stevedores don't see him." He left with a worried expression. I watched as he trudged across the dock and through the sally port.

Two more carpet buyers came during the afternoon, and both promised to come back after dark with boats. They wanted 10 dozen each, at 1500 *gourdes* a dozen.

About 1500 hours Ronald returned with the *houngan*, a jolly little brown man in a black suit, with a cream-colored tie that looked like it might have been white at one time. He carried a green carpetbag.

The little man came up the pilot ladder without problem, and when he got to the deck he stood there for a moment looking around. The hubbub on deck died as the stevedores realized who was on board. I saw their shocked faces and heard a swell of murmurs. The *houngan* ignored them and turned to me. Ronald translated as I told him that I wanted to keep thieves out of the accommodations.

A quick little man, he grasped immediately that the two hallways, the only entrances to the accommodations, were the keys to our security. He went up to the doors and studied each in turn. When I looked forward, all the stevedores and hangers-on had slid down into the hold or over the side into the boats. Several of the lighters had cast off and were drifting slowly away.

The old man dragged a five-gallon bucket over from the bulwark and stood up on it. The Haitians on the *Gitan Express* crowded on the starboard deck, staring at him.

He was all jollity until it came time to earn his money, then he got a serious look. He turned around and stared directly at the stevedores on the *Gitan Express*. They shrank out of sight. He fumbled in his bag until he found a brush and a small black jar which he uncapped and held up in front of him. With the brush dipped in the tarry mixture, he carefully drew something onto the bulkhead above the starboard door. He dragged the bucket over to the port door and made a similar mark. After putting away his brush and paint, he got down from the bucket and stood crouched over for a long time, mumbling. He dug in his bag again and took out a pink plastic pouch that looked suspiciously like a lady's lipstick case. He sprinkled a pinch of powder on the floor of the doorway, then repeated the crouch, the mumbling, and the powdering at the other doorway. Finished, he gathered himself, closed his bag, and straightened up.

I had Ronald explain loudly that I wanted the same thing done in the back, and we went aft. The crew were on the fantail, taking their mid-afternoon break with their girlfriends. The crewmen regarded the old man curiously, but the Dominicanas, who recognized him immediately, jumped up and ran through the accommodations to the main deck.

I told Ronald to tell the old man that he didn't actually have to do anything, since there were no Haitians to witness it, but he insisted that his magic wouldn't work without going through the proper steps. I left him to it and went back on deck. All the stevedores and the whores had left the ship in the last of the lighters. They stared back fearfully at the ship.

When the *houngan* came forward, I gave him $50 and we shook hands. He went to the side and called over a boatman in a canoe tied alongside the *Gitan Express*. The man reluctantly paddled over and took the witch doctor ashore.

A few minutes later Jean arrived, furious. I met him at the boarding ladder.

"What is this?" he demanded. "You bring a *houngan* onboard and stop discharging?"

"I didn't stop discharging. I just hired a *houngan*."

"Captain, why you do these things? How do I discharge this ship?"

"They'll come back. They just won't come in the accommodations." I pointed to the marks above the doors.

"The *houngan* put that there?" He retreated to the boarding ladder. "Captain, why you play with these things? This is serious business, Captain, very serious business." He went up the steps and felt with a foot for the pilot ladder. "I take the ship off-hire until stevedores come back." He climbed down.

"Bullshit," I called down. "Go ahead and note a protest. . . 'Stevedores stopped discharging because an old man painted marks on accommodations house.' The broker will laugh at you."

He stepped into the boat and looked up. "You will be sorry about this, Captain. When you suffer misfortune onboard your ship, you will remember what you have done." He waved to his cowering boatman to take him ashore. I went up to the saloon chuckling.

Just after dark, four carpet buyers arrived at the same time, in the same boat. Ronald had been onboard for a while, pretending that he wasn't worried about the *houngan*. The crew and the girls were sitting on deck because the girls wouldn't go through the accommodations.

Apparently, the second two buyers were bitter rivals of the first two, and all four came onboard stiff and angry. Within three minutes they were shouting about whether the rolls already selected and marked with tape by the first two had been bought or not.

Egg and Ferret could only come up with 22,000 *gourdes* between them, out of the 30,000 agreed upon, and it took almost an hour to convince them that 22,000 *gourdes* would only buy 16 dozen rolls.

They took to their boat twice in anger, but came back each time to plead for all 20 dozen rolls. Finally they managed to discover another 5,000 *gourdes* between them and agreed to take 18 dozen. But one of the other buyers had been removing their tapes while they were haggling with me, on the ones with the brightest colors, and when Egg and Ferret discovered this, fists started flying.

I broke it up. "Look, men," I said, "I'm tired. Goddamn tired. If you want to buy some carpet, let's deal. Otherwise you'll have to leave the ship."

They agreed to behave, and the other men let Egg and Ferret take the rolls that they recognized, or claimed to recognize, as having been tagged. Their workers swarmed up the ladder. I was waiting for them to try to get an extra roll or two over the side, but they only took 18 dozen. But while I was counting their rolls from the deck, I noticed that the rolls looked thicker than they had before. I jumped down in the boat, landing on the carpet, and discovered what I suspected. Egg and Ferret had rolled up smaller rugs into the larger ones while they were going through them that morning.

I pulled myself up on deck grimly. They faced me, ready to bluster it out, but all I said was, "Bring all the carpet back on deck. All of it."

First they claimed that the rolls were like that when they selected them, then they said that they would pay for the extra rolls. Egg even had the audacity to pull out another wad of *gourdes*, but they still only had enough money to buy an extra dozen. I made the men in the boat hand up the surplus. After another half-hour of complaining, they got in the boat and slid off into the darkness.

The last buyer onboard searched through the carpet until 2300 hours, then bought two dozen rolls for 700 Haitian dollars. He handed them down into the boat himself, cradling each one like a baby.

We kept the usual watch hours that night, but there were no thefts. Kokimo, who usually woke up and got a plate of food from the back of the stove about midnight, complained in the morning that he'd gone hungry rather than go through the hallway. I told him to ask the crew watchman to get him a plate from then on.

The next day half-a-dozen carpet buyers came onboard before noon. They carefully marked the rolls they wanted, now under Ronald's supervision, and agreed to come back in the evening.

Discharging continued uninterrupted throughout the day, and at 1700 hours Yussuf reported 14,505 bags discharged and 44 bags damaged. We were almost half-way through. The stevedores climbed out of the hold and dragged their way across the barge in exhausted silence. The ship got quiet.

After supper the Haitian buyers showed up, the four men from the morning and two women who hadn't been onboard before. They spent three hours dragging rolls of carpet out on deck and arguing about them. Several times I looked over toward the army building, but the men lounging on the roof paid no attention to us.

Finally the women bought 10 dozen rolls without haggling, paid in U.S. dollars, and loaded their carpet without further ado. One of the men bought four dozen rolls after an hour of haggling, and one bought seven rolls for 1500 *gourdes*, about $120. The other two men had no money, and at 2300 hours, when I ordered them off the ship, they were still trying to convince me to let them have a couple of dozen rolls each to take back to Port-au-Prince on credit.

We finished discharging three days later. By then we had managed to paint the starboard side with the last of the marine paint. I still had 16 dozen rolls of carpet that I hadn't been able to sell, even at half-price.

"The ca'pet buyers know the ship is sailing," Ronald explained sadly. "They are waiting for you to give the ca'pet away."

"How much is giving it away?"

"Maybe they pay 50 dollars Haitian a dozen."

We were sitting in the officer's mess. I jumped up. "They think I'll sell carpet for a dollar a roll? I'll show their stupid asses." I hastily wrote out a note to Jean with Time of Completion and ETD and sent it ashore in one of the boats. Then I sent Ronald to spread the word that the ship was sailing, and that the captain was going to be giving away the remaining carpet.

I called Yussuf and Manuel on deck. "Men, take all the carpet left on the ship and put it on the No. 1 hatchcover. Get a gallon of diesel fuel ready to pour on the carpet, but leave it out of sight until we're ready to leave."

"What we doing, Captain?" Yussuf asked.

"The carpet dealers think I'm going to let them have carpet for nothing. I'll show 'em."

He shook his head with a half-grin and went forward to the forecastle, where the last rolls were stored. As the AB's dragged the carpet out on deck, the carpet dealers in their polyester triple-pleats began to gather on Bonvillain's barge, which was only about 50 meters away.

We had to wait for Jean, since I hadn't been given sailing orders, so after we had tied the rolls of carpet into one great bundle, I gave the crew the afternoon off. The Dominican musician, Humberto, came onboard with one of the boatloads of girls. I watched him carefully, but he joined the party on the fantail without doing anything suspicious. Sonia and Yussuf came out of Yussuf's cabin, and some of the girls started a chicken barbecue on the grill on the boatdeck. I had paid Yussuf and the AB's several hundred dollars each for helping with the carpet, and from the bright looks on their girls' faces, trickle-down economics were at work.

The carpet buyers watched all this with patient amusement.

Jean arrived at 1845 hours with instructions to sail for Miami Roads and to call the agent on arrival. He gave me a scrap of paper with the agent's telephone number. I gave the crew another half-hour to wind the party down, and after Ronald and the Dominicans went ashore, Yussuf and I made a thorough stowaway search together. We locked the forecastle, pantries, steering flat, and spare cabins as soon as we had inspected them. The hold was swept clean and empty except for a pile of dunnage against the collision bulkhead. I noted the search in the Drug and Stowaway Search Log, had Yussuf sign it with me, and went on deck.

There was a stir on the barge when I appeared. The telegraph in the wheelhouse clanged. I sent Manuel forward to get the diesel fuel. When he started pouring it over the carpet, a howl went up on the barge. Egg and Ferret were in the center of the throng, waving fistfuls of money.

Yussuf cranked up the crane and swung the boom around. I hooked the bundle of carpet to the crane runner and pointed a finger to the sky. Yussuf swung the carpet overboard. Manuel had gotten a little enthusiastic with the diesel oil, and a fat trail of shiny drops followed the bundle across the deck and over the side. The oil kept dripping into the still water, spreading into slicks that caught the setting sun.

I soaked the end of a long sliver of dunnage in diesel, lit it, and touched it to the bundle. The fire spread slowly to the ends, gouts of yellow flame sheeting up. Yussuf swung the bundle farther from the ship's side.

The rope caught fire, and after a few minutes it snapped with a shower of sparks. The burning carpet fell to the ocean. It floated heavily, still burning, drifting off toward the sunset and sending a pillar of black smoke straight up into the darkening sky. The carpet dealers on the barge yelled and cursed. I went up to the wheelhouse to get ready to sail.

With Ronald overseeing the casting-off ashore, we took in our anchors and steamed in a wide half-circle around the point of town and north toward Gonave Bay. The town dwindled to a cluster of weak yellow lights under the brow of the mountain.

I handed the ship over to Yussuf at midnight, as the ship rounded the tip of Gonave Island. The next morning at dawn we were above Cape Tiburon and steaming for the Old Bahama Channel. The fourth morning found us off Miami Beach.

We dropped the port anchor at 0520 hours. At 0800 hours I called the ship's agent on VHF. His voice was distant and curt. "Stay at anchor, Captain. The pilot will call you on channel 16 when they're ready to bring you in."

I signed off and turned to Yussuf. "Stand by to stand by. I guess we're still on charter to Garot, so we don't care if we stand by six weeks."

Yussuf shrugged. "I would like to see Miami. Never been here before."

We looked at the art deco hotels on Miami Beach, shining pink and blue in the morning light. A small freighter came out of the channel as we watched, the pilot boat trailing her like a puppy. We didn't recognize her.

There was a yell from the deck. I looked down. Ricardo was standing below me, eyes wide. "Captain," he yelled, "*polizontes*! Stowaways, stowaways! There are men in the hold!"

"Aw, my God," I said. "Fucking stowaways." I got the ship's .38 from the safe, loaded it, and went on deck. Ricardo and Manuel were leaning into the open stevedore hatch. I peered over their shoulders and saw a man on the ladder, his head just below the hatch. He was a brown man with close-cropped hair and a flat, lumpy face. "*Agua*," he croaked.

"Get down," I ordered. "*¡Abajo, señor!*"

He retreated down the ladder. I sent Manuel to get a jug of water from the galley. I called down, "*¿Cuantos estan ustedes?*"

"*Tres, Capitán.*"

"*¿Sola' tres, seguro?*"

"*Sí, Sí, Capitán*, there are only three of us."

"Then lie down on the floor face-down and stretch out your arms above your heads." I went half-way down the ladder and looked at them. Two were wearing shorts and one was wearing only underwear. The air in the hold was hot and close. The men were panting, their bare backs dusty and streaked with dirt. "Are you Dominicans?" I asked.

"*Sí, Capitán.*"

"Do you have any identification with you?"

"*No, Capitán.*"

I looked around the hold. Some of the dunnage timbers that had been piled neatly against the collision bulkhead were strewn on the floor. Short pieces had been stacked on each side to create a cavity, and neither Yussuf nor I had noticed that the pile was larger than it should have been.

I let Manuel lower a plastic jug of water to the men. Yussuf looked down from the wheelhouse. "Three of them," I yelled up to him. "What a fucking hassle."

I went up and called the Coast Guard on VHF to report the stowaways, then went down to the galley and told Victor to make extra rice and beans for them, but to give them no meat.

He shook his head sadly. "There is little enough meat as it is." He pointed to the boiling pot. "This is the last of the *pollos desnudos*."

I went up to relieve Yussuf on radio watch. An hour later the pilot boat called to say they were on their way out. I picked up the glasses and saw that the boat was already coming out of Government Cut. "Sonofabitch," I muttered to myself, "give us some warning, will ya?"

Manuel and Ricardo went forward and Yussuf came up to the bridge. The pilot came onboard, a young man with sandy hair and mustache. When he learned that we had stowaways onboard, he went down on deck to take a look at them, then came back up and lit a cigarette. "Scruffy looking rascals, ain't they?" he said.

When the chief signaled ready engine, we upped anchor and steamed slowly through the clear green ocean toward the sea buoy. A Cigarette boat with a couple of dark beauties on the rear couch came roaring past, throwing a roostertail 30 feet into the air.

We slowed to Half Speed to enter Government Cut, then to Dead Slow to let the Fisher Island Ferry cross in front of us. The tugs and the pilot boat were waiting at the mouth of the river. The pilot got off and the *Erika*'s crew took the tugs' lines.

With *Ring Power* in front pulling and *Hercules* in back steering, we proceeded up the narrow Miami River, past the marinas and condos and under the I-

95 bridge. The river was full of small European ships, maybe two dozen. Some were loading and some were just sitting. With nothing to do, Yussuf and I stood on the port wing of the bridge and waved to the other crews. We were taken to a dock just northwest of the 27th Avenue Bridge. The tugs continued upriver to take another ship out.

The usual army of officials was there, and when they were all assembled on deck I led them up to the saloon. Even with the windows open and the fan going, it was hot. The agent was a heavy-set Irishman with a permanent sunburn named Bill Monahan. When the INS man asked me where the stowaways were, Monahan turned to me angrily. "Stowaways? Why didn't you tell me you had stowaways onboard?"

I looked around at the assembled Customs, INS, and USDA personnel. "I wasn't thinking about you," I said stiffly. "I've got enough to worry about without some Limey ship's agent."

"I'm Irish," he said, in a scalded tone. His face took on the color of a brick, but after a moment he set to sorting out the documents and handing the proper ones to the proper authorities, and he didn't say anything else. The USDA man went downstairs to inspect the galley. The Customs men asked me a few questions, then went snooping around the ship on their own. The INS agent, an elderly gentleman with white hair, interviewed the crew and gave everyone a shore pass except Jacek and Jerzy.

Jacek stood in front of the INS man after the others had gone. "Why no shore pass for me, Mr. U.S. Government? Why am I criminal in this country? Why my wife cannot visit her sister?"

I pushed him out of the saloon gently. He was neatly dressed but stank of rum. He didn't resist, and went down the companionway and into his room. I started to apologize to the INS man, but he waved it away. "It's a stupid policy, Captain, I don't mind saying so." He put away his stamps and pads. "If it was up to me, I'd give 'em shore passes, but. . ." He shrugged and went out.

A young INS agent had gone down into the hold to interview the stowaways. He came back up and handed me a form. "Their names are on the form, Captain. As you know, INS policy for ships with undocumented aliens is to require that they be retained onboard."

"Sir," I said, "I'm sure my owner would be glad to pay their airfare back to the Dominican Republic. . ."

He shook his head shortly. "That's not policy. And if any of them escape, the ship can be fined between $3,000 and $10,000 each."

I glared at him. "This is disgusting."

He shrugged, packed his kit and left the ship. Monahan said, "Do you have some place to keep those men onboard, Captain?"

"I'll have to go buy some handcuffs. I don't have anywhere to keep them except in the hold."

He gave an unsympathetic snort and put the ship's papers in his briefcase.

Miragoane, Haiti, Christmas, 1987
Bonvillain's barge is in the foreground

Relaxing during discharge, Miragoane
From left: the author, Daniela, Yussuf, and Haitian stevedores

Sonia and Amanda on Miragoane Bay

The *Queen of the Sea* (ex *Marion P. Billups*)
First arrival in Haiti

The *Erika* and the *Veronika*
Rafted up off the coast of Honduras

Stowaways getting a taste of the lash
Rio Haina, Dominican Republic

CHAPTER FIVE

I ASKED THE AGENT FOR A RIDE TO THE ALAMO OFFICE, WHICH he gave without enthusiasm, where I rented a Geo Metro for $15.95 a day. I was driving toward town on Le Jeune Road when I saw a pawn shop and whipped in. It was one of those pawn shops that specialize in police supplies. The proprietor was a big, bearded man with an automatic in a quick-draw holster. I bought three pairs of Smith & Wesson handcuffs at $28 each. I also picked up two jumbo cans of pepper spray.

As I was going out I noticed a rack of Wrist Rocket slingshots on the wall by the door. I picked one up. "Ah, hah," I said. "I know what I need this for." I stretched the rubbers a couple of times, then put it on the counter. The man tried to sell me a pack of steel balls as well, but I said, "I'm on a ship. I got all the ball bearings I need."

I drove back to the ship and went up the gangway. Yussuf was sitting by the stevedore hatch with a stick in his hand. "How's the prisoners?" I asked him.

"They're crying down there," he said grimly. "They say it's too hot."

"They're goddamned right it's too hot. It was too hot when they sneaked onboard. Okay, get Manuel and Ricardo. I'm going to go down and cuff 'em to something."

He stood up and put the stick down. "Captain, I don't feel right about this. We are seamen, not jailers."

I put the bags of supplies on the hatchcover. "Right now, I'm sorry to say, we're both."

Yussuf went to get the AB's. I put the cuffs in my back pockets and hooked one of the cans of pepper spray on my belt. Manuel and Ricardo followed Yussuf out of the accommodations, looking sullen. I opened the hatch carefully. The three men were still down on the hold floor. "Get back away from the ladder," I ordered them. "Manuel, you don't have anything on you they could use for a weapon?"

"*No, Capitán.*"

"Okay, come with me." I went down with Manuel right above me. When I got to the floor I said, "*Señores*, I'm sorry about this, but in order to open the hatches, I must secure you. This can be easy or hard. It's your choice."

"*No, Capitán*," the older man cried, "not the *esposas!*" I had forgotten that Spanish slang for handcuffs is "wives."

"Yes, the *esposas*." I moved toward him. "Give me your left hand."

He held it out. I slipped a cuff around it. I pulled his arm over and put the cuff around a staple on a frame. The tall one also submitted silently, but the sharp-faced man drew back with a snarl. Manuel cried, "Watch out, *Capitán!*" I unhooked the pepper spray. "*Tranquilo, señor.*"

He yelped something and ran the length of the hold. At the port stern corner he turned and crouched. "I will not be chained like a dog," he yelled.

I held the pepper spray out and approached him slowly. "*No, Capitán,*" Manuel murmured, but then he closed his mouth tight and stood where he was. I moved across the hold toward the stowaway. His nostrils flared, his eyes rolled, and his narrow chest heaved.

"*Tu mano, tu mano, señor,*" I said softly, over and over. "Give me your hand."

He lurched at me with his arms outstretched, his hands like claws. I jumped to the side. He stepped on the loose end of a board over the port bilge, just forward of the bilge box, and it gave way under him. He pitched forward. I snapped a cuff on his left wrist and dragged him out of the bilge box by the arm.

He tried to run again, but I jerked him up sharp, and when he rebounded toward me I knocked him down with a wicked forearm to the side of the head. I dragged him over to the side and clamped the cuff to a staple. He moaned and struggled.

"Goddamn," I panted, standing back from him. "Goddamn this bullshit."

"*Muy malo, Capitán,*" Manuel kept saying, "*Muy malo.*"

My shirt was plastered to my chest. I felt like I couldn't get air into my lungs. The stowaways were hunched against the steel side, their dusty bare chests streaked with sweat. I looked them over. "How did you get onboard?" I asked them.

They said nothing.

"Who brought you onboard? When did you come onboard? Where are your papers?"

They were starting to relax, sliding down the frames, but they said nothing.

Finally I called to Yussuf, "Open up a hole forward. Five or six boards'll do. I need some light over the dunnage." I started rooting around in the oil-stained boards. The men had made themselves a cozy enough nest, with short blocks of wood chocked in at the sides to make it look solid. In honesty, though, I couldn't remember even having looked at the dunnage when we did the stowaway search.

I found their stash inside a vent duct and pulled it out, a square packet in a yellowish plastic bag. Inside was a Dominican passport, two *cedulas*—Dominican national I. D. cards—and three wallets. One had 40 U.S. dollars, one had 65, and the third had a small number of Dominican bills. The last had a badly posed photograph of the tall stowaway with his wife and three children in front of a cheap paper backdrop of a waterfall.

I compared the documents with the prisoners, bound each man's things together, and put them back in the plastic bag. Victor called down that he had brought the men's supper, so I said to lower the plates and I would distribute them.He dropped them down in a bucket, one plate at a time. I saw pieces of chicken in the rice, but I didn't say anything to Victor about it. I put a water jug where the center man could hand it to the others and went back up the ladder and on deck.

The sea breeze was cool against my throat. Yussuf was standing by the hatch. "Everything okay, Captain?"

I was out of breath. I gulped the cool air. "Yeah, just peachy. We've got to make a brig somewhere on this ship, Yussuf."

He laughed. "A brig, Captain? To keep the stowaways in?"

"Of course. We've got to put them somewhere when we start loading." I started aft. "Get me your stores list. I'm going shopping tomorrow."

I went looking for Jacek to get his stores list, but he wasn't in his room. The door was closed and locked. I went to the engine room. The ship was on the harbor generator, and the engine room was silent and laced with shadows. I found Jerzy aft, changing the packing in the Borga pump. "Where's the chief, Jerzy?" I asked.

He looked uncomfortable, and shrugged to show he didn't know. He had been learning a little Spanish from his Dominican girlfriend, so I asked, "*¿Afuera?* Out?"

He nodded. I grimaced and went upstairs.

At suppertime, I got two beers from my refrigerator and joined Yussuf in the officers' mess. He thanked me and took a long drink from his can. We sat for a while without talking.

I finally said, "Did you know that the chief's left the ship?"

"What? He's detained onboard, isn't he?"

"That's right. If INS pulls a spot-check, it's a $3000 fine."

He pushed his plate away half-eaten. "Jacek's a good chief, but plenty *loco* sometimes."

I leaned over the table. "Yussuf, we can't trust the Hondurans to stand watch over the stowaways. Until we get the brig built, you and I will have to take four-and-four. I'm sorry."

"I understand, Cap'n."

I took the 10-to-two watch. Nothing happened. I sat under the floodlights on deck and read. I could hear the stowaways in the hold yelling and cursing sporadically, but I never bothered to check on them. At breakfast Yussuf told me that they had started hammering on the shell plating during his watch, but he had just turned up the volume on his little teevee and kept watching.

Jerzy came in and nodded to us. He sat down heavily. "*No hay* Chief?" he asked.

I shook my head. "*No hay.*"

We sat in numb silence. When Jerzy was finished eating, I took him down to the pantry and showed him with drawings how I wanted the brig constructed. He understood that I wanted a barred door constructed and a vent cut into the deck overhead, but he couldn't understand why. Finally I drew a sketch of a man in jail, holding the bars.

"Ah," he said, "the *polizontes.*"

"Yes, for the *polizontes*. Use the steel rebar in the forecastle. The steel rods." There were some rebar rods left over from a past cargo, and I showed him with a detailed sketch what I wanted. "Weld the bars together to make a jail door. Put a horizontal opening here to pass food in. And I want you to cut an opening in the wall so we can take out their shit bucket without getting attacked."

The English went right by him, but he understood the drawings. "Okay, Captain," he said sadly, "I make jail for ship."

I went on deck and opened the stevedore hatch. A ball of hot air rolled out. The three men were sitting up with their backs to the frames.

"Captain," the tall one called, "please! I must go to the bathroom. My intestines are killing me."

The rat-faced man said, "God will punish you for doing this. We are dying down here. It is too hot. . .there is no air."

I lowered a plastic bucket down with a roll of toilet paper tied to it. "Here's your bathroom. When you're finished, yell and we'll pull it back up."

It was 0730 by the time we started opening the hatches. Manuel and Ricardo came out of the accommodations pulling on their gloves, hatchboard hooks hanging from their belt-loops. Yussuf looked out his port-hole, saw us climbing up on the hatchcover, and came hurrying on deck with his shirt unbuttoned. We started opening No. 1.

A middle-aged black man came up the gangway from the dock. He ducked under the crane boom. "Good morning, men. Is the captain on board?"

"I'm the captain," I said.

He stared and laughed. "I never saw a captain working hatchboards before." He held out his hand. "I'm Morton, the dockmaster."

I shook his callused paw. "I have only a mate and two AB's," I said. "You know three men can't work hatchboards."

"You're right about that, Captain. Well, we will start loading the ship at nine o'clock. Will you be ready?"

"Of course. All we have left to do is shift the beams. What is the cargo?"

He looked at a sheet of paper. "We will load some pallets of Carnation first. There are some bales of *pepe* coming this morning. That's used clothes. And we have 2000 bags of rice in the warehouse."

I nodded. "The usual Haitian shit. Okay, we'll be ready. Start forward, get the bow down a little. Put the milk in first, up against the forward bulkhead, then put the rice around it. You got Kraft paper?"

"Of course, Captain." He pointed. A forklift was coming out of the warehouse with a big roll of brown paper on a pallet. The shore crane cranked up with a heavy clatter, popping black smoke, and moved forward on giant treads, its outriggers sticking up in the air like a spider's extra legs.

Morton clapped me on the shoulder. "How are your stowaways this morning?"

I grimaced. "Everybody knows about those fucking stowaways. How are they? They're taking their morning shit. After that they'll have breakfast. Then they'll lie around all day while I work my ass off. I'm the captain and they're the stow-aways, but I'm the one carrying the shitbucket."

"Get the agent to hire a guard. That's what the *Rosalind B.* had to do. They had five stowaways."

"I don't know. I hadn't thought about it. But the crew and I are pretty goddamned tired. We had to pull night watches in Haiti, and now this bullshit." I rubbed my face. "I'll call the owner."

"You can use the dock phone any time you want." He pointed to a steel ship-ping container with a window cut in the side. "It's in the dock office."

"Thanks."

The men had the coaming clear of boards, so I jumped down to help work the shifting beams. When the stowaways saw Morton looking down they called to him in Spanish, "See how we are being treated, *hermano*? We are dying down here."

Morton looked at me. "What're they saying, Captain?"

I translated.

He regarded them somberly. "Bad luck for the ship, Captain. We've had a lot of problems at this dock with stowaways."

"Well, I'm having the welder build a brig for them now," I said. "Speaking of which, he'll probably be ready to start welding this afternoon. Can I get a Hot Work Permit?"

He nodded. "We have a running permit. All I have to do is write you a ticket."

The crane lifted the roll of Kraft paper onboard choked in a nylon sling. Sev-eral black stevedores in ratty street clothes started climbing down the ladder. "Whoa," the first man said. "What is this? Some kind of slave ship?"

I explained the situation. The stevedores continued down the ladder and gave each other heavy looks. "Don't look too good fo' the brothers," one of the steve-dores said.

I went aft and found Yussuf. "Look, First," I said, "I wasn't thinking right. It ain't gonna work keeping the stowaways in the hold until Jerzy gets the brig ready. The stevedores are freaking out. Some kind of incident could happen."

"Where can we put them, Captain? In a spare cabin? They'll tear it up."

"Let's put them on the fantail. It's cool there, and they're out of sight of the stevedores. We're going to have to make sure those handcuffs are on tight."

I went forward and got a length of small stuff, then rounded up the crew and went down in the hold with Ricardo. The stevedores were starting to roll out the Kraft paper, but they stopped to watch as I tied the rope from the wrist of the first man to that of the next, and from him to the third. I made a loop in the end to hold, then unlocked each man's cuff.

I went up first, holding the end of the rope. The stowaways came on deck unsteadily. I herded them aft through the accommodations and onto the back deck. I cuffed one to a drain pipe from the boat deck, one to the grabrail on the aft bulkhead, and one to the ladder handrail.

"Be careful of them, Victor," I warned the cook. "Don't get close to them. If they bother you in any way, come get me and I'll take care of it."

Victor kept his head down, chopping vegetables. "*Sí, Capitán.*"

I went on deck. Jacques Garot was coming up the gangway wearing a polyester shirt half-unbuttoned, showing his hairless chest under a gold mooring chain. I held out my hand. He did not take it. I rubbed my hand on my pants leg and let it fall.

"Let us go to your office," he said.

I led him through the doorway and up the companionway. He came in and took a seat in one of the armchairs without waiting for an invitation.

"Here's the charterer's logs and my Notes of Protest," I said. "They start when the ship went on-hire at the Lake Charles seabuoy inbound."

He tossed the papers to the table without a glance. "Captain, you caused me plenty problems in Miragoane. You cost me very much money. I do not know if you know that."

"No, I don't know that. Coke?"

He waved it away. I got myself one and took a long drink. He wiped his forehead and went on, "You did not sign the Bills of Lading properly, and I was forced to make a heavy payment to the port director in Miragoane."

I laughed shortly. "You had to make a heavy payment because he caught you trying to smuggle rice. That didn't have anything to do with the Bills of Lading."

His yellow eyes snapped. "You may work for Dickie, but you're the captain onboard. You have to think of yourself."

"What does that mean?"

He leaned back. "Jean told me about the *houngan* you brought onboard."

"So?"

"That was a good trick. Haitians are ignorant people, easy to fool." He paused for effect. "I know how to use voodoo also. But I know a magic in Haiti more powerful than voodoo." He stood up without effort and looked down at me. I sat back in the low armchair and regarded him coolly.

"Do not cross me again, Captain," he said. "I do not like to lose money."

I stood up, a head taller. "I don't like getting threatened. I'm going to have to report this conversation to my owner."

He laughed as he walked toward the door. "Dickie? You do that. I talk to Dickie every day. Very nice young man." He stopped and turned around. "Dickie does not know this business, Captain. You should think of yourself."

He went downstairs. I watched as he walked along the deck. Several Haitian stevedores were coming onboard, and when they saw Garot their faces lit in alarm. They started backpedaling to clear the gangway for him. They averted their faces as he walked toward a green Range Rover, but after a barked order from Morton they came onboard and went down in the hold. I went on deck.

Yussuf was restacking the dunnage in the hold to get it out of the way of the cargo. It was a few minutes after 0900, but the cargo hadn't started coming out of the warehouse. The stevedores on shore were sitting on the forklifts with their hardhats in their hands.

Yussuf came topside and stood by me. "Captain, you know the charterer?"

"Yeah, he was just onboard. His name's Jacques Garot."

Yussuf looked around. "You know he was head of the Ton-Ton Macout under Papa Doc?"

I started. "You're kidding!" Then, "So that's what he meant. And that's why the stevedores were so scared of him. One of the stevedores told you that?"

He nodded.

"Well, I don't care if he's Baron Samedi's ghost. No one comes onboard this ship and threatens the captain. We'll see who comes out on top when the charter's over. He doesn't know any more about ships than the rest of these gold-chain shitheads."

I stormed off the ship and went in the dock office to use the phone, but the container was full of Haitians arguing, so I went to the pay phone on the street. Dickie answered, mush-mouth with sleep. I told him about the stowaways.

"Oh, my God, " he said, now awake. "How'd they get onboard?"

I described the pile-of-dunnage trick.

"How much is it going to cost to send them back to Haiti?"

"They're Dominican. But they've got to stay onboard anyway." I told him about INS policy. "I'm building a brig, but it's slow going. It may not be finished in time." It wasn't the moment to tell him the chief engineer was missing. "Look, Dickie, you got to send the agent some money for a private guard. Yussuf and I can't work all day and keep watch all night. We just can't do it anymore."

"Well, I'm coming down tomorrow. I'll take care of it then."

"What about crew wages?"

"I'll bring the wages."

"Good. Then I'll see you tomorrow."

We hung up. An ancient wino in an army raincoat was pushing a shopping cart down the sidewalk, chewing on something behind his yellowish beard. I had to step off the sidewalk to avoid getting rammed by the cart.

The dock was full of Haitians and their trucks. Morton was arguing with a Haitian in a straw hat, shouting over the roar of the crane. A huge Haitian woman in a dress the size of a mess tent was trying to make a driver move his truck. Behind the *Erika* a ship named the *Hayti Family* was loading drums of motor oil in slings.

When I looked in the *Erika*'s hold, the Carnation was almost stowed. Another pallet was swinging onboard. Morton came up. "Rice next. You want to start in No. 2?"

"It doesn't matter. We can if you want."

"No, we'll continue in No. 1 so we don't have to move the crane."

I started aft. "Make sure Kraft paper is over all the metal. My first officer is watching you." I went through the accommodations and onto the fantail. Victor was sitting on one of the bitts, trimming fat off pieces of meat and chatting with the stowaways. They were sitting comfortably against the bulwarks.

Victor jumped up when I appeared, almost dropping the pan of meat. He gathered his things with his head down and ducked into the galley. The stowaways stared at me defiantly.

I went in the galley. "Victor," I said softly, "I know these men are Hispanic, just like you. I know they're trying to find a better life, just like everybody else. But they're the ship's enemy. . .if they escape, it could cost the ship $30,000. The owner doesn't have the money for a fine like that, so the ship would get seized and rot away here on the river, and we'd all be out of a job."

He nodded, carefully breading the pieces of meat and laying them into a pan half-full of bubbling fat. He did not look at me.

"I don't mind if you talk to the *polizontes*," I went on, "but you have to be careful not to give them anything they could use to get free, or use for a weapon."

"Oh, no, Captain," he protested, "they are peaceful men. They are not from Santo Domingo. . .they are from a small town."

"That may be so. And I don't want to mistreat them. But they have to be kept onboard, and I know they'll do anything to get off." I put my hand on his shoulder. "I need your help in this, Victor. It's hard on everybody."

He nodded. "I will be careful, Captain."

I went upstairs and did some paperwork. The rice started coming onboard. Yussuf came to the saloon to tell me that a strange Haitian was onboard asking about the captain. I frowned and looked out the window. A big brute in blue work clothing and bug-eye sunglasses was standing on deck. I got the .38 from the safe, loaded it, tucked it into the small of my back, and went down.

"How do you do?" I said to the man, holding out my hand. "I'm the captain, Max Hardberger."

He shook my hand. There was a piece of his left ear notched out. He didn't look like he missed it. "I am Andre," he growled. "From Mr. Garot."

"Great. How's it going? When do we finish?"

"I know not'ing about ship, Mr. Captain. I am from Mr. Garot. Understand?"

"All too well. Now I must ask you to leave."

His face was impassive behind the sunglasses. "What?"

"If Garot sent you to scare me, it's not working. Get your Macout ass off this ship."

I saw Yussuf's shocked face out of the corner of my eye. A Haitian was peeking up out of the stevedore hatch. Andre said, "I will tell Mr. Garot about this."

"Oh," I said, "that really puts me in the hurt locker." I put my hand behind my back. "Now get off my ship."

He turned and went down the gangway slowly, to show me he didn't have to if he didn't want to. Yussuf said quietly, "Captain, you should be careful what enemies you make."

I took out the .38 and showed him the little horse stamped on the frame. "God made men, Yussuf, but Samuel Colt made them equal." I put it away. "That Macout motherfucker shows up again, I'll feed him two pills and make it look right afterward."

He shook his head and said, "Is Mr. Dickie coming today, Cap'n? Is he bringing the crew wages?"

"He says he is."

He smiled. "I will send some money to my family in Egypt. I try to do that every two or three months."

I ran my hand through my hair. "What am I going to do if the chief doesn't come back, Yussuf? Jesus, three stowaways and a missing chief engineer. If we have to leave without him it'll be a $3000 fine."

"Very bad, Captain."

"Well, let me go call the cops and see if they've got him." I unloaded the pistol and stowed it in the ship's safe, then went down to the pay phone on the dock. After using up $1.50 in quarters, it appeared that Jacek was not being detained in Dade County. I went back to the ship and sat down to lunch with Yussuf and Jerzy.

Two minutes later a Coast Guard officer stuck his head in the mess, a muscular young man with bristly black stubble on his meaty skull. He looked at me. "Captain?"

"Yessir?"

"CWO Parrott, U.S. Coast Guard. We're here to make a Port State Control inspection."

I kept a smooth face. "Very well," I said. I got up. "Yussuf, when you finish, can you come up to the saloon?"

He nodded unhappily. I led the Guardsmen upstairs and tried to direct the fan toward them as they slid along the bench. With CWO Parrott were a short, pasty-faced woman named Ensign Horta and two young male trainees with acne and big feet. Ensign Horta had one eyebrow and an unfortunate overbite.

Parrott pulled a computer print-out from his briefcase and looked it over. "Captain, the first thing we want to inspect is your sanitary system. Can you have your chief engineer show it to us?"

"I can show it to you. We have one Type III holding-tank toilet, and the other toilets are sealed off inside territorial limits."

Horta got interested. "What do you mean by that, Captain? You have toilets onboard that are not connected to the ship's holding tank?"

"We don't have a ship's holding tank. I have a toilet with a built-in tank to use in port. The other toilets discharge overboard. The bathrooms are locked up and the overboard discharge valve is locked. I have the only keys."

"That's not legal, Captain," Parrott said, still studying the print-out. "I'm going to have to issue a detention for the sanitary system."

"It was passed by the Mobile Coast Guard," I said earnestly. "You're looking at the print-out from Mobile now, aren't you?"

He put the paper on the desk. "Captain, the Miami Coast Guard has full Port State Control authority to inspect this vessel, regardless of what Coast Guard district inspected it previously."

"Yessir," I said, "I understand that. But the CFR's don't require that all my toilets be hooked up to the sanitary system."

He said, "Let's take a look at the regulations." He took a well-thumbed copy of the CFR's out of his briefcase and opened it. "Um, Sect.159.7, subpart (c), says, 'After January 30, 1980, no person may operate any existing vessel equipped with installed toilet facilities unless it is equipped with an operable Type I, II, or III device.'"

"Well," I said, reaching into the low bookcase against the bulkhead for my copy, "let's see." I found the passage. "That's right. But it doesn't say that every toilet onboard has to be connected to that operable device. And we do have a Type III toilet onboard."

Parrott put a finger in the book and closed it. "What's the tank's capacity, Captain?"

"Oh, it's five gallons or so. It's part of the toilet, under the seat. It's a camping toilet."

The woman barked, "A camping toilet! That's not a sanitary system."

"M'am," I said patiently, "that toilet is a Camden Model Four with a Type III approval tag on it. That's all the regulations say I need."

Parrott pressed his lips together. "If you have a toilet, you have to have a sanitary system."

"The reg's don't say that if you have more than one toilet all of them have to be connected to the sanitary system."

"That's what it means," Horta said.

I shook my head stubbornly. "But that's not what it says."

"Sir," Horta said, as if to end some kind of silliness, "the meaning of the regulation is clear. This vessel will not leave Miami without a proper sanitary system onboard."

I stood up. "Madam, are you trying to tell a native speaker what plain English words mean?"

A flush worked its way up her neck and burned hot on her cheeks. Parrott stood up as well, a hint of a smile on his heavy face. "Captain, we'll check with the Captain of the Port about this."

I figured they would start looking around for other detention items, but they must have had bigger fish to fry. They shook my hand perfunctorily and left the ship.

I went on deck. A netload of flour was coming onboard. I heard Yussuf yell, "Captain, Captain!" and looked up to see him on the starboard wing of the bridge. "Captain," he called down, "did you see the teevee people?"

"What teevee people?"

He pointed toward a pile of waste-paper bales on the dock. "They're gone now. They were taking movies of the stowaways. From on top of those bales."

"What the hell?" I went down to the dock and walked around the bales, but didn't see anybody. Then I walked out to the street, where a white van with an antenna on the roof was pulling away from the curb, heading southeast on North River Drive.

I went onboard and down to the pantry, where Jerzy was grinding off ceiling fittings. "Just get it finished," I told him. "*Finitado*. We'll do it right later."

"But, Captain," he protested, putting down the grinder. "I engine room. Plenty work generator running."

I kicked at the old pantry door, now lying sideways in the landing. "Where the hell is the chief?"

He shook his head. "Don't know, Captain. Chief plenty problem no Daniela."

"What do you mean? What else has he done? I know he's been drinking."

His discretion—or his lack of English—overcame him, and he didn't explain. I went back to the accommodations. Victor handed me a long grocery list. "We are almost out of everything, Captain," he said apologetically.

I tried to focus on the list. "Hell, Victor," I said, "it's not your fault. You've done a hell of a job. . .I don't know how you can stretch food like you do."

He ducked his sleek head. "It is nothing, Captain. In Honduras it is how we must cook."

"Okay, I'll try to get everything this afternoon. What is this, *zanahoria*? Oh, carrots."

When I went on deck Yussuf and Manuel were closing No. 1. We got No. 2 open and the shore crane pulled up its outriggers to crawl along the dock to a new position. A hi-top truck with a crumpled fender was backing up, its doors open. It was full of boxes of hair relaxer. A girl from the front office arrived in a golf cart with a phone message for me to call Lt. Burkhalter at the Miami Coast Guard office.

I used the phone in the converted container. I was passed from underling to underling, then connected to Burkhalter. He had a nasal Downeast accent. "Captain, I understand you gave my inspectors a hard time today."

"Negative, sir. I merely refused to be told the meaning of plain English."

"Captain, would you be able to come down to my office this afternoon? I'd like to speak to you personally about this matter."

I agreed to go, and got in the car without returning to the ship. I had to drive around the downtown area for a quarter-hour before I found a parking spot. The Coast Guard offices were in an old Stalinist-style building near the bay. I went through the metal detector and up to the third floor, where I was shown into Lt. Burkhalter's office.

He was a young man with a buzz cut and freckles on his pink scalp. He pumped my hand briskly and indicated a seat in front of his desk. "We don't see many American captains on these Haitian freighters," he began.

"I'm not on a Haitian freighter. The owner is an American. The flag is Honduran."

He dismissed that. "I understand you have toilets onboard that discharge directly overboard."

I shook my head. "Negative. Those toilets cannot be used. I have the key to the overboard discharge valve on me."

He leaned forward. "There is no provision in the regulations for merely locking the overboard discharge valve, Captain. CWO Parrott tells me that you think the regulations don't require you to have all toilets onboard connected to the sanitary system."

"That is correct. They do not."

He regarded me levelly. "There's no point in rereading the regulation together. We both know what CFR 159.7 says." He got up and went around the desk and closed the office door. It was a very small office—I had my knees jammed up against the front of his desk—and when he closed the door there arose between us a kind of unpleasant intimacy. He sat down again. "Captain, you're right. The regulations are not specific about that. But I'm going to tell you something. Your ship will not leave Miami without a sanitary system. Do you understand what I'm saying?"

"I think so. You're saying that you are going to break the law in order to ruin the owner of my ship, who happens to be an American with two baby girls." I leaned forward. "The regulations clearly do not forbid having those toilets onboard as long as I have a sanitary system."

"And you are claiming that the portable toilet you have onboard is your sanitary system."

"It's a Type III MSD. Read the label."

He kept looking at me. He was getting a little white around the edges. When he spoke again, his voice was tense. "Captain, when do you finish loading?"

"Tomorrow."

He opened a file on his desk. "My inspection teams are tied up for the rest of the day." He smiled thinly. "Re-inspecting detained vessels." He closed the file and pushed it aside. "However, I can do one of two things. I can put your file aside until you call to tell me that the sanitary system is in place and ready for re-inspection, or I can send a team to the ship to make a general inspection under Port State Control authority."

I thought for a second. "Sir, I don't want to cause a problem for the ship by trying to insist on my interpretation of the regulations, but I know that the owner doesn't have the money to get a Gas Free Certificate, and there's just no other way to install a sanitary system here in the States. I would now like to ask respectfully if the regulations would allow me to sail if I took out the direct-discharge toilets. The ones that are now installed and locked up."

"You mean, to sail out with just that camping toilet for the entire crew?"

"Yessir."

We both knew this was crazy, but we were constrained by our roles to play it out.

He hesitated. "Well, I think the regulations would allow that. But the other toilets would have to be removed and taken off the ship."

"All right," I said. "You can send a re-inspection team tomorrow morning. That will allow us to sail without going off-hire."

We stood and shook hands on the deal. I opened the door and went downstairs. Latin American shoppers crowded the streets, escorted by Cuban guides who shooed them along through the heat from one electronics discount shop to the next. I drove to a lumber store on North River Drive, where I bought three shower heads with flexible hoses and six sacks of Quikcrete. The springs on the little Metro stayed bottomed out all the way back to the ship.

I parked by the gangway and led Manuel and Ricardo to the trunk. "Put two sacks by each toilet," I told them. "Then get a sledgehammer and meet me at the starboard head on the main deck."

They looked at each other. Ricardo asked, "A sledgehammer, Captain?"

"*Sí, señor. Un martillo grande.*"

I went aft to the fantail, where the stowaways were in bad shape. They had deliberately yanked their wrists against the cuffs, and had given themselves some respectable abrasions. The tall one was languishing on the deck with his feet stretched out toward the galley bulkhead, moaning and writhing. He was spitting up chewed rice in a white foam.

I looked at Victor through the porthole. "How long have they been doing this?"

"Ever since the *filmaderos* were here this morning."

"You fed them lunch already?"

"*Sí, Capitán.*"

I went on deck. Yussuf was standing at the corner of the hatch coaming, looking down into No. 2. Sacks of sugar were getting piled around a late-model pickup truck parked against the engine room bulkhead.

"Chief back yet?" I asked. He shook his head.

I nodded toward the truck. "You see any paperwork on that truck?"

He looked at me. His eyes were red and bleary, half-closed. "No, Captain. Was I supposed to?"

I sighed. Morton was in the hold. The stevedores were covering the truck as fast as they could. "I know you haven't been getting much sleep, First," I said. "Me neither. But the ship could get in trouble if we take undocumented cargo. You know that Morton and the dockowner are snakes, just like everybody else in this business. You've got to stay on top of it."

"Yessir." He moved closer. "Captain, Manuel and Ricardo are very unhappy about the stowaways. They say you are treating them badly. I think they are going to talk to you about it."

"Good. Any crewman can talk to me at any time."

He didn't say anything.

"Yussuf," I went on, "those stowaways are the ship's enemy. They're the fucking enemy, I tell you. Stowaways, smugglers, agents, charterers. . .they're all the enemy, and every crewman's job is to keep the enemy at bay."

He made a placatory gesture, but I was getting wound up. "It wouldn't matter if a stowaway was his goddamned brother-in-law. A crewman's first loyalty is to the ship."

Morton came up through the stevedore hatch. I broke off and looked at him. "So, Captain," he said, "how's the prisoners?"

"They're sick. It's a terrible thing. But I wanted to ask you about the export documents for that truck."

He looked down at the truck. "What documents, Captain?"

"Specifically, the Customs export permit."

He laughed. "Oh, sure, Captain, Mr. Garot has that."

"Have you seen it?"

He pointed a finger to his soft, broad chest. "Me? I'm just the stevedore foreman. No, I haven't seen it."

I shook my head. "You might as well stop covering it up, then. If I don't see the export permit in about an hour, I'm ordering it taken off the ship."

"Oh, don't worry, Captain. The truck is legal, very legal, everything taken care of."

"Fine. Get the permit faxed over to the front office and I'll take a look at it. Otherwise, the truck comes off at. . ." I looked at my watch. "Well, hell, it's already 4:30. Okay, it comes off at 10 a.m. tomorrow morning."

He nodded. "Okay, Captain, I'll get you a copy. The export permit, you say?"

"That's what I say."

He made a note on a piece of greasy paper and went ashore. Another truck backed up, full of brightly colored bales of *pepe*. I sat on the hatchcover for a while. The sun was low over the freighters at the Tropical and Hybur terminals upriver. Another jet was taking off at the airport. It came roaring overhead, so low I could see the rivets in its belly.

Yussuf came up and sat down. "What's wrong, Cap'n?"

"Oh, nothing. I'm just tired."

"When we get night watchman, Cap'n? It's not fair we have to stay up at night and work all day too. Dickie can afford a night watchman, can't he?"

"Well, we'll have that brig finished tomorrow if Jerzy can find time to work on it. Goddamn that Jacek. . .where the hell could he be?"

"You called all the jails?"

"Yeah. They say they don't have him."

"Did you tell the agent yet?"

"That smartass son of a bitch? Not yet. But I've got to start looking for another engineer. . .you know of one?"

He shook his head. "How about asking over there?" He pointed across the river to the Falcon Bar.

"Yeah, that's an idea. I'll go over and see if anybody knows a chief engineer looking for work. It can't be too hard to find one on the river."

"But. . .a good one, Captain? Plenty bad chiefs on Haitian ships."

"You're right about that. And a good engine room is about all this poor old girl has left. I'd hate to see a bad engineer ruin it. One thing about Jacek. . .no matter how much he drinks, he seems to keep the ship running without too many problems. When he's onboard, that is."

Yussuf nodded. "He's good, Captain. He knows everything. Electricity, engines, formulas, everything. He was a lieutenant in the Polish navy, you know."

"Come on!"

He nodded. "Daniela told me. He got kicked out for drinking."

"Huh. I bet that took some doing. Well, I've got to find another chief engineer. We'll be ready to sail tomorrow night." I got up and brushed off my pants. "You watch the ship. I'm going over to the Falcon Bar on official business."

He grinned and went back to the loading. I got in the car and drove across the river. The door of the Falcon was propped open with a stool. Two men were drinking mixed drinks at a table against the wall, and two others were drinking Buds at the bar. They were watching a teevee on a shelf on the back wall.

The bartender was a thick-necked old man with ruined hands. I climbed up on a stool in front of him and ordered a beer. "Say," I said, when he slid a draft in front of me, "you don't know any chief engineers looking for a job, do you?"

He shrugged and looked around at the customers. "Anybody know a chief engineer looking for work?" he called out.

One of the men at the table, a short Hispanic with a large black mole on his forehead, said, "What ship, sir? Maybe I know a man who will be interested."

"The *Erika*, across the river. At the All Seas Terminal."

The bartender stared. "The *Erika*? You work on that ship?"

"I'm the captain."

He grinned. "You're the guy that's mistreating those stowaways, eh?"

It was my turn to stare. "What are you. . .where'd you hear about that?"

He waved at the teevee. "Hell, Captain, you're famous. There was a thing about the *Erika* on teevee at noon."

The Hispanic man said, "I saw that. Big problem, those stowaways, aren't they, Captain?"

I took a swig of beer. "They're a fucking headache. And now my chief's run off in a drunken binge."

"Yeah," the bartender said, awed, "They showed them stowaways talking about how cruel you are, how you only feed them rice and how you keep them handcuffed all the time."

"Guilty as charged. And that's the way they're going to stay until we get back to Haiti. Those fucking reporters. I knew it was going to come to this."

The Hispanic man got up and brought his drink over to me. "I am Jesus Esquivel, captain of the *Harlequin*, out at Dodge Island. I am visiting my friend, Capt. Menendez of the *Plata Trader*, upriver."

I bowed to Capt. Menendez, a dark, bald man with gold teeth.

Capt. Esquivel slipped onto the stool next to me. "You know, Captain," he said loudly, "you ought to do like the Japanese. They don't take stowaways." I stared at him. "Take stowaways? I don't take stowaways either. They sneaked onboard. . ."

I looked around. Everybody was grinning at me. I felt around for the straw in my hair. "Oh, you mean, when they find them, they kill them."

He shrugged. "They just aren't onboard when the ship comes into port." He finished his drink. "And there is another interesting thing. Very seldom does anyone stow away on a Japanese ship."

He ordered another drink and downed it. A trail of shiny sweat started along his hairline. "A friend of mine had an engine breakdown in Jacksonville," he went on. "Last November There were four stowaways onboard, and INS wouldn't let the owner fly them home. The crew had to keep them in the accommodations for two months while the crankshaft was being repaired." He drank. "It was such hell for the crew that half of them quit."

Capt. Menendez said, "You heard about the AB on that German ship in Tampa? He was on watch. The stowaways got loose and busted his head open with a piece of pipe. Doctor on teevee said it would be a miracle of God if he ever talked again."

Two Filipino crewmen came in, and the people in the bar drifted back into their own conversations. The bartender promised to keep asking about a chief and Capt. Esquivel promised to look up the man he had in mind. I went back to the ship.

The stevedores had left, and the dock gates were shut and locked. I went in through the sally port and started for the ship when a big old man with a shiny bald head came out of the office. "Captain," he called to me, "wait a sec." He hurried over. "You're Capt. Hardberger, right? Ernie Rollo, the dockowner. Did you know the *Erika* was on teevee today? It looked like they were standing on top of those bales by the south warehouse." He pointed. "Jerks. I oughtta sue 'em for trespass."

"I saw them. They were in a white van."

"Captain, this is bad publicity for the dock. Isn't there someplace else you can put those men?"

I shook my head. "I'm having my second engineer fix a brig now. It should be ready tomorrow."

He nodded. "It's not your fault, Captain, but it don't look too good for the dock to have men in handcuffs lying around. Especially black guys, if you know what I mean."

I turned to face him. "Mr. Rollo, I'd like nothing better than to be shut of them. I would pay for their airfares back to Dom Rep out of my own pocket if INS would let me. This is the biggest piece of crap I ever saw. Forcing me to detain those men onboard under conditions like this, in this heat. . ."

"I know, I know, Captain," he said hurriedly. "You're not the only one. Two weeks ago we had a nice little Bahamian ship in here with two Haitians onboard. There was no place on the ship to keep them, so we put them in the bonded-stores room in the warehouse. Solid concrete walls."

I turned to walk toward the ship. He had to come along to finish the story. "You know, those bastards tore a piece of rebar out of the ceiling during the night and used it to smash through the wall and into the warehouse. After that they busted a hole in the outer wall and escaped." He shook his head in wonder. "You should have seen the hole they squeezed through." He put his hands together with his forefingers and thumbs touching. "No bigger 'n this, no shit."

He clapped me on the shoulder. "It's no big deal, Captain. Get 'em below and it'll blow over. At least they aren't Haitians. Then we'd have all the goddamn civil-rights groups down here raising hell."

I went up the gangway and into the hallway. Victor stuck his head out of the galley. "Captain, Captain, *El Flaco* is dying!"

"*¿El Flaco? Sin duda.*"

"No, Captain, really. . .come quickly."

I went aft. The three men were lying listlessly in the heat, cut off from the faint wind by the bulk of the house. Their dusty chests heaved and their shackled hands dangled from the cuffs. They rolled listless eyes at me. El Flaco, The Skinny One, had managed to vomit something up, and was lying motionless with his face in it.

I nodded and went down to the pantry, but nothing had been done since I left. I went to the engine room. We were on the harbor generator, and I could hear Jerzy working in the quiet. One of the MWM's heads was off, and Jerzy was working on it at the workbench. I came up behind him. He looked at me hollowly, his eyes sunken into his grimy, dripping face. He started trying to explain what he was doing, then gave up.

"Chief?" he said hopelessly. "No chief?"

I shook my head. "No chief, Jerzy." I threw my hands out. "Very bad. Very, very bad."

He went back to his work with grim Polish determination. I went up to Yussuf's cabin. He was sitting slumped at his desk, a cold can of Shaefer's held loosely in his fist. "First," I said, "we've got to get those men off the fantail. The dockowner's crying about that bullshit on teevee. Let's put the pantry door back on and post a guard. If they start causing trouble, all he's got to do is sound the alarm."

He put down the beer and stood up. "Okay, Captain. I'll take care of it."

"Get the AB's to do it."

He hesitated. "Captain, Manuel and Ricardo say they will not help make a jail for the stowaways."

"What? They will disobey me?"

"No, no, Captain," he said quickly. "But I think they will quit if you try to make them."

I blew out a short, angry breath. "All right. Belay working on the brig tonight. I'll figure out something in the morning."

I took a light supper in the saloon, served by a subdued Victor. After eating I went up to the bridge and sat on the port wing. A Haitian ship at the Caribe Terminal across the river was still loading rice with its deck crane, an ancient lattice-boom artifact with an unmuffled engine.

After a while the 27th Avenue Bridge opened and a Hybur container ship came through under tow. It was a boxy, mid-Seventies ship stacked with containers, the short, square house perched like an afterthought on the wide stern. The crew lounging on the fantail nodded to me as it went past. I could smell their supper cooking.

Darkness fell. Yussuf came up to the bridge to ask if he and the AB's could go ashore. I gave permission. A few minutes later they appeared in street clothes and went down the gangway. Jerzy came on deck in a sodden boiler suit and drank a Coke, staring at nothing and wiping his face with a rag. He went back to the engine room.

At 2200 hours I checked on the stowaways. They seemed to be sleeping. Victor had given them some left-over carpet to lie on. I went up to the boat deck and sat on a folding chair where I could keep an eye on them from above.

Another plane started its take-off run at the airport, engines whining. It came overhead at 200 feet, a big cargo 747 covered with lights, and roared off to the northeast, shaking the fabric of the ship. The stowaways slept through it, like everyone on the river eventually learns to do.

It got quiet again. I could see the flicker of the teevee in the bridgetender's hut, and past the bridge the lights of freighters docked downriver. Somewhere a radio was playing *salsa*.

About midnight I got up and fixed a snack from the food Victor had left on the back of the stove. I looked out at the stowaways through the aft galley portholes while I ate.

They were asleep, but restless, squirming and twisting on the carpet. The self-inflicted scratches on El Flaco's wrist were now infected—probably with his own feces—and clearly visible in the dock floodlights. He licked his lips, eyes still closed, and muttered something. The sunken skin over his temples made a skull of his head.

I went back to my perch and settled in. Yussuf was scheduled to take over at 0200, but some time around 0130 I fell asleep in the chair.

Yussuf woke me with a hand on my shoulder. He was in street clothes. "Captain, where are the stowaways?"

I jumped up, still groggy. "What? What do you mean?"

"The stowaways aren't on the fantail. You didn't move them?"

"No, no, they're there. . .Oh, my God!" I stared down. They were gone. The handcuffs were gone. There was nothing left of them but three pieces of carpet.

I rushed down and stared around, then ran through the house to the deck. Manuel and Ricardo were coming up the gangway, half-drunk. They hadn't seen the stowaways.

Victor came out of his cabin in his boxer shorts, puffy-eyed with sleep. "No, *Capi*, nothing!" he cried. "I hear and see nothing!"

I sat down heavily in the crew's mess and put my forehead against the table. "And the fucking owner'll be here this morning, just in time to get the news." Yussuf sat down across from me. I raised my head and stared at him bleakly. "Minimum fine will be $9000. Minimum. I might as well go pack my shit."

"It wasn't your fault, Captain," he said. "We're all exhausted. Dickie should have hired a guard."

"He was going to do it today." I pummeled my face. "Okay, I'm going to bed. I'm going to get four good hours of sleep. After that, we'll see what happens."

He didn't say anything. I went upstairs, took off my clothes, and climbed up into the bunk, my head full of useless, spinning thought. I got up again at dawn, dry-mouthed and still exhausted, put on clean clothes, and went downstairs to start the day.

At 0800 I called INS from the dock phone. The man on duty said an agent would come out to investigate. He didn't seem to care one way or another.

Morton was standing on deck when I got back to the ship. The sun was rising over the buildings on 27th Avenue, shining hard and yellow on the ship's wet back. Yussuf, Ricardo, Manuel, and Victor were humping hatchboards, but when I got onboard I took over from Victor and he went aft.

"I heard the stowaways got away," Morton said. "Sorry to hear that, Captain."

"It was my fault. I fell asleep on watch. I might be carrying my bags down the gangway myself this afternoon." I kicked a hatchboard down to the deck. The AB's looked at each other and kept their heads down.

"Don't say that, Captain," Morton said. "Is the ship going to be fined?"

"Of course. Only question is how much."

He shook his head and left.

The agent arrived at 0900, while we were loading five-gallon buckets of cooking oil, and right behind him came two trim young INS men in tight uniforms. They escorted me into my saloon without preamble and started taking down the details.

"You had the stowaways on the back deck?"

"That's right."

"In handcuffs."

"That's right."

"And you considered that a secure arrangement?"

"Obviously it wasn't, but I had nowhere else to put them."

The older one was asking the questions. He scratched on a printed form. He tore off the second sheet and handed it to me.

"So," I said, scanning the entries, "what's the fine? I don't see it on here."

He put his pen away and straightened the flap over his pocket. "That will be determined by the Agent in Charge. We don't have anything to do with that. All we do is report what happened."

I nodded. The agents slid out from behind the table, sweaty and anxious to get away. They shook my hand and fled. "Don't worry," Monahan said, "it won't be over $3000 each."

"Great," I said. "That's just peachy."

Victor appeared with coffee for me and tea for Monahan. His hand trembled as he set the saucers down.

Dickie Vance appeared in the door five minutes later. "Good morning, Captain," he said. He was wearing an Izod shirt, open at the throat, and pleated golf pants. We shook hands and I introduced him to Monahan.

He sat in a chair. "Captain, I took a real hit on off-hires on the last voyage. Here's the list of off-hire times."

He handed me a faxed, typewritten list. I glanced over it. "These are bullshit. I don't even have to look at the log to tell you that these are bullshit."

"Well, I got paid after the ship had already left Miragoane. I knew you were going to call in the evening, but I couldn't wait to get the money. That's how tight things are. So I agreed to take the $22,000."

"You can still dispute off-hires. Did you get the Statement of Facts and my Notes of Protest from the Lake Charles agent? Did you compare the off-hires?"

"I never got a Statement of Facts from Carleton. In fact, he's out of business. The phone's disconnected at the dock and his home phone doesn't answer."

"That doesn't surprise me. Well, it complicates things, but we have my log. I always log stoppages, and it's a legal document you can take to arbitration. There weren't any stoppages in Lake Charles to ship's account anyway. All delays were weather-related. As far as these off-hires in Miragoane, they're bullshit too. You and Garot will just have to fight it out."

"Could you look that over and write me up something?"

"Sure." I put it on the table.

"Well," he said, "I've got the crew wages."

"Excellent."

He waved a hand. "So, let's go see the stowaways."

"They're gone."

"What?"

"They escaped. Last night. I was on watch and fell asleep."

He jumped up. "Jesus Christ, you gotta be kidding!"

I spread my hands and said calmly, "No, I'm not. I haven't had a whole night's sleep in a month. I just fell asleep. Somebody must've slipped 'em a handcuff key, and as soon as I fell asleep they unlocked the cuffs and walked away."

"What's it going to cost?"

"Mr. Monahan says $3000 each."

He turned and slammed a fist into the bulkhead. An old framed photograph of a windmill jumped off its hook and fell behind the refrigerator. "There's no fucking excuse!" he shouted. He turned back, his face swollen. "Nine thousand dollars because you fell asleep?"

I stood up slowly. The deck felt unsteady under me. We had just taken a car on the hatchcover, and the ship had rolled. "I'm ready to go home, Dickie," I said. My voice sounded far away to me. "But I'll need my wages before I go."

He stared. "Sorry, Captain," he said in a strangled voice. "I'm sorry. I lost control of myself."

"No, no, I'm tired. I'm ready to go home and let this poor old ship sink."

He swallowed and worked a weak smile onto his face. "I'm not blaming you, Captain. I know you've been working too hard. In fact, it's my fault. . .I should have told the agent to hire a guard."

I remained standing.

"Captain, you know I need you. At least until I can get some money saved up. I'm still paying back the money I borrowed in Mobile."

I didn't say anything.

"Captain, will you stay on?"

"All right," I said, "I'll stay."

"Thanks." He brightened. "It just means I won't be able to pay the crew until next month."

I shook my head in disgust. "These men have families. They can't tell their families there's no money coming home because the captain fell asleep."

Morton stuck his head in the door. "We'll be finished about noon, Captain. When do you want the tugs?"

"Four o'clock. What about the export permit for that truck?"

"I'll get that." He hurried out.

Monahan wished me a safe voyage, shook our hands, and left. I told Dickie about Jacek. He took the news calmly, even after I told him that Jerzy would have to go as well. "Get another chief and second, then," he said, pulling out a thick manila envelope. "Fuck that drunken bastard. They're due $3800? Here's four thousand. It's all I got left. Here, take it. If the chief doesn't come back before you sail, give his wages to the rest of the crew."

He thrust the money into my hand and made a show of looking at his watch. "Well, I gotta head for the airport. Tell the crew I'll catch up on the wages next month." He rushed out.

I went down and led Manuel and Ricardo to the starboard crew's head, where the cement and sledgehammer were standing by. I picked up the sledgehammer and smashed it into the ceramic toilet. It felt good. I kept hammering on the toilet until I had reduced it to shards. Then I stepped out so the AB's could clean it up.

After we had smashed all the toilets down to their bases, leaving only filthy holes in the floor, I stuck rolled-up pieces of tin into the drains and had the AB's cover the floors with 10 inches of cement. When the cement started to dry, I used a piece of wood for a trowel and formed shallow basins.

"Okay," I told the AB's, "let's make some shower gratings."

After I got Manuel lined up on cutting and screwing together thin pieces of dunnage, I borrowed a drill from Jerzy and drilled through the bulkheads. Under Yussuf's supervision, Ricardo cut the ship's water pipes behind the sinks. He ran PVC pipes up the bulkheads and connected them to the shower heads I'd bought. The ship now had six showers and one camping toilet.

Yussuf shook his head. "Very bad, Captain. We'll be a clean crew, but we'll have to shit in buckets. We cannot keep emptying that portable toilet every hour of the day."

"Watch this." I lifted up the grating to expose the basin in the floor. "You're from Egypt. You never saw a Greek toilet before?"

He gave a sudden laugh. "We call them Turkish toilets. Very clever, Captain. We leave the gratings down in the U.S. and take them out when we leave. But how do we. . .?"

"Flush?" I took the shower head out of its holder and held it down close to the floor. "With the shower head."

I went to the dock office and called Arcadio Munoz, the crewing agent, who said he had a chief engineer with a Honduran license who'd just called from another ship in the river, looking to change jobs. He would work for $1800 a month. I told him to send the man to the ship as soon as possible.

I had just hung up when Jacek came shuffling along the dock. His hair was matted and his face was swollen. His clothes were torn and limp with filth.

"Jacek!" I called. He stopped and turned. His left eye was blackened and almost shut. I went up to him. "What the hell happened to you, Chief?"

"I was mugged, Captain."

"What? You've been in the hospital all this time?"

"I was in jail, Captain. I got in a fight."

I took his elbow and steered him toward the foot of the gangway. "You fought the muggers and got arrested for it?"

I never did get the whole story, but apparently he had been mugged outside the Pussycat Club, a notorious strip joint at the corner of North River Drive and 36th Street, and had gone looking for his assailants. He claimed he had found one of them, but got arrested when he attacked the man. After three days he was kicked out of jail without charges.

I told him to get cleaned up and come to the saloon, and to bring Jerzy with him. Then I went to the phone and told Munoz to find me a second engineer as well, one who could weld.

When Jacek and Jerzy came up to the saloon, both were in street clothes. I spoke to Jacek and let him translate for Jerzy. "Jacek, you're a good chief, a damned good one, but I can't have a drunk onboard. It's dangerous, and it sets a bad example for the crew. I'm going to sign you off here in Miami. Jerzy, I don't have any complaints about you at all. I think you're great. But the new chief engineer won't be able to speak Polish, and it's too important that the engineers be able to talk to each other. I'm going to have to send you back to Poland as well."

Jerzy slumped when Jacek told him, and nodded unhappily. "Okay, men," I said, "as soon as I pay you off, go get your bags packed. It's almost 11, and the agent will be here to pick you up at 1400 hours."

I paid them off and they left. Fifteen minutes later Jacek reappeared in the door. "Captain, may I talk to you?"

"Certainly. Come in."

"Captain," he began, "I very sorry big problem on shore. I very sorry too much drink. But you see Daniela. . .she very angry when I call now. Plenty problem in Poland. No work, no shipyard in Sczeczin anymore."

I held up my hand, but he went on, "Captain, you know I work plenty hard, never complain, even so I cannot get off ship since leave Europe except in that shithole Miragoane."

"I know, Chief, and it's a goddamn. . ."

His eyes flashed. "Captain, please give me one more chance. Please do not send Jerzy and me to Poland."

I shook my head. "It's too late, Jacek. Everything's arranged. I'm very sorry, but I can't take the chance. If your drunkenness caused a catastrophe, it would be my fault."

"Captain, Daniela. . .she will kill me." His voice trailed off. He looked into my face, saw no hope there, and shuffled out. His wooden clogs thumped on the steps going down.

I went on deck. The stevedores had already left the ship. A heavy-set man with white hair, dressed in a clean boiler suit with "United Fruit Co." above the pocket, was coming up the gangway. "Captain?"

"Yes?"

"Angel Cienfuentes, chief engineer."

We shook hands. "Chief," I said, "are you ready to work?"

He looked around the ship, at the ongoing welding and the worn, splintered hatchboards, and gave me a doubtful look. "Let us take a look at the engine room."

We went down. The engine room was still and hot. Jerzy had left everything spotless and orderly, with the tools racked against the forward bulkhead and the floor plates as shiny as silver. The chief looked around, nodded, and said, "Okay, I'll come onboard."

"Excellent. When can you join the ship? We sail this afternoon."

He frowned. "Where's the old chief? Can't he show me around the engine room before he signs off?"

I shook my head. "He's leaving at two p.m. to catch a flight back to Poland. Plus he's not feeling very cooperative. I got a feeling he won't show you anything. Can you take over without him?"

He shrugged. "Of course. I am familiar with Werkspoor. But this is very irregular."

"It's the Caribbean. Okay, Chief, I've got to get some supplies. Get the cook to show you your cabin. . .he's from Puerto Cortes. Victor Barahona. Know him?" He laughed. "He is my neighbor. He is on this ship?" "Yeah. I hired him in Mobile." We shook hands. "Well, Chief, good to have you onboard. By the way, you know any second engineers looking for a job?" "Hmm. Not right now, Captain, but I will call home and have my wife ask. Many engineers in Cortes, you know." "Fine. Well, I'll see you this afternoon. If there's anything that we absolutely have to have in the engine room before we go to sea, let me know as soon as possible. We're sailing at 1600."

We went topside. Jacek and Jerzy were standing on deck in their shore clothes, their cheap luggage on the hatchcover. The agent's boy drove up as I was walking toward them.

I shook hands with Jerzy, but he pulled me to him and gave me a big, impulsive hug. I stuck out my hand to Jacek, but he turned his back to me.

The boy came up the gangway. "You men ready to go?"

Jacek nodded curtly and grabbed his suitcase. Jerzy gave me a last sad look, picked up his bag, and followed his countryman down the gangway. They piled their luggage in the trunk and got in the car. As it bumped onto the street Jacek turned back and gave me an odd, bitter smile.

I called Munoz. "Angel Cienfuentes took the job. He's signing on this afternoon."

"He did? Oh, dear, dear, he has not paid me. I must run down for to catch him before you sail."

"What about a second engineer? Find one?"

"Ah, unfortunately, Captain, I have not. I will keep trying today. Maybe I will drive up to Dania. There are good men on those Bahamian boats, you know, Captain."

"That's okay. Just find a licensed, warm, and breathing second engineer and send him to the ship as soon as possible."

I had just gone onboard when a white Ford sedan pulled up. CWO Parrott was driving, with Ensign Horta in the passenger seat. They got out, adjusted their uniforms, and came up the gangway followed by a different pair of young male trainees with big feet.

"Captain," Horta said, "we are here to inspect your toilet facilities."

"Welcome onboard," I said. "May I get you coffee or soft drinks?"

"No."

"Very well." I led them into the accommodations and down the port hallway to the crew's head. I had told Manuel to take the lock off the door. I threw it open proudly.

They stared. "You had the toilets made into showers?" Parrott asked.

"Correct."

Horta leaned in and turned the valve. A sprinkle of brown water squirted onto her natty blue sleeve. She jerked her arm back and stared at the stain in dismay.

Parrott struggled to keep a grin off his face. I reached past her and turned the shower off.

She bent down and lifted the grating. The cement was still fresh. She let it fall. I took them to the officer's head, where they looked in briefly, then we went up to the master's head. I showed them the cement floor with the basin and drain hole. The crew hadn't had time to install shower fittings or make a grating.

"This isn't a shower," Horta said grimly.

"It's not a toilet either," I snapped.

There was a thick silence between us. Parrott said mildly, "As long as it's not a toilet, Captain, it's okay. We'll clear the detention."

Horta clicked her teeth together.

"Thank you, sir," I said to him. He scribbled on a form and handed it to me. They left the ship. A battered white delivery van pulled up at the foot of the gangway and two men started unloading coils of cheap, ungalvanized wire to lash the cars down with.

I looked at my watch. Almost 1100 hours. A small British freighter, the *Celtic Rover*, had been brought in behind us during the night, and stevedores were crawling over her. Her cargo of plywood, neatly bundled and strapped, was ready on the dock. I saw Morton and whistled. He walked over.

"Good morning, Captain," he called.

"Good morning, Morton. What time do the stevedores start?"

"Stevedores?" He scratched his grizzled head. "We done loaded the *Erika* already, Cap. You feelin' okay?"

"I feel wonderful. It's always a pleasure to leave Miami. But I can't leave until that Toyota's unloaded."

"The truck? Captain, what are you talking about? Everything is okay with that truck."

"Except for one thing. You agreed to bring me the export permit by 1000 hours. It's now 1100 hours. Time to jettison the contraband."

"Oh, no, no, Cap'n. I just forgot about the export permit. I'll get it brought to the dock right now."

He bustled off toward the front office. A few minutes later he went to the *Celtic Rover* and brought some stevedores over. We opened the hatch above the truck, a cherry-picker rolled up, and they took the truck out. A skinny black kid got in and drove it around to the back of the south warehouse.

I called the crew up to the saloon. They filed in, and I realized with dismay that they thought I was going to pay their salaries. I spoke in Spanish. "Men," I said grimly, "I am sorry to tell you that Dickie will not be able to pay your January salaries. He brought the money to Miami, but INS is going to fine the ship $9000 for letting the stowaways escape. He has told me that he intends to use your salaries to pay the fine." I paused. "I'm sorry."

The AB's took it in stone-faced silence. Yussuf fidgeted, anxious to get back to work.

"Fellows," I went on, "Dickie is a good owner. Of course he's going to pay you as soon as he can. Out of the next charter-hire. It's not his fault that I fell asleep and let the stowaways escape. I would like to ask you to let the ship sail."

The Hondurans and I looked across the saloon at each other. "*Sí, Capitán,*" Victor said firmly, "we will sail with you." He looked at his countrymen. "*¿Sí, muchachos?*"

"*Sí, Victor, Sí,*" Ricardo said, and Manuel gave a big clown's grin, and that was that.

"Thank you, men," I said. "Now let us prepare for sea. I have received an urgent message from Miragoane that the girls are waiting."

They laughed politely. I went down and called the agent with the name of the new chief engineer. I promoted Ricardo to second for the voyage, counting on the fact that it was unlikely Coast Guard would conduct a license check before we sailed. I was also counting on finding a second engineer in Miragoane.

At 1500 hours a Hispanic youth in a jogging suit brought the ship's clearance and an updated crew list, neatly typed, but the tugs didn't arrive until 1900 hours. Rollo never showed his face. It was almost dark by the time the tugs hauled us out into the river and we headed downstream. As we passed a big apartment building on the starboard side, the wheelhouse level with the third floor, I could see the denizens getting ready for the evening. Oblivious to the ship sliding past in the dark, they shaved and showered and dressed and drank and snorted coke. One woman, a heavy-set Hispanic with shoulders like a sack of cement, drank from a bottle of muscatel and danced by herself in the middle of a bare living room.

We passed under I-95 and through the Brickell Avenue Bridge. Early diners sipped frozen drinks at an open-air restaurant on the south side of the river. They watched idly as the ship ghosted past and out into the bay.

The pilot boat came idling up as the tugs dropped our lines. Yussuf brought the pilot to the wheelhouse, a pale young man with a cigarette dangling from his bloodless lips. He nodded casually, put his bag on the dashboard, and ordered Half Ahead. I rang for the engine room, and after a few minutes the chief responded.

"We've got a new chief engineer," I explained to the pilot. "I guess it's taking him a little time to get the engine room figured out."

"No problem," the pilot said. "We've got plenty of room here."

The engine started with a couple of soft hiccups, and I signaled for Half Ahead. The ship gained steering-way. Yussuf brought the bow around to point it toward the narrow gap between Dodge and Fisher Islands. We idled past the rusty side of a Carnival cruise ship.

The Fisher Island ferry was crossing the channel as we approached. The pilot ordered Dead Slow Ahead. The engine spluttered. I stared at the engine console. The rpm needle fluttered and sank toward zero. The engine coughed twice more and stopped.

"What the hell. . .?" the pilot said. I jumped to the telegraph and rang for power, then ran out on the wing of the bridge. Manuel and Ricardo were still working on the lashings.

"Manuel," I yelled, "drop anchor! *Rapido, hombre, rapido.* The starboard anchor, one shackle."

"Looks like your chief hasn't quite got a handle on things down there," the pilot said dryly. "We'll be all right. The wind's out of the north. . .we'll go aground without doing any harm."

I cut a tight look at him. "Until the Coast Guard comes onboard. Then they'll ruin my owner for sure." I went to the speaking tube and yelled down for the chief, but he couldn't hear me. The anchor chain rattled in the quiet night, briefly, and stopped as Manuel set the brake. The ship slowly turned her bow to the north. I waited for the stern to ground, but we swung free.

"That's lucky," the pilot said. "Go see if the chief can get her started again. That way I won't have to call Coast Guard."

"Thanks." I hurried down the companionway.

The new chief was up on the catwalk by the heads, twisting valves. He saw me and shook his head angrily. "She's not getting fuel, Captain. I haven't found the problem yet."

I stared. "No fuel? We've got 60 tons. . ." A thought hit me. "Wait a second, Chief."

I ran back up to the main deck and into the starboard hallway. I opened the plexiglass cover over the emergency shut-down valves. The main engine fuel shut-off handle was pulled up to the closed position. I freed it and let the spring pull it back into place. Then I went downstairs.

"The old chief sabotaged us, Chief. He pulled the emergency shut-down. It's back open again."

He scowled. "*Puta madre*, Captain. Now I have to bleed the injectors."

"Okay, Chief. Let's hope we can get it done before the Coast Guard sees us sitting here. Their station is right around the corner, you know, at the end of Dodge Island." I shook my head grimly. "Slimy drunken bastard."

I went back to the wheelhouse. The pilot and Yussuf were smoking together on the port wing of the bridge. I told them the story. "I hope he didn't do something else," I finished. "Hell, he could have put sand in the sump."

"You'd know by now," the pilot said. "How long before we can get going?"

"As soon as the new chief bleeds the injectors. Thirty minutes."

The pilot shook his head. "I dunno, Captain. I'm supposed to report this to the Coast Guard. And the pilot boat'll be calling in a few minutes to see why we aren't offshore yet."

"Can you stall 'em? If the Coast Guard hears about this, they'll tear us a new asshole."

He shrugged. "Let's wait and see. There's a ship coming in. . .as long as we get the anchor up before they get here, we'll be alright. Otherwise, I'll be in trouble myself for not reporting the breakdown."

The three of us looked toward the tip of Dodge Island, where the Coast Guard station was hidden behind the warehouses. The wind was starting to come up. A cool breeze eddied against my sweaty forehead. The pilot threw his cigarette overboard. His radio crackled and a raspy voice said something unintelligible.

"That's the boat," the pilot said. "I'm going to have to . . ."

The telegraph rang suddenly, making all three of us jump.

"Impossible," Yussuf said. "Chief bleed injectors already?"

I didn't wait. I went to the window and made the up-anchor sign to Manuel on the foredeck. With only one shackle out, just enough to pin the bow, it was only a minute before he signaled the anchor clear of the bottom. I rang for Half Ahead.

The main engine was running rough. I grimaced. "There's something wrong with the engine, First. Can you feel it?"

Yussuf nodded. The pilot frowned. "What do you want to do, Captain?"

"Let's go out to anchor and see if the chief can get it straightened out."

He nodded. "Okay. Quartermaster, port five. Steady as she goes."

With the engine loping along, brap-tockity-tockity-brap-tockity-tockity, we drew past the fishing pier and nosed out into the darkness. A container ship, one of the little Bahamas fruit ships, came chugging past on the port side and into Government Cut. We turned into the channel, the bow rising on the low ocean swell, and threaded our way along the buoys.

The pilot boat was waiting for us, rolling in the swells just off the seabuoy. I signed the pilot's chit and shook his hand. "Many thanks, Pilot," I said. "My owner thanks you."

He smiled in the darkened wheelhouse. "We're all seamen, Captain. Good luck." He went downstairs.

Yussuf said, "Drop anchor again, Captain?"

"Turn southeast. I'm going down to talk to the chief."

The chief was still on the engine catwalk. I went up close and yelled in his ear, "What's wrong with the engine?"

"Nothing, Captain. I knew we had to get going, so I only bled four injectors. If we can shut down for a few minutes, I'll bleed the rest. I think everything else is okay."

I sighed deeply. "Thank God." I clapped him on the shoulder. "That was good thinking, Chief. You'll get a case of beer from the slop chest for that."

He nodded absently, watching the pyro gauges. I went back topside. "Let's get a few miles south," I told Yussuf, "then the new chief'll finish bleeding the injectors." I sat on the port stool. "I think he's going to work out okay."

We shut down a little later, with the lights of the Florida Keys stretching into the blackness to the southwest. The ship rolled silently. A big, fast container ship, ablaze with lights, steamed northward between us and Bimini.

An hour later the chief appeared on the bridge, drenched in sweat, to announce that the engine was ready. I took another position from the satnav while he got oil up, then called for Full Ahead. The old engine settled down to her usual steady thumping. I turned the ship toward the Santaren Channel. The lights flickered as the chief switched over to the tailshaft generator, and the noise of the Deutz died away.

The next morning, before I went on watch, I looked around in the engine room until I found a drawer of old bearings. A good chief engineer never throws away a bearing, no matter how badly worn, because someday it might be better than a frozen one. I chose half-a-dozen of the worst, broke the races with a ball-peen hammer, and gathered up the steel balls. They were about half-an-inch in diameter and perfect for my purpose. During the long morning, between satnav and radar fixes, I practiced with my new Wrist Rocket slingshot using a plastic jug on the hatchcover as a target, but without much success.

Two days later we approached Cape Tiburon. The wind had been building steadily out of the northeast, and now it was roaring down the Windward Passage and tearing the tops off the long Atlantic swells.

I sent Yussuf around the ship to make sure all was secure, and when he came back he had a square, canvas-covered box in his hand. "I found this in the lifeboat," he said.

I looked it over. "Emergency transmitter. Somebody must have gotten into the lifeboat locker." We went out on the boat deck, but the lifeboat locker was locked, and when I opened it, the supplies appeared complete and properly packed. I stowed the transmitter and relocked the cover.

At dawn the next morning we were off Miragoane Point, the rising sun peeping over the mountains and glowing fire-red on the roof of the church. Fishing boats were setting out from the southern shores, black dots on the green water. Several ships were at anchor in the bay.

Yussuf signaled the chief for Half Ahead, and a few minutes later the generator engine cranked up with a clatter. The ship slowed.

"You think the whores have recognized us yet?" I asked Yussuf.

He laughed. "They recognized us last night by our lights. *Las aduanas* will be ready for us when we drop anchor."

"Hah. *Las aduanas*. The Customs ladies. First onboard and last off. You think your girlfriend will be here?"

"Of course. She's probably getting off one of the other ships right now."

I shook my head. "I hope you're taking precautions, Yussuf. Wearing your oilskins, you know."

He nodded. "I've been a seaman all my adult life, Captain. I know the dangers."

We glided through the break in the reef, the giant rock of Miragoane Point a half-mile off the port side. We could see ships backed up to the shore with lighters swarming around them. The *Bahia Mar* and the *Dieu Puissant* were at anchor, among others I didn't recognize.

As soon as we had dropped the hook a boat put out from shore toward us. Yussuf trained the glasses on it and announced the impending arrival of *las aduanitas*. Propelled by a hard wind off the mountains, the boat made it to the ship in record time, even laden as it was. The girls climbed up the pilot ladder, some new and some the same.

Ysadora, Jerzy's girlfriend, was distraught to learn that he was already back in Poland, but she improved her position onboard considerably by graduating to the new chief. Sonia came up wearing a loose sleeveless blouse and stretch shorts. Yussuf met her on deck for a long kiss. The long-haired girl, Lucerna, climbed over the bulwark in a minidress, making a production of it. Amanda came last.

We went to anchor stern-to late in the afternoon, between Bonvillain's barge and the northernmost ship in the line, the *Gracias a Dios*. After our lines were ashore and the crew had gone to supper, I sat in the wheelhouse for a long time, looking at photos of my family. I could hear music and laughter from the fantail.

I got in bed, buried my head in the pillow, and soon the music and laughter were gone.

When I woke the ship had taken a list to starboard. I went down and knocked on Yussuf's door. He slipped the hook and opened the door in his underwear. Sonia was asleep behind him, lying naked on the sheet with her soft pale breasts flattened against her chest. "I don't know, Captain," he said. "Let me take soundings."

I went to breakfast. Yussuf came in with a worried look. "No. 2 starboard is full, Captain."

"What?" I jumped up and rushed down to the engine room. The chief was grinding a valve seat on a spare Deutz head.

"Chief, check your valves. No. 2 starboard is full of water."

The chief went to the manifold and jerked on the valve handles. "All closed, Captain."

"Have you transferred any ballast water since yesterday?"

"No sir."

I went topside and asked Yussuf, "What about the starboard bilge? I hope to God it's not full."

"No sir. Still 10 centimeters."

"What about the No. 2 starboard tank-top? Is it good?"

"I think so, Captain."

We sounded Nos. 1 and 3. They were empty. "I guess the tank-top is holding," I said. "How much cargo is on top of the manhole?"

"I'll go look."

We went down the stevedore hatch together. The rising sun was already baking the starboard side of the hull. The after manhole of the No. 2 starboard double-bottom tank was under the midbridge, in an area stacked with bags of sugar. We went back topside.

The first of the lighters were sculling toward us from the southern rim of the bay, full of stevedores. "Well," I said, "let's see if the chief can keep up with the water by pumping. Maybe we can get to the manhole tonight."

It took an hour to pump down No. 2 starboard, and within two hours it was full again. The cars on deck went into the lighters without incident, and the shoreside stevedores walked them up the beach. I told Roger to discharge the cargo above the after manhole of No. 2 double-bottom first, and by 1700, when they knocked off, they had gotten a hole cleared down to the floor.

As soon as the last stevedore had left the ship Manuel and Ricardo broke up the cement over the manhole and lifted off the plastic sheeting that kept it from sticking to the steel. The manhole had been opened at some point in the last couple of years, and the nuts backed off easily enough. In half-an-hour the cover was up. I stuck my head down into the tank.

Water was running aft in a steady stream. The pump was running, and I could hear water gurgling in the intake. I pulled my head out. "We're breached to the sea, Yussuf. You know the drill."

He nodded grimly. "Okay, Captain." He told the AB's to get one of the automobile jacks and some bags of cement.

"Get 10 bags," I told them. "It's a big hole."

I took off my clothes and let myself down into the sweltering tank with Yussuf right behind me. My flashlight stabbed into the dark tunnel forward, lighting the wasted, cracked frames. The water poured through the limber holes and made little bow waves against my knees as I struggled forward. My bare shoulders scraped against the knife-edges. The tank smelled of salt water and marsh mud.

We kept going in the close, hot darkness, but still the water kept running downhill from ahead of us. "It looks like the hole is right forward, First," I said. "We should have discharged forward." I spat out a mouthful of rotting sea water. "I don't like getting this far away from the manhole."

We were almost to the forward bulkhead before we got to the point of ingress. My flashlight picked out the crack in the hull, in a damaged area about four meters long. The shell plating was bent up from some unknown impact, buckling two frames. One of the frames had broken free from the shell-plating entirely. The damage was at least four or five years old.

The crack in the hull was about 30 centimeters long, at the top of the indentation, running fore-and-aft, with water spurting up in a thin sheet and flowing down the slope of the bottom. I pulled myself through the frame and crouched in a ball to the side so Yussuf could see past me. He whistled.

"That's a bad one, Captain. It's going to be hard to stop the flow with the plating bent up like that."

"No shit." We watched the water spraying in, sparkling in the flashlight's beam. I sighed. "All right. I'll wait here. You go back and get the AB's to hand the jack and lumber forward to us." I grinned at him in the play of light and shadow. "And get the thickest gasket material you can find. It's too long a crack for bacon."

He gave a faint smile and started aft.

I sat with my back against a frame. The water splashed and gurgled. I turned off the flashlight to save the batteries and waited in the hot stinking darkness. The light from the after manhole was a long way away, coming and going as Yussuf crawled through the lightening holes.

He came back with the jack and some lengths of heavy timber. He laid several squares of heavy rubber sheeting and a piece of steel on the shell plating.

"The pump still keeping up with the water?" I asked him.

"Yessir. It's about six inches deep under the manhole."

"Okay, let's see what we can do."

We scraped the area around the crack clear of mud and rust, exposing the pitted inner surface of the steel. We laid the rubber down and put the piece of 3/8" plate on top, then adjusted the base of the jack over it. With the top of the jack jammed against a timber spanning two frames, we started jacking down.

Yussuf and I worked the handle together. My back and neck started aching, but there was no way to stretch out. We strained to pull the handle down with each click. The water kept coming in. We jacked a few more clicks and stopped. The flow was reduced to a trickle, but it was still there. We jacked some more. The plating creaked.

"I don't like this, Yussuf," I said quietly. I looked at his rust-caked face. He wasn't smiling now. I sat back and tried to ease the fire in my shoulders. "I don't know if we're going to be able to stop it."

"It's almost stopped now, Captain. Let's try a little more."

I wiped the sweat out of my eyes with the back of a filthy hand. "All right. A couple of clicks more."

I worked myself back for a better purchase, and we hauled on the handle. It yielded slowly, reluctantly, finally giving up another click. We pulled again, and this time the click came fast. I stopped, a cold hand around my heart, but it was too late.

The jack jumped sideways, throwing the handle backward through the lightening hole and sending the timber above it thumping into darkness. My flashlight got knocked out of my hand. The compartment was filled with green light from the ocean, streaming in through two long cracks. The light poured upward onto Yussuf's horrified face.

"Get back," I cried, "get back! Get to the manhole."

We both dove for the lightening hole at the same time. The space between the frames was already half-full of cold water. We got jammed together in the lightening hole, both struggling to get through, ignoring the tearing of steel against our flesh.

Yussuf fought his way backward and I shot through the hole with the pressure of the water behind me. Yussuf's head got tangled in my feet. Then we were at the second lightening hole, the water splashing past my face. Yussuf was gasping and spitting behind me.

We kept going through the lightening holes, the water level lower in each space as we scrambled aft. I started to feel stinging in my cuts. Past the last frame and up into the manhole, Ricardo's shocked face above me. The compartment below was half-full of water already.

"Get the manhole cover," I shouted as I climbed out. "Get the manhole cover!" They stared at me blankly. I was yelling in English.

Yussuf came up behind me, blood streaming from a hundred cuts. I said in Spanish, "Get the manhole cover. Get it on the manhole. *Rapido*, or we're sunk!"

Manuel grabbed the manhole cover and threw it over the bolts. Yussuf was already scrabbling for the nuts. The water was almost to the upper edge of the lightening hole.

"Get four nuts on the cover," I said. "Hurry, for God's sake."

We took a nut each and worked furiously to get them started. Manual took the spanner and managed to get the four nuts screwed down tight before the water reached the manhole. He and Ricardo screwed on the rest of the nuts.

I climbed up on top of the bags of sugar and collapsed, eyes closed, chest heaving. Yussuf climbed up and lay down beside me. I could hear his ragged breathing. After what seemed like a long time, the AB's were finished.

"Water stopped, Captain," Manuel called up. "Manhole sealed tight now."

"Any water get in the hold?"

"No, Captain. Cargo all dry."

"Thank God."

He climbed up and knelt beside me. "You okay, Captain? You're bleeding."

I pushed myself up. "I'm okay. I'm okay." I looked around. Yussuf was sitting up with his head between his knees. The blood from his cuts thickened and trickled down his sides.

I got to my feet. "The bilges," I said. "We've got to go on deck and sound the bilges to see if the tank-top is holding."

We made our way across the top of the cargo and climbed out of the hold into the cold air. It was almost dark. The girls were sitting on folding chairs in front of the accommodations. They squealed when they saw us.

Victor came running up. "Captain, Captain, you're bleeding! What happened?"

I let him help me aft. "Get us some towels and bandages. I'm okay. Make sure Yussuf is okay."

The girls got up and we sank into the chairs. My shoulders and thighs were on fire from the saltwater in my cuts. Victor appeared with towels and bandages, and he and Amanda started cleaning me up. Sonia worked on Yussuf with a proprietary air.

I looked at Manuel. "Sound the bilges. The starboard side first. If the water's coming in, it'll go to the starboard bilge box."

He got the sounding tape and lowered it down the sounding pipe. It came out with the same 10 centimeters. I let out a ragged sigh. "We're okay, men. The tank-top is holding."

Yussuf sat up and motioned Sonia away. "How can we fix a crack from the outside, Captain? We'll have to go into drydock."

I stood up and wrapped a towel around my waist. Miragoane was having one of its brief evenings of electricity. Dim yellow lights twinkled around the rim of the bay like jack-o-lanterns. A pale round moon peeped over the mountains.

"We'll worry about that later," I said. "We saved the ship. That's all that matters. We saved the ship."

CHAPTER SIX

AT BREAKFAST THE NEXT MORNING YUSSUF SAID, "CAPTAIN, there's a Guyanese AB on the *Bahia Mar* named Lionel Johnson who might be able to help us fix the crack. He's the one who goes diving whenever they have a problem."

"Oh, yeah, the guy who fixed the hole in the *Santo Filipe*." I looked at him. "What do you have in mind? It's too big for underwater epoxy."

"What about this?" He drew an oval on the table with a finger. "We put a big, thick rope of tar on a piece of plastic, big enough to go all around the cracks. Then we have Lionel take it under and smooth it on the shell plating. It might stop the leaks long enough to make a cement box."

I nodded. "It's possible. You'd have to make some oakum and mix it with the tar to bridge the gaps."

"Yessir."

I nodded again. "It could work. The pressure of the water'll keep the patch against the hull. Biggest question is whether we can keep even the tiniest leak from coming in."

"That's why we have it on a piece of tarp. Lionel can keep pressing the tarp against the hull until all the leaks are sealed."

"You think it'll stay soft enough?"

"Sure, Captain. We give it to him hot. The water's warm. If he gets it on quick enough, it'll still be warm."

"Okay. Go ask him to come over when he gets a chance."

Just after 1700 hours, as the stevedores were climbing off the ship, a ship's boat came alongside and a small, round-headed man came up the pilot ladder. He spotted me on deck and came over. "I'm Ian 'arrison," he said. "Are you the captain?"

"Yes."

He pointed to a big cement ship at anchor. It had been there when we arrived. "I'm the second engineer on the *San Iago*. Are you looking for a second engineer?"

"I sure am. What's your license?"

"I have a Honduranian chief engineer's license, Cap, but really I'm a second."

"I see. How long at sea?"

"Ten years. Well, sar, actually I was eight years on a dredge in Venezuela. Chief engineer for four years. Now two years at sea."

"You're from Guyana?"

"Yassar."

"Okay, Ian 'arrison, the job pays $1100 a month, no overtime."

"Okay, Captain. Dat's all right."

"Good. Report to the chief engineer when you get yourself squared away."

We shook again and he motored back to the *San Iago*. About 1800 hours a canoe came up to the pilot ladder with a muscular black man standing in the bottom, arms crossed on his chest. He kept his balance easily as the tiny boat bobbled toward the side of the ship. I went forward. The man came up the ladder holding a pair of battered swim fins.

"Good evening, sar," he said, holding out his hand. His palm was as hard as a rhino's foot. "Lionel Johnson here, sar. From de *Bahia Mar*."

"Oh, the two-minute man!"

He laughed. "I guess you can call me dat, sar. But I can hold my breat' for more dan two minute, you know. You will see."

"Excellent." I led him to the side of the ship, at about the middle of No. 1 hatch. I pointed overboard. "There's a big crack in the hull down there. In the bottom, about eight feet from the side."

"A crack, you say, Captain? Plenty hard fix one long crack. I fix holes wit' epoxy and button-patch, but no crack."

I outlined what we wanted to do. He shrugged. "Big problem will be stopping all de water, Cap. Even wee trickle too many for cement."

I nodded. "Exactly. But we've got to give it a try. No way the owner can go into drydock. You think you can put a piece of plastic on it?"

"Sartainly, Cap."

"You think. . ." I was about to offer him 10 dollars, but instead said, "Would 50 dollars be enough for the job?"

He nodded. "Dat okay, Cap. You ready?"

"You mean right now?"

"I have to work during the day, Cap. I'm welder, you know." He laughed. "Plenty welding on de *Bahia Mar*. If I don't weld on dat old bitch every day, she sink like a potato machine."

"All right," I said, "I'll get the chief to start pumping." I sent word to the chief to pump out No. 2 starboard. A few minutes later the pump started discharging.

Lionel shook his head. "No guarantee from my side de patch stop de water, eh, Cap? I t'ink maybe no good."

"We'll see," I said. "It's worth a try."

He stripped to his underwear, grabbed his fins, and leaped over the side. I sent Ricardo to get Yussuf and hump all the cement onboard down into the hold. I found a meter-square piece of tarp in the forecastle, and I was trimming it with an old galley knife when Yussuf called from deck, "Captain, the AB from the *Bahia Mar* found the cracks. They're only about 30 centimeters long."

I went out and aft on the starboard deck. "They looked two meters long when we were down there, eh? So how many bags of cement onboard?"

"Twenty-two."

"Should be enough. Got some rebar?"

"Yessir."

I held up the patch. "Okay, where's the tar?"

He had already gotten some chunks from the forecastle and had melted them in a paint can with the propane torch. I put the patch on the hatchcover, mixed the soft tar with oakum—shredded hemp—and smeared the hot, sticky mass over the surface of the plastic. Johnson was lazily paddling around in the water. Ricardo dropped the patch to him.

Johnson took it and submerged. The last we saw of him were his black fins in the blue depths, heading under the hull. Yussuf said something to himself.

"What's that?" I said.

He pushed a button on his watch. "Oh, I'm timing him. I want to see if he really can stay down two minutes."

We waited. I looked around the bay. I could see the old man on the abandoned freighter in the bay, the *God Only One*, tottering around on the littered boat deck. On the beach, the last sacks from the last boat of the day were being landed, the exhausted stevedores wobbling up the muddy bank caked in rice powder and cement. Only two trucks were left. The squatters were back on the dock, their fires burning between the huts and sending a sulfurous blue smoke out over the bay.

Johnson broke the surface with a poppling sound, breathing heavily. Yussuf said, "Two minutes exactly."

"Okay, Captain," Johnson called up, "it fixed on de crack good."

A half-hour later the pump lost suction. We confirmed it by sounding, then opened the manhole. Yussuf and I looked down into the tank with flashlights, searching for a telltale trickle of water, but nothing. We went down and started forward. Still no water. Wavelets lapped against the hull, but the tank was empty.

When we got forward we found the tarp bulging as hard as iron into the cracks. There was no water running aft.

"Wonder how long it'll hold?" Yussuf said, his voice hollow.

"Long enough for the cement to set. That's all we care about."

"Better than a slab of bacon," he said. "Cap'n, you should hire this Guyanese man."

"Think he might be looking for a job?"

"Everybody on the *Bahia Mar* wants to get off. The captain is crazy."

"Same's been said about me." I started aft through the lightening holes. "You think he'll come over for $700?"

"Sure, Cap'n."

We climbed out. I went up and got a 50-dollar bill from the ship's safe and took it to Johnson in the crew's mess. "You did a good job," I said. "Want to join the *Erika*?"

He raised his eyebrows. "You have job onboard, Captain?"

"Yeah. I'm looking for a welder/AB. I can pay $700 U.S., plus overtime."

"Yassar. Dat's okay. When de job sta't?"

"Right now."

He held out his hand. "I'll go back and get my bags."

We shook. I called Victor. "Show Mr. Johnson to a cabin. If there's anything he needs let me know."

Victor bowed to Lionel, shook his hand, and led him forward. I went down into the No. 2 starboard tank and crawled forward toward the flickering lights where Yussuf and the AB's were mixing cement. When the last of the cement was spread evenly in the box made by the frames and stringers, we crawled out of the tank and went up into the hold. "Okay," I told the AB's, "bolt her down. We'll sound the tank in the morning to see if the box held." I carried my clothes up on deck.

After a late supper, I went down to the engine room and cracked some more ball-bearings before climbing to my perch in the darkening wheelhouse. I ranged my ammunition on the dashboard and put the Wrist-Rocket slingshot close to hand on the autopilot console. Things had settled down on shore, with only a few cooking fires still burning. The electricity was off again. The streets were dark, with candles flickering in the windows.

The ship rocked quietly. The moon rose huge and lopsided into a lattice of high clouds. The only noise left was the thumping of generators. About 0200 I went downstairs and found Kokimo asleep on a piece of carpet, his knees curled up under his chin and his head on his hands. I fixed a cup of black coffee and went back up to the bridge. The decks of the ships to the south were empty. The fires were all out on shore, and the roof of the army building was deserted.

I lowered the pilot ladder on the starboard side, to make it easier for anyone wanting to come onboard. About 0300 hours my first customer arrived, a dreadlocked figure gliding across the bow of the ship in his canoe. I got a couple of ball bearings from the dashboard and went out on the wing of the starboard bridge, behind the deck lights. I didn't have long to wait. The pilot-ladder ropes started shaking. I put a ball in the leather pouch and positioned myself.

His head eased up over the bulwark, dreadlocks first. He studied the front of the house carefully, then slid over the gunwale and took up a low crouch on deck.

He moved silently aft. I leaned over to keep him in view as he approached the front of the house. I let him get to the rear corner of the hatch, about 20 feet below me, before I drew the tubing back and let the ball fly.

My aim wasn't good. The ball pinged against the deck and landed in the water with a splash. He spun around. I took aim again and the next ball got him behind the ear. It whacked against his skull like a lugnut hitting an oak tree. The would-be thief dropped to the deck without a twitch and sprawled against the hatchcoaming with his head in darkness.

I ran downstairs. No one was awake. I could hear snores through the cracks in the doors. I went on the dew-covered deck. The Haitian was still motionless, one arm across his chest and the other flung wide.

I picked up a piece of broken dunnage and held it ready as I bent close to him. He was breathing slowly and regularly. I looked at his face. He had a large boil in the middle of his forehead that made him look like he was about to sprout a horn.

I went back and knocked softly on Yussuf's door. "Yes?" I heard him call sleepily.

"It's the captain. I need some help. Keep it quiet."

He opened the door in his underwear.

"I just knocked a thief out with my slingshot. I need help getting him into his canoe."

His eyes opened wide. He closed the door to drop the hook and came out. He stared at the thief, still motionless, and knelt down beside him.

"He looks dead, Captain. You sure you didn't kill him?"

"He's breathing. That's all that counts. Let's get him into his canoe and shove him off."

"That where you hit him?" he asked, pointing to the man's forehead.

"Naw, that's some kind of sore or something. I got him behind the ear."

The man snored loudly, once, and turned on his side. Yussuf stood up. "He's okay. But what if we put him in the boat and he rolls out of it? He might drown."

I gave a sharp grin. "He shouldn't go boating at night. Dangerous creatures about."

"Let me go get the AB's."

I shook my head. "Let's do it ourselves. The fewer who know about this the better."

We made a bight in a one-inch rope—a smaller rope would have cut into his skin—and looped it under his arms. We handed him over the gunwale and lowered him to his boat. When his feet were a few inches above it, we made the bitter end fast and I went down. Yussuf lowered him into the boat as I guided his feet. I unfastened the rope and pulled it out from under him. He never regained consciousness, but he did call out once in Creole, a small, lost cry that disappeared into the darkness as soon as it was uttered.

I stood on the bottom rung of the ladder and untied the boat. The bow wheeled away. When I got up on deck it was already at the edge of visibility, and a few minutes later it was gone toward the western reaches of Miragoane Bay.

I chuckled. "I bet he has a hard time figuring out how he got there when he wakes up."

Yussuf nodded. "You were lucky, Captain. You could have killed him."

"Yeah, I'm glad I didn't. If I had, I wouldn't have called you to help."

He was shocked and hurt. "Captain, you know you can trust me. Why, if you ever need help of any kind, you must call me. I could never say anything to anyone. I am Arab." He took my shoulders. His face was caught for a moment by the white light from the front of the bridge. "You are my brother, Captain. Your enemy is my enemy."

I took his hands. "Thanks, Yussuf. I feel the same way. But if I had killed him, it is best that no one else know about it."

We both turned and looked out to the west. I thought I saw a speck on the water, but I couldn't be sure. "Well," I said, "I've still got another couple of hours on watch. You get some more sleep. If I thump another one, I'll call you."

He went to his cabin. "Good hunting, Captain." He slipped inside and put the door on the hook. I went back up to the bridge. Dawn came and I went down to begin the day.

Five days later the last of the cargo went over the side and into the lighter. Boys with homemade brooms and plastic bags came onboard to sweep the hold for what they could get. I went up to call Dickie on the SSB. I had tried several times during the day, but the high-seas operator could only leave messages on his answering machine. This time he took the call.

"Hello, Captain," he said, his voice drifting in and out, "how's it going?"

"We finished discharging at 1600 hours."

"Excellent. When can you leave?"

"We're ready now."

"Okay, Captain, sail for Savannah. You have a load of fertilizer to take to Rio Haina."

I groaned. "Bulk fertilizer, I hope not?"

"Wait a sec." I heard the sound of paper rustling. "It says 1550 metric tons of ammonium nitrate in bulk."

"Dickie, be advised that this ship cannot take that much. We can only take about 1500 tons, maybe less."

"Why is that, Captain? The broker says a 1600-ton ship ought to be able to carry 1550 tons."

"I can't discuss it right now. I'll call you when we get there. But for sure we can't take that much."

"Okay, I'll tell the broker."

"And you know we're not set up for bulk fertilizer. Tell the charterer he'll have to put plywood over the floor timbers before we load. That way he won't have to keep the ship on charter an extra week."

There was a silence. Someone was shouting in Greek. The ether popped and sizzled. "Why is that, Captain?"

"We can't leave fertilizer under the floorboards. It'll rust out the steel. The boards'll have to be taken up to wash the fertilizer off the tank-tops."

Another silence. "Okay, Captain, I'll talk to the broker about it. What's your ETA to Savannah?"

I thought. "Five days with good weather."

"Okay. Here's the agent's phone number." He read it off. "Give the agent 72/48/24 hours' notice."

"Roger that." We signed off.

I told the crew that we would sail at 2100 hours. A few minutes before 2100 the girls came on deck and climbed tearfully over the gunwale. The boatman sculled them toward the darkened town. Ronald was standing by on shore to supervise the casting-off of stern lines. When Yussuf rang the bell for anchor-up, I turned the ship north and steamed past the flickering lights of candles in the windows of the town, and an occasional headlight picking its way down the hill.

We were running along the edge of the Bahama Banks three nights later. It was just before midnight, and a few minutes earlier I had turned the ship northward into the Santaren Channel. A cold Atlantic wind was blowing out of the northeast. The barometer had fallen to 29.12. The waves off the Banks had risen to a short, angry chop that slapped noisily against the empty hull.

I had just finished the charterer's log for the previous day, and was idly waiting for another satnav pass, when a hard white light bored across the night in front of me from the starboard stern quarter, casting the gear and forecastle into nightmare relief. My heart jumped. I rushed onto the starboard wing. A big U.S. Coast Guard cutter was wallowing in the low sea astern, its rooftop light rotating toward me. It pinned me like a fox.

The radio crackled to life. "Motorvessel *Erika*, this is the U.S. Coast Guard cutter *Cape Henry* off your stern. Do you read me?"

I went inside, still blinded, and groped for the microphone. "*Cape Henry*, this is the *Erika*."

"Is the master on the bridge?"

"I am he."

"What is your destination?"

"Savannah, Georgia."

"What is the name of your captain?"

I spelled my name in alpha-bravo-charlie.

"Stand by, Captain."

The cutter kept station a hundred meters astern, its wheelhouse a black strip of bulletproof glass. The searchlight stayed nailed on my starboard door. The radio popped again. "Captain, we are going to board your ship. Have your crew put a pilot ladder over the starboard side. Bring all your crew on deck."

I thought that over. "*Cape Henry*, this is the master of the *Erika*, a Honduran-flagged freighter in international waters. Are you asking permission to board this vessel?"

The response was immediate. "Captain, we can get a fax copy of permission to board your vessel from the Honduran consul in Washington 24 hours a day. I repeat, we are going to board your vessel."

I kept my voice crisp. "Since you are not asking permission to board I cannot give it. Therefore I will note a forced boarding in the log. Of course your boarding will be unopposed."

Yussuf appeared on the wing of the bridge in a pair of shorts, eyes wide. I released the mike button and told him, "Go lower the pilot ladder on the starboard side. Send the chief into the engine room and get everybody else up on deck."

"Yessir."

"Captain," the radio barked, "reduce your speed to zero-five knots. I repeat, reduce your speed to zero-five knots."

"Aw, fuck," I said. Into the mike, "Roger that, *Cape Henry*. Be advised I will have to go off the tailshaft. It might take a few minutes."

The cutter's engines roared to life. I stuck my head out into the light and saw that it was bow-high, surging toward the stern of the *Erika*. The boarding boat, a hard-bottomed inflatable with a radar arch on the top, was already in the water and plowing toward us. "Captain of the *Erika*," the cutter called, "reduce your speed immediately! You are being boarded now!"

I saw two figures in orange vests making their way toward the cutter's 20 mm. bow gun. I dropped the mike and jumped over to the engine-room telegraph. In my haste I rang for Stop Engine, then had to ring again for Half Ahead.

I could hear the cutter's commander, again ordering me to slow down. I picked up the mike. "*Cape Henry*, I have rung the engine room for Half Ahead. We are on the tailshaft generator, we are on the tailshaft, do you understand?"

By then the cutter was some 30 meters astern, the bow high over our low stern, the gun trained on me through the back windows of the chartroom.

The auxiliary engine came on and the lights flickered. The engine slowed, sending a shudder through the ship. Guardsmen climbed onboard and conquered the deck. I couldn't hear what they were saying in the rising wind, but they made the crew sit on the wet tarp with their hands behind their heads. Two Guardsmen kept their M-16's pointed at them the whole time. I bit my tongue and watched as a party broke off and followed Yussuf up to the wheelhouse.

A burly man in a bullet-proof vest stepped over the coaming. He had an automatic in a nylon holster. "Captain?"

"That is I."

"Lt. Oliver Gannett, United States Coast Guard. Captain, let me see your hands."

I showed them to him.

"Captain, why did you not obey the order to slow down?"

"I told you. . .I had to wait for the engineer to take the ship off the tailshaft generator." I waved. "I can't slow the ship down from up here. I have to use the telegraph. If the chief had slowed down right away, we would have had a blackout. Then you would have fired on me for sure."

His hand still hovered near his pistol. "What are you talking about? What does this generator have to do with slowing down?"

I explained how a tailshaft generator works. He watched me, a hulking black silhouette against the brilliant blue-white light from the open door. Others crowded in behind him, weapons ready. "Why did you refuse permission to board?" he asked.

"I didn't." My voice rose. "I asked if you were asking permission to board. You never did. How could I refuse if I was never asked? After I've filed a protest with the Honduran ambassador, maybe you'll check the tapes. I never refused permission to board."

His face moved into the light. He was a big, smooth-faced farm boy with cheeks rosy from the wind. "Stand by, Captain." He went out on the wing of the bridge. I could hear him muttering into his walkie-talkie. I couldn't hear what they were telling him, but he came back in and said, "Captain, do we have your permission to board this vessel?"

I spread my legs. "No, you do not. Now that you have accomplished a forced boarding, and taken control of my vessel, you may proceed without hindrance. But I will enter this into the log as a hostile act."

He went back on the wing. His underlings and I stared at each other while we waited. The ship shouldered its way through the low sea on autopilot. The cutter's engines whined and growled from the darkness as she struggled to stay slow. The farm boy came back in. "Captain, you have been boarded under the authority of the United States Coast Guard because you have stated your destination as a U.S. port. Your permission is not necessary for boarding and search."

I rolled my eyes. "Oh, for God's sake! You've got my off-duty watch up and my crew crouched on deck like criminals. You've got a cannon trained on my ship and you tell me that my permission is not necessary?" I shrugged. "You have taken command of my vessel away from me, Mr. Gannet. I will make a note of it in the log."

The chief appeared in the door in his boxer underwear and old-man's undershirt, his shower sandals flopping on the steps. A beefy Guardsman with an M-16 appeared behind him.

"This man was in the engine room, Lieutenant."

The chief looked at me apologetically. I stepped forward. "All right, this has gone far enough. I'm holding the Coast Guard responsible for your reckless conduct. I have to have an engineer in the engine room at all times during navigation."

Gannett said to the Guardsman, "Take the chief engineer back down and stay with him. Keep your R/T on."

"Yessir." The man nudged the chief. They went downstairs.

Another young man appeared. "Lieutenant, looks like a manhole in the front has been opened recently. There's fresh scratches on the nuts."

Gannet looked at me. I said, "We did some cleaning in the forepeak. Routine cleaning."

He looked out on the deck. My men were still hunched over like prisoners of war. The wind was blowing hard enough to rattle the cables on the cherry-picker boom and swing the SSB antenna. He turned back. "Captain, get a couple of your men to open that tank."

"Negative. My men work for me, not the U.S. Coast Guard. You want to open that tank? Open it yourself."

His eyes narrowed in the narrow light. "Captain, if you want, we can escort you into Key West and make a thorough inspection there."

I laughed. "Go ahead. We're on time charter. I like Key West, personally. But if you want to open that tank, send your men down to the engine room for a couple of spanners. We opened that manhole about a month ago, and it only took a couple of hours."

He studied me and gave a shake of the head. "That's all right," he said to the Guardsman. "Anything else?"

The boy sneered. "She's plenty dirty, Lieutenant. But we couldn't find anything else."

"All right." He went out on the wing and talked to his masters again, then came in and said, "We're finished, Captain. Have your men remain on deck until the last Coast Guardsman is off the ship."

I didn't answer. He followed the others down the steps. The cutter had dropped back with the searchlight off, the falling moon streaking its white deck and lighting the orange stripe on the hull. The inflatable had pulled away and kept station alongside. Now its outboard engine revved as the driver brought it up to the ladder to take the Guardsmen off.

When the last one was off the ship, I leaned out the window and told the men to go back to bed. I rang for Full Speed Ahead. Yussuf came up shaking his head. "Big assholes, eh, Captain?"

"Yeah, stupid jerks." I told him about the tailshaft incident. "They don't even know what a tailshaft generator is, and they're out here risking our lives with their damned cannon."

He took out a cigarette and snapped a lighter at it angrily.

"Well," I said, after a moment, "*Insh'Allah*, right?"

He grinned. "*Insh'Allah*, Captain."

After the ship was switched back to the tailshaft generator, the chief came up to the bridge, shaking with outrage. "You did not give them permission to board, Captain? This is an act of war against Honduras. *¡Estoy furioso!*"

"Well, Chief," I said, "I don't like it either, but there's nothing we can do about it. In fact, I've seen 'em do worse. At least they didn't tear up the cabins, I hope."

"No sir, the cabins are all right. *Puta* Coast Guard." He went downstairs grumbling.

At 0600 I went back on the bridge, fighting a splitting headache, and took my watch. The ship was almost out of the lee of the Bahamas, and the wide Atlantic was starting to heave against the starboard side. The empty ship pointed its bow to the sky and fell back against the sea with a hollow crash that shook her all the way to the rudderstock. Yussuf was gathering his things to go below, and the lurch sent him against the bulkhead. He steadied himself with an elbow.

"Bad weather coming, Captain. You see the glass?"

I looked back. The barometer was at 98.76. I whistled. "What's the radio say?"

"VHF from Jacksonville says storm in Atlantic, going northwest. We ought to miss the center of the storm, but Jacksonville says Force 7 winds and 20-foot waves."

"Yikes." I looked out over the narrow hull. "She's too long. She can't take ballasting in heavy weather."

Yussuf stood watching me.

"Go on, First. It'll be all right. I'll slow down if I have to."

He went below. The wind was rising to a howl, whistling across the aftermast. It smelled of ocean, clean and empty. I turned the autopilot to put the bow a little straighter into the waves. She took another lurch and bottomed heavily in the trough.

We continued on until 1145 hours, when I had to call for 3/4 Ahead. Yussuf came up early with a cup of coffee. "She's pounding, Captain," he said glumly.

"No shit. Watch this." I took him forward to the windows. "Watch the bow on the next high wave."

I waited. A big roller appeared in the distance. "Watch the bow against the top of the crane boom. Watch this!"

The wave heaved at the bow, lifting it bodily toward the slate-colored sky. "Jesus," Yussuf breathed, "you mean the way the ship is bending?"

"Yeah. You can see it easily against the boom."

"Is she breaking up, Captain?"

I laughed. "I hope not. But she sure is bending in the middle. Whoever put that 10 meters in her took the heart out of this old girl." Then I called for Half Ahead. At this point we had to go off the tailshaft, but when the engine slowed, the ship's motion eased.

"First," I said, "go down and tell the chief to fill No. 1 and No. 2. We're empty now, so a little water in the bilges won't hurt anything. And sound No. 3 both sides to make sure they're full."

Just as I spoke a wave hit the bow and swung it to port. Before the autopilot could bring it back, another breaker, just as high and shot with foam, smashed into the starboard side and rolled the ship violently to port. Yussuf went skidding across the floor. I was launched out of the stool, but I managed to grab the railing under the front windows and hang on.

The ship kept going, all the way to 30° to port, before rolling 25° back to starboard. I could hear things smashing around in the saloon below. Someone on the main deck yelled.

"Jesus," Yussuf said, "can we keep going, Captain?"

"We've got to, First. Dickie can't even pay our salaries. . .you think he could afford to pay for an extra port call?"

"That's better than the ship sinking."

I thought about a sarcastic reply, but it wasn't the time for it. "Go make sure everything is secure, First," I said. "If we've got to heave-to, we will."

The combers kept coming. Spray from every third wave flew across the deck in a white cloud. I had to raise the windows to keep the spray out of the wheel-house. The bow kept working, up and down, up and down, as the old ship took its punishment and struggled steadily on under Half Ahead. In late afternoon I went down on deck and studied the crack, but Jerzy's repair was still holding.

With the help of a two-knot current flowing north, we passed Jacksonville just after dark. We could see cars on the beach road, their lights stabbing out over the water. The wind was no higher, but we were getting bounced by rogue waves that churned out of the blackness and hammered the starboard bow. We were making about five knots over the ground, and still the ship kept soaring up the faces of the waves and dropping heavily in the troughs.

At midnight, after Yussuf came on the bridge, I took a flashlight down to the port side of the deck and trained it on the repair. In the middle of the rust-red primer that had been slopped onto the weld was a black line. I looked closer, bending over to get my face out of the wind and spray.

The crack was back.

As I watched, the bow rose on the face of the next wave, and the crack disappeared. The wave passed under the middle of the vessel, and the crack opened again, an eighth of an inch wide.

I stood up and shined the light across the deck. The weld had broken along the length of the original break, stretching from the ribband to the hatch coaming. It yawned again, a wicked little crack that could snip off a piece of flesh if you pressed your finger to it.

The coaming was still holding. I turned the light over the side, and the weld on the shell plating was still holding. I went up and told Yussuf.

"Is she going to break up, Captain?"

"I hope not," I said. "She can't take much more of this, though. If we can reach Savannah I'll have Lionel weld a doubler on the crack. That's what we should have done as soon as we left Mobile."

The ship took a wicked roll to port again, but we were already holding on.

"Watch this," I said. "I'm going to time the next big roll."

I shined my light on the clinometer. Five minutes later a big beast came tearing out of the darkness and threw the ship over on her side. I clicked the start button on my watch when the ship reached 33° of port heel, and the stop button when she reached 30° on the other side.

"Three and a quarter seconds," I said, braced against the binnacle. "Sixty degrees of roll in three seconds. Jesus H. Christ. No wonder the old bitch is breaking up."

"What are we going to do, Captain?"

I went to the chart table. "Let's turn for Savannah now. That'll put the waves on the beam. She'll roll worse, but she won't pound as hard. We'll cut it close to the seabuoy. We ought to be there by dawn."

I turned the autopilot, and the rolling went wild. She heaved to port, held there with everything clanging and banging, and started back, the roll gaining speed as the ship reached the vertical. She whipped over to starboard, caught an off-period wave, and shuddered to an even keel for a second. The next big crest-heavy wave thundered against the flat of the side and shot straight up into the air.

Yussuf went down to an uneasy rest. I monitored the ship's position on the satnav as I tried to cut the corner to Savannah. It turned out that the empty ship was making far worse slippage than I had expected, and I had to point her bow back into the wind. We endured another two hours of pounding before I could turn the ship to the northwest again.

When Yussuf relieved me at midnight we were still rolling. He had a hollow-eyed look.

"You okay, Yussuf?"

He gave me a tired grin. "Two nights no sleep. But I'm okay. No problem, Cap'n. Such is the life of the sea."

"Such it is," I agreed, and got up from the stool. "Well, we'll make it. Wake me up when we get to the seabuoy. It should be about 0500. And call the pilot station when you get 50 miles out."

I went down to my bunk and bundled up in blankets with the portholes closed, but the wild rolling of the ship kept me from sleeping, thanks in part to the Frisian shipwrights who had built the master's bunk athwartships.

We picked up the pilot at dawn, the little launch bouncing in the swells as the driver tried to match the gyrations of the ship. The pilot stood on the catwalk with his bag over his shoulder, hanging on the railing with an intent look. At the exact moment the boat rolled toward the ship and its bow rose on a wave, he stepped across to the ladder as calmly as a widow negotiating her front steps. He jumped up on deck and came aft.

"Rough today," he said as he came in. Yussuf took the ship off autopilot and stepped behind the wheel. The pilot steered him toward the channel, cutting off the seabuoy by half the distance to the second buoy. I excused myself and went down to Lionel's cabin, where I found him brushing his teeth.

"Hey, man," I said, "We've got a crack in the deck. Can you weld while we're going upriver?"

He looked at me with his mouth full of toothbrush. He took it out. "Sure. Where is dis crack?"

I took him on deck and showed him. "Get the AB's to help you," I said, and went back to the bridge.

We passed a low marshy coastline and entered a wide, slow river. It wound past cow pastures and sere brown fields until the city appeared, glittering like Oz in the distance. We slowly approached it. Ricardo chipped the port deck while Lionel uncoiled his welding leads. The pilot looked down at the work a couple of times, but if he saw anything remarkable in welded repairs being effected on the way upriver, he didn't mention it.

The welding was finished by the time we reached town. We steamed at Half Ahead between downtown warehouses and the backs of old dry-goods stores. There was a preservation waterfront with some "No Docking" signs and hardy old pensioners bundled up on benches. We puttered upriver under an interstate bridge and pulled over to the south bank to dock. There was a railhead there, with a line of freight cars waiting for us. Behind the railhead was a cluster of concrete silos.

The dock was a rusty steel affair made of latticed pipe. We docked without incident and I went down to look at the repair of the crack. "Pretty ugly," I said to Yussuf. "Tell the AB's to cover it up with some wood or something. Better to look sloppy than have people see this thing."

The agent was standing on the dock with Customs, INS, and USDA. They piled onboard as soon as the gangway was lashed in place.

When the agent came onboard I asked him, "Did the charterer make arrangements for plywood to be put on the floors?"

"No, Captain. He just told me to have some plastic delivered to the ship. It's coming now."

A truck pulled up and two men started discharging rolls of thin plastic sheeting.

"Fat lot of good that's going to do," I said. "This is going to cost the charterer a wasted week."

A Customs man brought a black Labrador up the gangway. The dog jumped down to the deck and starting sniffing for drugs around my pants cuffs. Not finding any, he dragged his master aft toward the accommodations.

I led the gang of officials to the saloon and we went through the formalities of clearing in. As soon as the last one left the ship I asked the agent, "Did the owner send the crew wages?"

He nodded and took a manila envelope out of his briefcase. "I've got it right here." He slid a pre-typed receipt across to me. It was made out for $5000.

"There's a mistake," I said. "Crew wages are $17,000. This is just enough for spares and provisions."

He looked pained. "Mr. Vance called me this morning. He said to tell you that he is sorry that this is all he can wire. He said try to give as much as you can to the crew."

I shook my head. "There won't be much left. We can't go to sea without spares and provisions."

He shrugged, closed his briefcase, and left. A tall character with a Zapata mustache came in. "Captain? Rick Swather, yard foreman. We've got 1650 tons for you today. Ready to load?"

I shook my head. "We can take only 1500 tons. Maybe a little more when we look at the marks."

He frowned. "We're supposed to ship 1600 tons, plus or minus 5%. Fifteen hundred tons is more than 5% under."

"Talk to the load line. That's how much cargo I can take, and not a ton more."

"Okay, Captain, I'll call the charterer. When will you be ready to load?"

"We're ready now. Which hatch do you want opened?"

"Open No. 1 first."

"Okay. But you'll have to switch to No. 2 after about 150 tons."

He nodded. "Roger that, Captain. We load this stuff all the time. We know it's heavy."

I went on deck and told Yussuf, "Make sure they keep the chute moving. You know this old hull is weak. They put too much weight in one place and she'll fold up like a pocketknife."

"Roger, Captain."

"We're probably going to finish tonight, so I have to get everything we need before the stores close. You got a requirements list?"

"I'll write it up now."

I got a provisions list from Victor and an engine-room list from the chief, then went into the yard office and called a rental car agency. All they had was a Lincoln Town Car, so I ordered it. A young man drove it down to the dock to pick me up.

I took Victor with me, and after the paperwork on the car was done we went to the nearest discount grocery store. We filled four buggies hurriedly, throwing in piles of beef, chicken, sausage, bacon, and cheese. I raided the gallon-size canned-vegetable shelves and the no-name generic racks. Fifteen hundred dollars later, the ship was provisioned for another month.

After dropping Victor and the groceries off, I put the propane cooking-gas cylinder in the trunk, knowing how illegal and dangerous that was, and headed off to get it filled. The first place refused, but the second place, the Yabba-Dabba-Doo Kampground on the edge of town, wasn't so squeamish. I got it filled and back onboard. The stevedores had finished No. 1 for the moment, and were bringing up another train car while the operator maneuvered the chute aft. I watched as he opened the chute's solenoid valve and the white granular cargo started flowing into the hold again. The operator moved the chute expertly, keeping the pile evenly spread across the floor.

I left again, this time on a hunt for AW 68 hydraulic oil, fan belts, DC light bulbs, and European electrical fuses. The oil and fan belts were no problem, but the others were a challenge.

By the time I had all the deck and engine-room requirements onboard, except for a few exotic items I just couldn't find, it was almost dark. About half the cargo was loaded, but it was so dense the hold was only a quarter full. After a quick supper I went on deck to supervise.

Two fuel trucks arrived with 20 tons each, but because I had been overreporting consumption since the beginning of the charter, we had 30 extra tons onboard and could only take 20 tons. I had the chief tell the drivers that he had a problem in the valve manifold, so we could only fill one tank. The second truck left.

We reached our marks at 2200 hours. The shipper's draft surveyor was onboard, and we were standing together amidships while I watched the loadline with a flashlight. When the Tropical Fresh loadline touched the surface of the water, I signaled the chute operator to shut it off. He released the button and the solid white column of fertilizer dwindled to a trickle.

The yard foreman came bustling down the gangway. By now the deck of the ship was far below the dock. "We're only halfway through this tankcar," he protested. "We can load the rest of this car, can't we, Captain?"

I shook my head. "Nope. We're at our marks now."

"Nobody's going to see your marks. We load ships below their marks all the time."

"Not this ship." He started to say something else, but I broke in, "How many tons already?"

He consulted a notebook. "Fifteen-oh-seven."

"So this is a 1600-ton ship. Subtract 30 tons for the crane and 50 tons for fuel, then subtract 20 tons of constant, and that's about right."

He snapped his notebook shut. "Maybe you'd better talk to the charterer."

I glared at him. "There's nothing the charterer can say that can make me overload this ship."

The surveyor coughed discreetly. The foreman looked up at the train car, then at the surveyor, then back at me. "Shit, this means we've got to send 20 tons back to the silo. This'll fuck up our paperwork."

"If I overloaded this ship," I said, "it could be proven just by the Bill of Lading and manifest. If she went down, it'd fuck up my personal paperwork for the rest of my life. I ain't gonna do it."

The foreman stamped up the gangway without replying. The surveyor, a rotund young man with sandy hair, leaned over and said quietly, "I don't blame you, Captain. I see them try that all the time. You wouldn't believe how many captains let themselves get buffaloed into overloading."

"Yeah," I said. "I was born at night, but it wasn't last night."

He started taking his draft soundings. I knew what was coming and went up to the saloon to wait. After a few minutes he came in and said, "Captain, something's not right here. I've gotten your bunker figures from the chief engineer, and I'm showing the ship taking 50 more tons of cargo than the yard figures."

I kept a blank face. "I have no idea why. I don't know how they're keeping tally onshore, but draft marks don't lie."

He didn't quite agree with that, but he saw my point. "I went with the chief to sound the bunker tanks. Are all the sounding pipes on deck?"

I knew there were two more sounding pipes in the engine room, but I nodded. "As far as I know."

He looked at his figures. "I can't be off 50 tons," he muttered to himself. "Maybe I should go retake the soundings."

"Don't forget the cherry-picker and the bracing for it," I said. "That's 30 tons all by itself." We had done no bracing for the cherry-picker, but with the midships high tank under it, he couldn't know that.

He nodded doubtfully. "Could be."

"And it's an old ship. Maybe it has a bigger constant...mud in the tanks. And maybe the figures weren't done right when the ship was lengthened."

"Lengthened?"

"Yeah, she was lengthened 10 meters in 1972. She got a new stability book after that, but you know how they bullshit things on a modification. She might have more steel in her than they thought."

He nodded again. "Well, all I can do is note the discrepancy."

He went out and I went on deck to help the crew close hatches. It was cold, with a steady wind, and it felt good to work hard. We had just finished chocking down the tarps when the pilot's car drove up and the pilot got out. He was a big, square-jawed man with a shock of white hair and eyebrows like hawk wings. He came onboard, laughed when he saw the captain working on deck, and waited until I was finished to walk up to the bridge with me. Yussuf and Ricardo went forward. Victor was standing by with Manuel aft.

It was almost midnight. I leaned on the wing of the bridge for a moment. My body felt like it was rocking in a heavy sea. I opened my eyes, and the rocking stopped. The pilot was adjusting his walkie-talkie.

I trudged into the wheelhouse and spun the wheel from lock to lock, testing the steering. Yussuf had turned the radar on. I tuned the range to 1/4 mile. The VHF squealed when I turned the squelch up.

The pilot's radio squawked on channel 13. Another pilot was calling from a ship coming upriver, approaching the interstate bridge. The pilot said to me, "Ready, Captain? Let's cast off."

I went to the wing of the bridge. "Single up?"

He shook his head. "Cast off all lines. We'll turn ahead of the other ship and pass 'em on the two."

I looked back toward the interstate bridge. The lights of downtown Savannah twinkled above it. "Very well," I said, and signaled to Yussuf to cast off all lines. He pointed at the bow spring line and made a question, but I shook my head and made the cast-off sign again.

"You don't have walkie-talkies onboard?" the pilot asked.

I shook my head. This was before they were required by SOLAS. He shrugged. As soon as the winches started grumbling, he said, "Dead Slow Ahead, starboard 30."

I rang for Dead Slow Ahead and spun the wheel. The engine burped and coughed and started thumping. I looked back through the chartroom windows. Now I could see the bow of a big bulkcarrier, at least 10,000 tons, nosing into the clear span under the bridge. It was coming up the narrow channel at a steady clip.

"Half Speed Ahead," the pilot said quickly. "Hard-a-Starboard."

I rang for Three-Quarter Ahead and called, "Hard-a-Starboard." The ship shuddered as the chief gave her the throttle. I ran out to the port wing. The stern was closing with the dock. I ran back to the wheel.

"We're going to hit the dock," I said. "I gotta midships the wheel."

"Hold 30 starboard," he barked. "Full Speed Ahead!"

I looked back at the bulker. Now she was half-way through the bridge and turning to port to make the bend in the channel. I put out my hand, hesitated, and rang for Hard Astern. The pilot had rushed to the starboard wing, but when he felt the engine stop he spun around.

"What the hell?"

"We won't make it," I yelled. "We've got to let her go by." I spun the wheel back to midships. The engine started in reverse. The bow slowly swung to starboard as the big ship drew abreast, but we were well clear of her. The pilot on the bulker was talking to our pilot, but I couldn't hear what they were saying. I ran to the port wing, gauged our speed, and called for Stop Engine. The engine rolled to a stop. The pilot was still on the starboard wing, but when the other ship was past he turned to me.

"You almost got your ship broken, Captain. Next time you'd better listen to the pilot."

I stepped forward. "You almost caused a collision, Pilot. If we had tried to turn in front of that ship it would have cut us in two."

He came inside. "Maybe I'd better call the Coast Guard, have them check your license."

Yussuf was yelling from the deck. "What's wrong, Captain? Throw the heaving line? Are we docking again?"

I looked at the pilot. "Maybe we'd better check licenses all the way around. I'm ready to tell my side of the story. Let's get that bulker captain in on it, too."

He hesitated, then looked away toward the window. "Hell, this damn ship ain't got enough power to get out of her own way. Ship shouldn't go to sea with no more power'n this thing's got."

I stifled a bitter grin and yelled to Yussuf, "Stand by, First. We're turning downstream. Just stand by there."

I rang for Dead Slow Ahead without orders from the pilot, and as the ship gained speed he recovered his composure. He gave me steering directions without further comment until we had gotten clear of the city, then Yussuf came up on the bridge and took the helm. Yussuf didn't seem to realize how close a call we'd had. He and the pilot started chatting about Paris—they'd both lived there— while I sat numb and exhausted on the port-side stool.

At 0315 we dropped the pilot off inside the seabuoy and turned southward. The sea and wind were still running high, but now the old ship had a full load in her belly, and she took the waves on her port stern with a heavy, comfortable wallow. Solid water washed harmlessly across her decks and sluiced off through the starboard scuppers. Yussuf set the course and leaned back against the bulkhead, rubbing his eyes.

"You okay, First?" I said. "Can you take the rest of the watch?"

He shook his head. "I guess so, Captain. Too long without sleep."

"Me too. Well, if you can't stay awake, come get me. After an hour I'll be all right." I stumbled downstairs and threw myself into my bunk without taking my clothes off. I fell into a dreamless sleep that ended when Victor woke me at 0530. With sand under my eyelids and a great weight pulling me earthward, I gulped down a cup of coffee and took another one up to the bridge.

By mid-morning the wind had backed to the north and eased. We rolled along against the Gulf Stream, making only eight knots. When Yussuf relieved me at noon I fell into bed without eating and slept straight through to 1800, even after Victor tried to wake me up twice.

After I had finished a plate of stewed chicken and rice and washed it down with a Coke, I was lounging on the port wing and watching the seagulls diving behind the ship when I saw, coming out of the looming darkness to the east, a huge submarine's conning tower, slicing through the water like the dorsal fin of a great robot shark.

At first I thought that the sub would pass behind us, but when it got closer I saw that it was going at flank speed, pushing a heavy sheet of water up over its bullet-nose as it stormed westward. I got out the binocs and studied the bridge, but there seemed to be no one on it. I went to the radar and worked out the CPA, and saw in a second that we were on a collision course. Since the sub was the give-way vessel, I was about to pick up the microphone when the VHF barked, "Captain of the gray-hulled freighter off Fernandina Beach, this is the USS *Moray*, a United States Navy submarine." Without waiting for acknowledgment, the voice continued, "Alter your course to the east immediately to pass behind my stern!"

I was dumbstruck. "USS *Moray*, this is the MV *Erika*. Sir, you are the give-way vessel. I suggest you alter your course to the south."

The voice came back, "MV *Erika*, alter your course to port at once. Sir, you are risking collision with a United States submarine."

I stepped to the autopilot console and spun the dial. The ship heeled suddenly as the hydraulic pumps groaned and the rudder swung. The chief came running up to see what was going on. He stared as the submarine shot past us at 20 knots, about half-a-mile away.

I got in the last word. "USS *Moray*, the *Erika* has changed course to 090. Sir, you have risked collision with a Honduran freighter."

The sub didn't bother to answer. I stepped to the starboard wing and shot them the middle finger for a long time, without seeing if anyone was watching. Then I turned the bow to the south again.

Six days after we left Savannah we arrived off the island of Hispanola. The wind had died as we rounded the eastern tip, and we steamed the last few hours over an oily, heaving sea that winked and flashed in the midday sun.

We found Rio Haina easily, by the wreck of a 3000-ton freighter lying on its side just off the beach. The mouth of the river was guarded by a long, manmade breakwater with lights on latticed towers to mark the entrance. A small outboard-powered pilot boat, its wooden sides splintered by ships' hulls, came streaking over the calm water to discharge the pilot. He was an old man who took his time coming up the ship's side.

We steamed at Dead Slow Ahead through the breakwater, close enough to the towers on each side to throw rocks at them, and into the river. The right bank held a giant shipyard with several vessels up on the ways, the bare ground covered with scurrying workers. There was a container port to the left. We kept going upriver for about a kilometer, then the pilot called over two grimy, soot-stained tugs to nose us up against an empty stretch of ground. There was no quay, just a low, bare wall of rock above the water. Two big crawler cranes were in position and trucks were waiting.

After we were All-Fast the pilot left and the officials came onboard, a motley collection of squat brown men in sweat-stained guayaberra shirts and worn uniforms. They left with their bottles of Scotch and cartons of cigarettes. The agent, a middle-aged man named Gustavo with a massive neck that narrowed down to a tiny flattop above his lumpy skull, pressed me to open the hatches immediately. I sent Yussuf, Lionel, and the AB's down to start humping boards, then asked him, "Did the owner send the crew wages?"

"Not that I know of, Captain. Of course I will send a fax right away to ask. But I am sure my bank has not received anything since the *pro forma* wire."

I nodded. "That's okay. I guess he didn't send it."

I gave the crew the rest of the day off, but since they had no money none went ashore. Between 1300 and 1700 the stevedores discharged 317 tons, according to the tally. At 1700 I called the crew together and told them, in English and Spanish, that the crew wages hadn't come, but that I was going to sell some fuel, and I would have some money for them later that night. I also told them that they were to tell everybody on shore, from the whores to the stevedores to the port officials, that the vessel's next port was Cartagena. I was reasonably sure no one would stow away for Colombia.

The crew disbanded, angry and dispirited. I put on street clothes and went through the sally port to the street outside. Squatters had built a line of rude stalls on the sidewalk, selling cigarettes and candy to the seamen and serving simple lunches to the stevedores. Now the lunch stalls were closed, their handmade chairs chained together and boards put up over the galley areas. I had to wait a couple of minutes for a Honda 50 motorcycle to putter up. The driver unloaded a seaman and I jumped on.

The boy drove me downtown, bouncing over railroad tracks and through mudholes. I managed to hold on all the way to the telephone office. A blast of airconditioning hit me when I walked in. The girl directed me to a phone labeled "U.S.," where I called Dickie collect. He was home for once, but he hadn't sent the crew wages.

"We may not be able to leave port," I warned him. "The crew is going to be furious when I tell them they aren't going to get paid here."

"Hell," Dickie said, "they wouldn't be getting paid any sooner if they were on a Haitian freighter. Tell 'em they're going to get paid as soon as I get the next charter hire."

"That's Thursday."

He made a lame little sound. "As soon as they get to the States, then."

"That's not soon enough. Dickie, these men have families. And they aren't on a Haitian ship, they're on my ship. I don't like having to tell them the money's not coming."

"Well, Captain," he said heavily, "I don't know what to tell you. I've been having to pay every cent I make back to the guy who gave me the money to get the ship out of Mobile. There just isn't any left." He laughed weakly. "At least the crew don't have to worry about somebody breaking their kneecaps."

"No," I said seriously, "all they have to worry about is their children going without food. You're a family man, think about it. This is what I'm going to do, with your permission. . .I have 30 extra tons of fuel onboard. We burn about 1.7 tons a day, and I routinely report 2.5 to 2.7 to the charterer. I'm going to sell some of that fuel here and give the crew advances. Is that okay?"

"Can you pay the crew off?" he asked hopefully.

"Are you kidding? We're almost $20,000 behind in crew wages. I might get only $4000, but it'll hold them until the next port. But God help you if we go into a U.S. port and they don't get paid. They'll be at ITF in five minutes."

"What is this ITF everybody's so freaked-out about?"

"International Transport Workers' Federation. They'll advance the crew the money to seize the ship for back wages. Of course ITF takes a big chunk when the crew gets paid, but at least the crew gets something."

"I'm going to pay them," he said, getting angry. "Jesus Christ, they're only two months behind. Hell, they live on 10 dollars a month. Sell the damned fuel, then, and give them the money."

"Roger that," I said stiffly. I hung up and went outside into a blast of heat. A motorbike taxi driver at the *mercado* knew where I could sell diesel, and took me to a large tire-repair shop on the edge of town, out by the highway. He introduced me to a huge, scowling black man with the index finger of his right hand missing, named Momo.

The man spoke only Spanish. I told him that I had diesel for sale off a ship, but that we would have to sneak the truck into the port. He offered me pesos equivalent to $1.00 a gallon. He said his truck could carry 20 tons. I countered at $1.40 a gallon. We finally agreed to 6000 gallons at $1.25 a gallon.

I waited until well into siesta time to go to the port office, where one man sat at a desk typing with two fingers. I told him I had hired a tank truck to take away oily slops. He wearily took out a pad, inserted carbons, and printed permission for the truck to enter.

I took a *moto* to the tire shop and rode back in the tanker with Momo and his driver. The guard took a cursory look at my *permiso* and waved the truck through.

The chief and the driver laid out the truck's hoses and started trying to hook them up to the ship's transfer system. After a few minutes they got something rigged together.

"Just a minute," I said, coming up on Momo on the dock. "Do you have the money? That's 103,000 pesos. I want to see the money before we start pumping."

Momo frowned at me. "The money is at the station. Don't worry, I send somebody with the money as soon as I get back. No telephone here."

I shook my head in disgust. "You might as well get your truck out of here, then. No fuel's leaving this ship until I see the *puta* money."

We started wrangling about it. The chief went back to the engine room. Momo left the truck at the dock and got on a motorbike taxi, but he came back half-an-hour later saying that the money had been taken to the bank, and he wouldn't be able to get it until the next morning.

"Well," I said, "that's it, then. Tell your driver to get the truck out of here."

"Listen, *Capitán*," Momo said, "let us do this. We will drive around with the fuel, you and I together, and sell it to the gas stations. That is what I was going to do anyway. That way you can be back before dawn with all the money."

"Yeah, if I make it back at all."

"Oh, no," he said, "*no te preocupues, Capitán*. You will be with me."

I didn't say the obvious. "Okay, Tiny, we'll do that. But only 3000 gallons."

He protested again, but gave in easily enough. The ship's transfer system took until midnight to pump 3000 gallons. I woke Yussuf to tell him what I was going to do.

"What?" he said, coming out of his cabin. "You're going to drive around Santo Domingo with that big black man? That's crazy, Captain. He won't pay you. He'll just kill you."

"There's that chance," I agreed. "I'm taking a knife and a can of mace, if they'll do any good. Anyway, if I'm not back by eight or nine in the morning, call the agent and tell him what happened. Get him to call the American embassy."

"Don't do it, Captain. At least let me come with you."

I shook my head. "You've got to stay with the ship. Don't worry, I'll be careful."

"How much money are you getting?"

"About four grand. If I make it back, I'll give it to the crew as advances, but don't say anything yet. Let's see what happens.

He eyed me doubtfully and shook my hand. "Be careful, Captain. I do not like the look of that man."

I didn't either, but it was too late for that. I went down and got up in the truck, sitting on the outside, and we rumbled off toward the port entrance. A new set of guards was on duty, but they let the truck out without question. The driver drove up the long hill toward the highway in first gear. As we passed the Manila Sunrise, a bar at the top of the hill, I saw Ricardo sitting in front with one of the Filipina whores, drinking a Presidente. We waved to each other.

We went through a toll booth and gathered speed for the run to Santo Domingo. The road was almost empty of car traffic, but the shoulders were lined with people walking in the dark, carrying buckets and bundles. They scrambled into the ditch as the driver barreled toward them.

We came to the outskirts of town. I hugged the door and clutched my knife with my hand inside the pack, but nothing suspicious happened. The city was blacked out, the buildings lit by darting headlights as cars negotiated the dusty streets. We came to a closed service station, looming out of the darkness. A kerosene lantern flickered yellow in the window.

A guard came out of the dark into the truck's headlights, carrying a pistol-grip shotgun. He talked to Momo, then a door opened and a well-dressed man with a flashlight came out. He shook our hands and counted out 35,000 pesos on the pavement in front of the headlights, which Momo handed to me. We hooked up the hoses and everybody watched the gauge as the truck pumped to the underground tanks. He had paid for 700 gallons, and that was what he got. We shook hands again, loaded the hoses into their tubes, and took off for the next station.

After six stations in four hours, we had sold all the diesel. I had 120,000 pesos, which was actually a little more than we had agreed on, but Momo was feeling generous. It looked like he had made 40,000 pesos himself for the night's work, or about $1300. I had $3900 to distribute to the crew. By then Momo and the driver and I were chatting comfortably.

The truck stopped at the tire shop at dawn, and Momo had a boy in a Ford Escort drive me back to the ship. I got onboard, my pack bulging with pesos, as the sun was coming up over the gantries of the shipyard across the river.

After breakfast I distributed the money to the crew in proportion to the money owed. I gave Lionel and Ian $200 advances and kept $500 for ship's expenses. The clam-buckets started up on schedule, at 0800, and the day's work started. I left Yussuf in charge, took a shower, and collapsed into bed.

When I woke at noon and went downstairs, a glum Yussuf told me that thieves had taken the outboard motor during the night. "Impossible!" I said. "I had it chained to the boat. Did they steal the boat too?"

"No, Captain. But they cut the boat all up. Come see."

We went up on the boat deck. The rescue boat was draped over its cradle. I had run a cable through the drain hole in the wooden transom and around the motor, with a lock on it, but the thieves had used a sharp knife to cut the transom off the boat, and had taken it and the outboard motor, leaving the ruined inflatable behind.

I cursed long and loud, but there was no clue. Ricardo had been on watch on deck from midnight to six, but he'd heard nothing. I believed him when he swore he'd been awake all watch. I surveyed the dock lines in a foul mood, then went to the chief and got two dozen small fishhooks. I tied them onto the hawsers, just out of reach from the ship, with monofilament.

Victor came aft to watch. "For the *ladron*es, Captain?"

I nodded grimly. "For the *ladron*es."

He laughed sadly. "That will be a bad surprise. Maybe ship get in trouble."

At lunch I warned the crew about the fishhooks. Yussuf shook his head. "*Ladron*es are very bad, Captain, but you don't want to go to jail in Dom Rep. I think jail would be very bad here."

I pushed the plate away. "I'm not a thief. Why should I go to jail?" I gave him a wolfish grin. "Those are emergency rat-guards. Thieves stole our rat-guards, so that's what they're there for."

The chief laughed loudly. "That's what they are, Captain. Ratguards. For human rats." He speared a chunk of stewmeat. "I think the captain is right. The *ladron*es deserve the fishhooks."

We discharged 400 tons with one crane that day. The other was broken when they tried to start it in the morning, and although men crawled over it throughout the day, they never got it going.

About 1800 Yussuf convinced me to go up the hill with him for a beer. We left Manuel and Ricardo on watch and walked through the gate together. Girls had gathered on the street, and as we passed they called and clutched at us, but we shook them off and kept going.

We went up the hill to the Manila Sunrise and ordered Presidentes from Hanio, the fat Filipino owner. He came to our table and sat down. He had been a bosun on banana ships for many years, had saved his money, and had bought the building we were in. He had been inspired to bring in Filipinas, who are famous among seamen. An amateur baritone of some talent and questionable musical tastes, Hanio presided behind the bar and sang for his customers while he looked through the wide front doors down to the port below.

Most of the girls were outside, on watch in folding chairs. Since we were with the boss they left us alone. After a while some Filipino seamen came in. They were from a ship that had just arrived in Santo Domingo. They'd heard about the place, and they were in a party mood. A couple of hours later no one could remember who'd ordered how many beers, and Hanio didn't seem to care. The Presidentes just appeared, and we drank them.

The next morning I woke with a fierce headache and a dry, stinking mouth. I drank a quart of water, took a quick, cold shower, and went on a circuit of the deck, but my fishhooks were gone. I knew that Yussuf had cut them off—no one else would dare—but he denied it until much later. I never replaced them, but starting the next night we stood two-man watches, one in the wheelhouse and one on the boat deck.

Yussuf came up to the saloon at 1400 hours the next day to tell me that the stevedores were quitting. "Are they on strike?" I asked.

"No sir. The foreman says they're finished. But there's still a lot of fertilizer in the hold."

"Well, that's exactly what I expected." I went down on deck with him. Through the open hatches I could see white drifts between the frames and in the corners of the hold. The stevedores were already ashore, but I caught the foreman as he was going down the gangway. "Who's going to clean up the rest of the fertilizer?" I demanded.

He shrugged. "That's not my problem. We have finished discharging the ship."

I rushed ashore and called the agent's office, but it was closed for siesta. I called Dickie in Miami. "I told you this was going to happen," I said. "And that damned plastic they put down in Savannah got all chewed up by the front-end loaders here, so there's fertilizer under the floorboards. All the floorboards will have to come up to get it out. Better call Garot."

A lighter snapped. He blew smoke into the mouthpiece. "This is a fucking disaster."

"What do you care? We stay on charter while we clean it up."

"No, I told Jack I'd pay for clean-up."

"What? Why'd you do that? I told you when you gave me sailing instructions that clean-up was going to be a bitch unless we put down plywood."

He coughed. "That was the day the charter-hire was due. Jack said if I didn't agree to clean-up, he was going to drop the charter. He said that if you and the crew were careful enough, there wouldn't be any problem."

"Let me see. Your own captain tells you clean-up's a problem, the charterer tells you clean-up's no problem, and you believe the charterer?"

"All right, Captain," he snapped. "Just use the crew and clean the fertilizer out of the hold. I'll wire $1000 to the agent for trucking and other shit. It better not come to more than that, 'cause I ain't got it."

"We can't do it," I said. "We're already exhausted. There's at least 10 tons of fertilizer in the hold. It'll take a week with shore labor."

"A week! No way. Jack says you're fixed for a load of cement out of Puerto Cortes for Miragoane. You have to be in Cortes by the 11th."

I checked the date on my watch. "It's the 5th now. You'd better push the laycan back until the 15th or 16th. And don't forget that the agent's going to be looking for more dockage and agency fees."

Another long drag on the cigarette. It seemed to help him think. "Then just clean out the hold and leave the fertilizer under the floorboards. We'll clean it out later."

"That stuff'll burn through the tank-tops, Dickie. You can't leave it down there."

"Just clean the hold, Captain. I'll wire the extra money for shore labor."

"Yessir," I said stiffly, and hung up. I called Gustavo and ordered a dozen men for 0800 hours. I gave the crew the rest of the afternoon off. We went up to the Manila Sunrise, but I returned to the ship about 2000 hours, leaving Yussuf and the AB's romancing the Filipinas. Things were looking promising for them when I left.

The next morning the agent's boy showed up with a dozen gaunt men in rags. The agent had said they would cost $7.00 U.S. each a day, but I knew he wasn't paying them over $4.00. I turned the deck crew out with shovels and improvised push-boards, and we started hauling the left-over fertilizer out of the hold in 55-gallon drums.

After three days of back-breaking shoveling, we were finished. I was just about to go downtown to call Gustavo when Yussuf came running up the companion-way. "Captain, Captain, there are people in the forepeak tank!"

I jumped up. "Fucking stowaways! How'd you find them?"

"We were cleaning up forward, and I heard noises coming from the forepeak tank. It sounded like somebody moaning."

I got the mace from the drawer. "Come on, let's go."

I got Ricardo and Manuel from the afterdeck, where they were taking their afternoon break, and the four of us went forward. I opened the forecastle door carefully and turned on the lights, but the compartment was deserted.

The manhole to the forepeak tank was covered with a folded-up tarp. We pulled it out of the way. The nuts had been taken off the cover. I put a finger to my lips and the four of us backed out on deck.

"Stowaways," I said. "Don't do anything. If they try to get away, let 'em go. I'm going for the police."

I ran to the port office and told one of the officials that we had stowaways onboard. He gave me a sour look and went down the hall to the port security office. Several men from that office, led by a young officer with close-cropped red hair, came back to the ship with me. The redhead carried a three-foot length of twisted electrical cable with a wooden handle.

We filed on deck and went forward. Two soldiers pushed the manhole cover aside, and the redhead shouted in Spanish for the stowaways to come out. After a long time, a dirty man with dreadlocks stood up in the manhole. He tried to push himself up, failed, and was dragged out by the shoulders. The soldiers took him on deck and tied his hands behind him.

Another came up, a small muscular man with a dusty bald head. He was taken outside and his hands tied. After a long time a third man put his head up into the opening, gasped a few times, and fell back. A soldier had to get down in the tank to push him high enough for the others to grab him.

Finally Yussuf and I went into the tank with flashlights and found three more. Two were conscious but unable to lift their heads, and the third was unconscious.

The rest of the deck crew joined us in the tank, and we dragged them to the manhole for the soldiers to lift out. Victor brought them water, and the two conscious ones were able to take their feet.

The unconscious man licked his lips when water was poured on his face, but he didn't wake up. One of the men told a soldier that they had come onboard on the 7th, so they had been onboard three days. They had already run out of water—there were two empty gallon jugs in the tank—and all they had brought to eat was a small bag of rotting mangoes.

The soldiers led them aft and down the gangway. By then the chief and Ian had heard about the stowaways and had come on deck. The redhead had the stowaways stretched out on the dock with their bound hands behind their backs, facedown. He started whipping them with the electric cord.

Yussuf averted his eyes. "This is horrible, Captain.

I pressed my lips together. "Yeah, but they're lucky we didn't take them to Cortes. They'd have been shot."

The braided wire came down on the unconscious man, stretched out with the others on the ground. He came to and whipped over on his back, howling and writhing, the cords in his neck standing out like cables. The redhead lashed him again and moved to the next man. The man moaned and bit his lips when the whip came down. The last time it came up red.

The engineers had gone back inside the accommodations. Manuel and Ricardo were pale-faced and silent. "Go on," I told Yussuf, "take the AB's inside."

They left the deck. A police van with steel grating over the windows, a little Mitsubishi, came careening up and squealed to a stop at the foot of the gangway. The soldiers piled one of the stowaways, the muscular little man, into the back of the van. He twisted and struggled until they got him in and locked the door. The van drove away.

The redhead called the agent over. He had been sitting in his van by the fence, watching the action, but when the redhead pointed to the remaining stowaways and indicated that he had to take them away in his van, Gustavo shook his head violently and cried, "¡Estan sucios! El sangre, el lodo. . ."

The redhead made it clear he expected the agent to take them. The agent came up the gangway. "I have to take the stowaways to jail in my van. Do you have something I can cover the seats with?"

"What about the police van? Why didn't it take them?"

He studied my face and moved closer. "This is the third time they have caught that one trying to stow away. They are taking him off to . . ."

"To where? To kill him?"

He didn't answer.

"Jesus," I said, "I would've let 'em walk if I'd known that." I went forward and got some left-over plastic bags and gave them to the agent. He put them on his seats, and the five remaining stowaways, two of them unable to walk unaided, were loaded into the van. Two soldiers got in and the agent drove off. The redhead and the other officials walked back to the port office. The redhead stopped to wash his whip in a bucket by the quarantine station.

For reasons which were never made clear to me, we did not sail the next day, but were kept alongside in Haina for another five days. I sold a small amount of fuel to one of the port officials, who sent a one-ton truck full of 55-gallon drums to take it away, and used the money to buy paint. When we finally got sailing orders on March 16 to steam for Puerto Cortes, Honduras, we had finished chipping and painting the port side of the hull.

I roused Yussuf at dawn for the drug-and-stowaway search. It was cool and wet on deck as we walked forward. I had forgotten my mace, but didn't bother to go back for it. As usual, we started in the forecastle. There was no one under the piles of spare hawser and bundles of gunny sacks. The AB's had bolted the forepeak manhole cover down.

I opened the door to the paint locker and stepped over the coaming. The lightbulb was burned out. I started to raise my flashlight when a shape loomed out of the dark. I struck out with the flashlight and missed. Something hit me a crashing blow on the side of the head that lit my brain like electricity.

I clutched at a bony, hairless arm. The man and I struggled for our footing among the paint cans. He shoved me backward. We fell together, locked in violent embrace. As his head flashed through the light from the door, I saw a square, brutish face and a mouthful of yellow teeth.

I got my hands around his neck, but he twisted free and got my right wrist in his mouth. He bit down. I could feel meat and sinew crunching. I howled. The light was cut off as Yussuf swung something. The stowaway yelped. I scrambled up and Yussuf hauled me out of the locker. My hand was smeared with blood.

The stowaway appeared in the door in a pair of matted, blackened underwear. He was bleeding above the left ear. His sweaty chest heaved. His lips drew back in a snarl.

I tried to grab the board from Yussuf, but by then the man had leaped through the forecastle door and out on deck. I ran out after him. I tried to shout for Lionel and the AB's, but a fierce pain in my jaw kept me from opening my mouth.

The man ran down the gangway and into the hazy dawn. I sat on the boarding ladder. Yussuf took my arm and turned it. There was a semicircle of gouges on the inside of the wrist, oozing blood.

"Ah," I said, but my jaw hurt too much to talk. The rest of the crew came boiling on deck. They took me aft to the officer's mess and Yussuf went to the ship's hospital for medical supplies. He smeared my wounds with antiseptic ointment and wrapped my wrist in gauze.

I wrote a note telling him not to say anything to the pilot, because I didn't want the ship's sailing delayed. He nodded and took Lionel and Ricardo with him to continue the search. I went up to the saloon and sat on a stool. I could see the three of them going forward, Yussuf with a piece of pipe and the others with dunnage.

The search turned up no more stowaways, and at 0700 we took on the pilot, cast off from the dock, and turned the ship's bow toward the south. I stayed on the port stool and let Yussuf do the talking. The pilot boat followed us out, pitching in the hard chop, and retrieved the old man and his bottle of Scotch. It was coming up on my watch, so I took the helm and sent Yussuf down to breakfast. I set a course to take us toward Isla Beata, an uninhabited egg-shaped rock off the southern coast, and climbed up on the port stool. I worked my jaw carefully. After a few minutes it popped back into place. I jumped off the stool in pain.

In mid-morning I cut west between Beata and the mainland. With the wind and waves behind us, the old ship gained a knot over cruising speed and tore along with sparkling bow waves rolling off her sides. I stared absently out over the bows until I began to get the quartermaster's hallucination, that the deck itself was going forward faster than the ship. It's an unnerving sensation, caused by the continual backward rush of water at the edge of vision. I shook my head to clear my eyes.

After lunch I went on deck to sit on the port gunwale, just forward of the house. I was alone on deck under a crisp white sun. A whale surfaced about 100 meters away, off the port side and forward of the bow. It blew a spout of steam and rolled under again. I was about to yell up to Yussuf when, right below me, about 10 feet from the side of the ship, a great, gray, barnacled back rose out of the sea.

A pink muscle inside the blow-hole opened up and the whale blew its hot breath straight up into my face, water and steam spewing past me and drifting across the deck. The whale took a deep breath with a hollow roaring sound, the pink muscle worked again, and the hole closed off. The gray spine sank into the blue water.

"Yussuf," I yelled, lighting a pain in my jaw, but he was already leaning out the port window.

"I saw it, Captain," he said, "I saw it. A huge whale, right by the ship."

The other whale breached again off the port bow, close enough for us to hear it sucking air, but that was the last we saw of them.

Three days later, when I called Dickie with my 72-hour ETA, he asked me for my position. I told him we were off the northeastern tip of Honduras.

"How much fuel do you have onboard, Captain?"

"Sixty-five tons."

"How much fuel can you spare?"

I thought. "Twenty tons."

"Excellent. Captain, there is a ship coming up from Nicaragua, the *Veronika*, that's going into Tampico. I want you to stop and transfer 20 tons when she gets there."

"Where is she now?"

"She's about 60 miles ahead of you. The captain is supposed to call me any moment. Keep going west, and you'll hear her on the radio."

We heard from the ship at 0900, 20 miles ahead. She had dropped anchor off Cabo Camaron on the northern Honduran coast. Yussuf laid out a course to meet her.

We came alongside and tied up with tires between us. She was an old wreck of a tweendecker, built in the late 50's or early 60's, about 3300 deadweight tons. I climbed up her rusty side and went on deck. The captain was a big Nicaraguan with a black beard named Brucello. He led me into his saloon and offered me a warm Coke. I took a couple of sips and left it on the table.

"Did you hurt yourself, Captain?" he asked, looking at my bandaged wrist.

"I was bitten by a stowaway in Rio Haina. Three days ago. I'm afraid it's getting infected."

"Ah, Rio Haina. A terrible place. You must go to a doctor in Cortes. There is a very good Cuban doctor there named Horatio Leon. His clinic is near the telephone office. You cannot miss it."

"Thank you. I will go to him."

"The new owner says you can give us 20 tons of fuel."

"That's right. I've been accumulating it since we started with the present charterer."

He laughed. "That's good. Very good. Every captain should do the same."

I looked at him. "Who is your owner?"

"This ship was just bought by an American. He came to Nicaragua to buy it. His name is Vance. Ricardo Vance."

"When did he buy her?"

"Two weeks ago. It has been laid up in Bluefields. The crew and I have been on it for two years. The old owner could not get the money to fix it."

"Huh." I stood up. "Well, let's see if the engineers have us hooked up yet."

We went on deck. The *Veronika*'s hatches were wasted and perforated. The cargo gear was in disarray. I said, "You're not on your way to pick up cargo, I hope."

He nodded. "Scrap steel from Tampico to Cartagena."

"Oh, scrap steel. Well, you might be able to take that."

"The hatches need work," he admitted, "but we have another problem."

"What's that?"

"We can't pump the double-bottom tanks. The pipes are rotten. We have to open up the manholes to empty the tanks."

"You mean you can't ballast up? I have the same problem, but it's because of the tank-tops. It's hell in a seaway, as we both know."

"Well, I never sailed on the ship until this voyage, and we have had good weather so far. I don't know what will happen when we get in high winds in the ocean."

Victor came up on the *Erika*'s deck and shouted across that he had some relatives who lived very close to where we were anchored, and that if he could go ashore he would buy some fresh meat cheap. Since our rescue boat had been reduced to scraps, Brucello agreed to have his bosun take Victor ashore in one of their lifeboats. I gave Victor $100 and they drove off, Victor sitting on the thwarts clutching his bag like a Dutch housewife.

The hose from the *Erika* jerked as the diesel started flowing. My chief came up, laid a hand on the hose, and told the AB's to tie it off so it wouldn't get pinched between the bulwarks. He went back downstairs.

"How many men you got onboard, Captain?" I asked Brucello.

"Seven. Six seamen and myself."

I winced. "I got seven including me, and I'm only half your size."

He let out a long, ragged sigh. "It's hard, Captain. Very hard. Nobody has slept since we left Bluefields three days ago. Plenty problems in the engine room."

"You'd better not go to the States until you get everything straightened out. Coast Guard'll seize this ship for sure."

The *Veronika* had some 50-kilo bags of sugar onboard, bought from a crewman on another ship. We traded a bag of rice for a bag of sugar, even-up. Victor and the *Veronika*'s bosun returned with a huge pig trussed in the bottom of the boat. Yussuf pulled it up to the *Erika*'s boat deck with the davit.

We were finished pumping by noon. Brucello and I shook hands and I went back to the *Erika*. Compared to the Flying Dutchman I'd just left, my little ship looked trim and seaworthy. We cast off lines at 1225 and resumed our westerly course. I entered an engine stoppage for bleeding injectors in the logbook.

On the boat deck, Victor began the—apparently necessary—process of killing the pig by degrees. The animal howled and sobbed for an hour, and when he finally succumbed to his wounds at about 1400 hours, I fell into a restless sleep under the lazy draft of the fan. About 1600 I woke with a throbbing pain in my wrist. I took the bandage off. The torn edges of flesh were red and hot, and my wrist was swollen. I sat up and worked my jaw. Better, but still sore.

I went up to the bridge at 1730. Yussuf was taking a bearing on the tip of Guanaja, easternmost of the Bay Islands. After he'd caught up the logs, he lit a cigarette and we sat together on the starboard wing, watching the island rise out of the sea. Ahead of us a big container ship was hull-down on the horizon, steaming westward. The last we saw of her was a thin thread of black smoke rising from the water.

"Yussuf," I said, "I wasn't thinking when I sent Victor to get that pig. I know we're getting short on other meat, and I know you can't eat pork. I should have told him to get a couple of goats."

"It's okay, Captain. I do not have to have meat with every meal."

"Does Victor cook you something else when he cooks pork?"

"Sometimes. If I ask him."

I grinned at him. "What about the beer and the Barbancourt? I thought Moslems weren't supposed to drink."

"Oh, but, Captain," he said, "the Koran says that when a Moslem is traveling, he may break the commandments. This ship is traveling, is it not?" He laughed, then got serious. "Captain, the AB's were asking me if Mr. Dickie bought the *Veronika*. The chief mate told me he came on board the ship in Nicaragua with a briefcase full of money and bought it."

"Yeah, the captain told me Dickie bought it. First time I'd heard about it." I picked up the binocs and trained them on a set of lights coming out of the southwest. It was a supply boat heading for Roatan, on a course that would take it across our bows with plenty of searoom. "We've got a problem with Victor and the AB's. They're Honduran, so if Dickie doesn't meet the ship with all back wages, we'll get detained."

"What do you mean?"

"A Honduran seaman can get a ship seized in Honduras with no money down. Cortes is full of *abogados* who troll the waterfront looking for unpaid seamen."

He chewed on a corner of his lip. "You know, Captain, I am a single man, so it is not so hard on me. My family doesn't need me to send money home. But Victor and the AB's have families. . .I've heard them talking about how hard things are at home with no money."

"I know, I know. Dickie sends my wife a check on the first of every month, because he knows I'll be on the next flight home if he doesn't. But I guess he thinks the crew'll put up with it." I put the binoculars away. "I told him he had to have the crew wages in Miami, and he didn't have it. Then he sent just enough money for spares and provisions in Savannah. He didn't send any money at all to Rio Haina." I spat over the side. "He's learned the first lesson in Haitian shipownership. Never pay the crew. Pay as little as possible otherwise, but never pay the crew."

"Very bad, Cap'n," Yussuf said. After a few minutes he went downstairs and I settled into the port stool for my watch. We passed between the islands of Utilla and Roatan during the night. A low overcast hid the moon and stars, and only a tracery of lights on the islands showed where they were. By dawn, when I went up to the bridge, we had reached Amatique Bay. Yussuf rang for Half Ahead.

"There's the seabuoy," he said, pointing toward the rocky Honduran coast in the distance.

"Good deal. You talk to the pilot yet?"

"Pilot boat will meet us at the seabuoy. Manuel's getting the ladder ready."

The pilot boat never came out to the channel. It waited at the mouth of the bay, where the pilot came on. He was a sallow young man with lank black hair that curled over his uniform collar. He gave no steering or throttle orders, but sat complacently in the port stool and watched as Yussuf conned us into the anchorage.

I directed Yussuf to a clear spot among the anchored freighters and looked at the pilot. "This okay?"

He waved a hand. "*Sí. Bueno.*"

Yussuf went forward with Manuel and dropped the starboard anchor. Puerto Cortes is a low, swampy port on the eastern rim of the bay. Three ships were at the dock, all doing cargo operations. Several freighters were at anchor, but some of them looked seized or abandoned.

Yussuf ran up the Q flag, and about an hour later the launch arrived with the agent and the port officials. They trooped into my saloon. The agent was a squat, sallow man in a white Guayaberra shirt. After the officials were finished and had gone down to the deck, I gave his briefcase a pointed look.

"I hope the crew wages are in there," I said.

He handed me a fax. It was from a company I'd never heard of, Navieras Caribes S. de R. L., addressed to me as master of the *Erika*.

"Max—I am arriving today with the crew wages. I will be onboard in the afternoon. Dickie Vance."

I folded the fax and put it in a drawer. The agent hesitated. "Captain, I must inform you that you are forbidden to use the ship's boat in this port. You and your crew must use the launch service to go ashore."

I waved a hand. "My rescue boat was vandalized in R. D., so it doesn't matter."

"Yes. I am sorry." He stood up and closed the briefcase. "Well, Captain, keep a watch on channel 16. I have a radio in my office, of course. I will call you when it is time for you to come alongside. As you see, the port is congested, and I do not know if it will be today or no."

I looked at the long concrete quay. It didn't look congested to me. "Very well," I said, shaking his hand, "I'll be standing by on 16." I went to the radio and called the launch back to pick him up. He was waiting on deck with the officials when Manuel went up to him and started talking, waving his arms and pointing toward the saloon. In a few moments the chief appeared and he and the agent greeted each other warmly. Manuel disappeared into the accommodations.

I opened the accounts to see how much in arrears the ship was on Manuel's pay. Almost $900. I had about $160 in the ship's safe. When Victor brought my lunch, I asked him, "Cookie, is Manuel going to the Ministerio de Trabajo?"

He slid my plate across with his head down. "*Sí*, I think so, Captain."

"Is anybody else onboard going?"

"I don't think so, Captain. Unless we don't get paid here. Then plenty problem."

"I know, Cookie. Thanks. Tell Manuel to come see me."

He went out with the tray under his arm. In a few minutes he came back wringing his hands. "*¡Capitán, ya salió Manuel!*"

I looked out the window to see Manuel ducking down into the launch's cabin with his suitcases. The launch pulled away. I shook my head sadly. "What a pity. If he had just waited until this afternoon, he'd still have a job."

Victor left, tsk-tsk'ing under his breath. I called the chief to the wheelhouse. He came in wiping his hands, his shirt plastered to his chest. "Chief, how many tons of fuel onboard now?"

He thought for a moment. "Thirty-eight."

I nodded. "How many tons in the log?"

"Sixteen."

"Good man." I picked up the microphone and called the agent. "The MV *Erika* needs to order 30 tons of marine gas oil. Repeat marine gas oil."

"Sorry, Captain," the agent said, not sounding sorry at all. "There is no diesel in Honduras. Even the trucks are being rationed so there will be enough for the buses."

"Then we have a big problem. Perhaps you should call the charterer and let him know about this. Do you have his number?"

"Mr. Garot in Miami? Yes, yes, I have spoken to him. Very well, I will let him know."

In the early afternoon a launch approached with a gringo on deck. It was Dickie Vance, wearing a pair of baggy shorts and a knit shirt, the leather laces of his Topsiders splayed across the deck. He handed up his bag and climbed the ladder.

I waited in the saloon. He came in smiling and sunny, laid the briefcase on the table, and asked for a Coke. I got him a cold one from the little refrigerator. He swallowed it.

"I have the crew wages," he said. He opened the briefcase and handed me a bank bag.

"Good, but Manuel already left the ship. He's probably at the Ministerio de Trabajo right now." I took the money into the office and put it in the safe.

"The what?"

"The Ministry of Labor. They seize ships for claims by Honduran crewmen."

"What? You gotta be kidding."

"I wish I were. Now that the MT's involved, it's going to cost extra."

"How much?"

I shrugged. "His back wages plus something to get the vessel released. Of course you can always let the ship sit here for six months waiting for trial."

He sat in the armchair. "Jesus Christ, this is crazy. You're a little behind in crew wages and they seize your ship?"

"Two months behind. That'll make anybody crazy. You're lucky the others didn't join in."

He rubbed his face. "Aw, it's been a bitch, Captain. That fucking Jacques is always shorting me on the charter hire, and I'm too scared of losing the charter to fight with him."

"Then you're throwing money away. I always amend the Statement of Facts before signing. I send my Notes of Protest and the ship's tally of off-hire times from every port. You haven't been getting my faxes?"

"Uh, yeah, I think I'm getting them."

"Well, you'll never get ahead if you don't fight the charterer over off-hires. It's not just Garot, it's any charterer. But that's not the crew's problem. They got to get paid whether you make money or not." He started to say something, but I cut him off. "And it didn't help when they found out that you just bought that big old wreck, the *Veronika*."

He started. "She's not a wreck. How'd they find out?"

"Hell, the crew of the *Veronika* told them. You didn't think we'd raft up in the middle of the ocean and the crews wouldn't bullshit with each other, did you?"

He shot me a calculating look. "Well, I was going to tell you, Captain, but I didn't want the rest of the crew to know. I didn't really buy it myself, you know. I just put together a group of golfing buddies to buy it. I think we got a hell of a deal. Paid a hundred grand. Did you take a look at her?"

"Just the deck."

"She'll be in Tampico tomorrow. We're doing some repairs to the piping, then she'll be ready to load cargo." He noticed my bandaged wrist. "What happened to your arm, Captain?"

"I got attacked by a stowaway in Haina. Sonofabitch bit me on the wrist. It's infected." I turned my head slightly. "Fucker hit me on the jaw, too. Dislocated it."

"Yeah, it's swollen. Still dislocated?"

"Naw, it's back in place. Still hurts, though."

He clucked. "Terrible, terrible. Have you been to a doctor?"

"No. I'll have to go today."

Victor called up the companionway, *"La lancha esta llegando, Capitán."*

"The launch," I said. "Come on, let's go."

The Hondurans and Dickie and I got in. They studied his face for a sign, but he didn't seem to notice. I nodded to them. They relaxed. The roar of the unmuffled exhaust precluded conversation. The launch landed us in front of a small warehouse.

We walked together to the sally port. A narrow-gauge train was being coupled up at the end of the line, dark faces staring out from the hot confines of the pre-World War II passenger cars. The Honduran crewmen bade Dickie and me hasty farewells and hurried toward their barrios. He and I crossed the tracks and walked along the narrow street, fronted by bars and whorehouses, until we reached the alley where the agent's office was. The agent gave me directions to the MT, and warned me that Manuel had told him onboard that he was going to have the ship seized.

The MT office was a bare cement building in front of a tree-covered square. The deserted lobby was dirty and smelled of disinfectant. I walked between two heavy mahogany doors into a hallway. A woman called to me from one of the rooms, and when I explained why I was there, she pointed across the hall.

The woman in the seaman's section gave me a hostile stare. She had papers stacked on every inch of her desk, and more piles on the floor.

"I'm sorry, Captain," she said smoothly, after I'd explained the situation and assured her that I had Manuel's back and current wages with me. "Señor Guillen has filed a complaint against the ship. Now the complaint must be investigated. I have already sent a message to the port director's office asking him to hold the ship until the investigation is complete."

I sighed. "What do I have to do just to pay Manuel his money? If I pay him today, can the ship leave tomorrow?"

She shook her head. "*No es posible*. Maybe in two weeks."

I stood up. "Thank you for your consideration. I'm sure I will be talking to you again very soon."

I went back to the agent's office and called Dickie out into the alley. "I need more money. I need to bribe the woman at the ministry."

His face got dark. "Bribe the woman? You've got the money to pay Manuel off, don't you?"

"Yeah, but that's not enough. That just gets him to release his claim. Now we have to pay this woman or the 'investigation' will take two weeks. I told you this was going to cost you money."

He gave me a sullen look. "How much?"

"I figure at least a thousand. I can go back with that and see what it buys."

"A thousand. . .! Okay, okay. Here." He took out a roll of hundreds. "If I see that asshole again, I'll knock his fucking head off."

He stamped back into the agent's office and I returned to the MT. It was almost siesta time. The office girls were filing out, chattering in bright Spanish. I caught the seaman's section woman in the hallway.

I gestured toward her office. "If we could go back in," I said politely. "It won't take but a few minutes."

She unlocked the door and let me in. I wiped the sweat from my forehead and sat down. "Señor Guillen put down that the ship owes him $1233, right?" I slid across an envelope. "What if I pay that amount to you, to hold until the investigation is over? That way he can get paid everything that is owed to him."

She started to say something, but I slid another envelope across. "And of course there is the MT."

She counted the money in the second envelope slowly, moving her lips, then she looked up and gave me a wide smile that showed a dead blue canine tooth on the right side. "You are right, Captain, and luckily there is another procedure. If there is any money left from the deposit you have put down, I will give it to the agent to forward to the ship."

I kept a straight face. She rolled a form into a typewriter and painfully pecked out a release stating that the MT had settled the seaman's claim for a total of 4866 *lempiras*, which was equal to the $1233. We shook hands and I left the hot little box of a room. She was humming as I went out.

CHAPTER SEVEN

I FOUND DR. LEON'S CLINIC WITHOUT TROUBLE. IT WAS A SMALL frame house set back from the street behind two frangipani trees, both heavy with red flowers. The boards of the narrow porch were worn from thousands of feet. There was a tiny wallpapered waiting room with four chairs, all empty. A woman who appeared to be Mrs. Leon led me back into an examination room. Flying termites had gotten into the frame of the house, and the room was wrenched. A chipped enamel bowl sat on a clean white towel on a chest of drawers.

Dr. Leon came in, a handsome man in his late 50's. He remembered the Nicaraguan captain, and even remembered that he'd treated him for chancres. He unwrapped my wrist and studied the puffy red flesh. The torn edges were now tinged with black. Red streaks were starting to appear on the forearm. Dr. Leon touched them lightly. "This is very dangerous, Captain. The infection is in the blood."

There was little he could do for the bite. He cleaned and redressed the wounds, gave me a shot of antibiotics, and wrote out a prescription on a piece of paper. I paid Mrs. Leon $8.00 and got the prescription filled at a *farmacia* on the way back to the ship.

Dickie was onboard. It was mid-afternoon, and his blond ringlets were plastered to his damp forehead in the sweltering cabin. He was finishing a Coke as I came in. He put the can on the table and said, without getting up, "I just talked to Jack. Your next port is the Bay of Flamants. It's in Haiti."

"I never heard of that port. Let's take a look at the chart."

He followed me up to the bridge. I got out the chart of Haiti's southern peninsula. The Baie des Flamants was on its southern coast, near the town of Les Cayes. I studied the bay. It was deep, more than 30 fathoms, but there was no indication of a port there. The *Coast Pilot* mentioned the bay, but only to say that a sand beach and fishing village were visible from seaward, and that a reef ran southwest on the eastern side.

"I don't think there's a port there," I said. "There's nothing on the chart."

He waved his hand. "Oh, you know. . .it's one of those things. Probably unload into little boats, like Miragoane."

"Yeah, but Miragoane is a port."

He shook his head. "Listen, Captain, can the ship go into the bay?"

"Yes."

"Can you safely drop anchor there?"

I looked at the chart again. It was a big bay, with a nice bight inside the reef. "Sure."

"Then I'd like you to do what Jack wants. We're on charter, and I need the money. What happens when you get there is his problem."

"Unless the ship gets seized. I know Haiti's in chaos, but the local officials have a powerful motivation—the value of the ship—to find a reason to seize it."

"Jack's got the locals bought. That's why you're going there."

I sighed. "All right, Dickie." I went out on the wing to go downstairs. The crew were assembled on deck in their street clothes. I went back in and said, "You'd better pay the crew. They're getting restless." I gave a little laugh. "If you want to get off this ship alive you'd better pay 'em."

"All right, all right."

We went down to the saloon. He opened his leather briefcase and put it on the table. "Well, send 'em in."

"How much you got?"

He hesitated. "One month."

"You don't have through March?"

He shook his head. "It was all I could raise, Captain. I'm sorry. It'll just have to do."

I gave him a sour smile. "You're learning some bad tricks, Dickie."

Blood rushed to his face. "I own this ship, Captain. Don't forget who you're talking to."

I stared at him without moving. He sat down suddenly and ran his fingers through his hair. "Look, Captain, you've done a hell of a job for me so far. . ."

"For you?" I said incredulously. "For you?" I stabbed a finger at him. "You got it wrong, Dickie. Whatever I do is for the ship. It's not for you."

He stared back at me blankly.

"All right," I finally said, "I'll go down and call 'em up."

The men took their month's salary with grim faces, but without hostility. We all rode the launch in together. The crew hurried off to the money-changers and Dickie and I went to the agent's office. He wanted to call his travel agent and make a reservation to Chicago, and I wanted to arrange for bunkers. The agent was all bows and scrapes for Dickie, and a little of his greatness must have rubbed off, for the agent had a lackey draw a chair up before his desk for me as well.

Dickie called Garot and told him the fuel situation in Honduras. He handed the phone to me. There was sweat on the handpiece. Garot's voice was hard and weak, sheared to whispers by the bad connection. "Captain, he said, "can you sail to Kingston?"

"Yes, I can make Kingston."

"Very good. Call me on the radio when you're a day out and I'll give you the agent's number."

"That's fine," I said, "but I have a question about the Baie des Flamants."

Dickie made a motion to cut me off, but I ignored him. "The *Coast Pilot* doesn't show any port in that area of the coast. Where is the ship going to clear in?"

"Don't worry about that, Captain," he shouted faintly. "I have taken care of everything. You can sail into the bay without problem?"

"I can sail in without a problem, but I must have a clearance, do you understand? I must have a clearance into the country."

"Don't worry, Captain. . ."

"Just tell me the port I'm going to. Is it Jacmel? That's the closest port of entry listed in the *Pilot*."

His voice rose an octave. "Go to Baie des Flamants, Captain. Go to Baie des Flamants. Do what I tell you. I will have a man there to meet you. His name is Pierre Boisblanc. Do not worry about anything. Now let me talk to your boss."

I handed the phone back to Dickie. They talked some more, then he hung up. He and I went outside. Waiters from the cafes fronting the alley were putting out tables and chairs on the stone paving. The sun was sliding down the western sky.

Dickie sighed. "Well, Captain, I guess you're going to Kingston to pick up fuel."

"Look," I said, "there's still 38 tons onboard. You know I always underreport. Why don't you tell Jacques that you managed to buy some blackmarket fuel at an inflated price, so we don't have to stop in Kingston? He'll be happy because he saves ship time and port charges, and you'll make a nice piece of change."

"But he'll know. All he has to do is ask the agent."

"Dickie," I said patiently, "diesel sale is illegal in Honduras. If we didn't buy it on the black market, where did we get it?"

He laughed out loud. "That's a hell of an idea. And a good way to get back some of the money he's been stealing from me."

"Don't say anything yet," I warned him. "I wouldn't want the port authorities to hear about it before we sailed."

We went back to the ship. Yussuf said that the agent had just called with orders to go alongside. The pilot boat arrived a few minutes later, and Dickie stayed onboard for the ride to the dock. The compulsory tug, unused and overpriced, made a perfunctory circle near us before returning to its berth.

After we were All-Fast, Dickie shook my hand, told me to assure the crew that he would catch up all wages next month, and left for the San Pedro Sula airport. At 1800 hours a crane, a gang of stevedores, and a couple of forklifts arrived alongside.

I watched the first hour of loading, enough to convince myself they weren't going to hurt the ship, then set up four-hour watches with Yussuf to match the stevedore schedule. He took the first watch and I went to bed.

At noon the next day Yussuf came into the officer's mess from cargo watch. The chief and second and I were already eating. The loading was going quickly, Yussuf said. He thought we might finish the following evening.

"Better knock off early and take a shower," I told the chief. "Tonight's the last night with mama."

"Mama plenty vex with me now, Captain," he laughed. "Ysadora put her picture in the pocket of my shirt, and the wife found it when she washed my clothes."

"Oh, la la," Ian said. "What she say about an old man like you with a young girl like that?"

"She called me an old goat," he said proudly.

After lunch I went up to the saloon and lay down on the bench and tried to find the vortex of the fan. A few minutes later Yussuf came in with a funny look on his face. "Captain, come see what's going on in the hold."

I sat up. "What do you mean? The stevedores are at lunch, aren't they?"

"Come quick. You'll see."

I followed him down to the deck. He tiptoed along the hatch to the hole in the boards and pointed down. I peered into the gloom.

Two stevedores, barechested young men dusted with cement, were lying together on a pile of sacks under the overhang of the deck. One had his head on the other's arm. I looked back at Yussuf. He was grinning. I looked in the hold. The two men were kissing.

"Hey!" I yelled, "stop that, goddamn it!"

The men looked at me without pulling apart.

"*No actividad homosexual en mi buque*," I called down. I shook my finger at them. Yussuf gave a stifled chortle. "Look at that shit," I told him. "They don't even care about getting caught."

The two men got up and went forward out of sight. The other stevedores were coming back from lunch. I met the foreman, a big, sloppy man with white stubble and a gut, at the head of the gangway. "There are two *maricones* in the hold," I said. "They were kissing each other."

He got a half-grin. "So?"

"Tell them not to do it again. This is a cargo ship, not a bathhouse."

He brushed past me. "It is their lunch hour, Captain. They can do as they please."

I told Yussuf about the foreman's cavalier response. "It is normal here," he said. "I walked in the Carreta Bar last night, the one by the railroad gate, and it was full of them. They were having a fashion show. It was disgusting."

We finished loading at 1630 hours the next day. I left a few minutes later to stock up on whiskey and cigarettes. There was a discount liquor store a few blocks from the port called *Mi Montañita*, or My Little Mountain, where I bought a case of Johnny Walker Red at world market price and two cases of Guatemalan Marlboros at $2.86 a carton. I got a taxi to take me back to the ship. Most of the crew were onboard in their work clothes, but the chief was still gone. I locked the whiskey and cigarettes in the office—the bonded-stores locker was sealed until we left—and went up to the wheelhouse. Yussuf was checking the radar.

The chief came up the dock a few minutes later carrying a cardboard box. I called down, "We sail at 2100 hours, Chief. Everything okay in the engine room?"

He nodded. "We okay to sail, Captain."

"All right. I'll signal when the pilot's onboard."

At 2100 hours the pilot came limping up the dock, an old man with a smoker's hack. His hollow coughing echoed off the tin walls of the warehouses. He pulled himself up the pilot ladder. A long time later he appeared in the door of the wheelhouse.

"Cast off all lines, Captain," he rasped. I looked out the port door and saw a tug approaching in the dark, its navigation lights burning. Yussuf was on the bow. I made a wave to cast off. The tug headed for its berth as the pilot called for Half Ahead and the ship slipped away from the dock lights.

The moon was still down. The channel lights floated in the blackness to the northeast. The pilot hunched over his cigarette on the port wing and let Yussuf con the ship out of the bay. When we got halfway down the channel he had me sign his chit and stood waiting for his cigarettes and whiskey. He wrinkled his nose when I handed him the Guatemalan Marlboros, but said nothing. He put the Johnny Walker and the cigarettes in his briefcase and went downstairs. The pilot boat pulled away and Yussuf rang for Full Speed Ahead.

The seabuoy fell behind. A half-moon rose up out of the sea. The chief rang for the tailshaft. The ship got quiet.

It was my watch anyway, so Yussuf went below. I was alone on the bridge. After a few minutes, a container ship came out of the channel from Santo Tomas de Castillo and overtook us on the port side. I adjusted our course to follow her wake through the gap between Roatan and Utilla. The big islands rolled by unseen in the dark. Then I aimed *Erika*'s bow toward Kingston, three days away.

The next morning I took the watch from Yussuf and sat on the starboard wing nursing a cup of coffee as the ship rolled through a low swell. Doomed land birds staggered about on the damp hatchcovers and fell in sodden lumps to the deck. The sun turned white and hot as it grasped the sky. The chief came on the bridge with a stricken look.

I straightened. "What's wrong, Chief?"

His mouth worked. "The bunkers, Captain. . .we do not have enough bunkers."

"What? We've got 38 tons, don't we?"

"We. . .we have. . ." His voice sank to a hoarse whisper. "We have three tons, Captain."

I jumped off the stool. "Three tons! That's not possible. You said we had 38 tons on arrival. What the hell. . ."

He cringed like a dog. "Yes, Captain, but I do not know what happened to it. Now we only have fuel in the settling tank and day tank."

I got a cold, light feeling at the back of my head. "You gotta be kidding."

He threw out his hands. "The second went to pump fuel from No. 5 center to the settling tank, and it was empty. There were 46 tons in that tank Thursday—I sounded it myself—and now it's empty."

I sagged against the stool. "Three tons! We can't even make Kingston on that. And we can't go back. There's no fuel in Honduras." I pressed my palms to my temples. "I don't fucking believe this, Chief." I started toward him. "What happened to that fuel, Chief? Did you sell it in Cortes?"

He threw himself onto the deck, his old knees making painful thumps against the planking. "You can kill me, Captain! You can kill me, but I don't know what happened to the fuel. I didn't sell it in Cortes, I swear by my mother's grave."

I reached down and helped him up. "Get up, Chief. I'm not going to kill you. Let's see what can be done."

I got Yussuf up and we sounded all the tanks. The fuel tanks, Nos. 4 and 5 center, were empty. The ballast tanks were also empty, so the fuel hadn't been pumped into one of them by mistake. There was nowhere else for it to have gone except overboard or ashore. I went into the engine room and studied the sight glasses. The settling tank held two tons and the day tank one ton. The chief and the second made themselves scarce.

Yussuf and I went up to the bridge. He lit a cigarette and blew the smoke out with a cough. "These Honduran Marlboros are bad, Captain."

"Guatemalan," I said absently. "They're Guatemalan." I turned on the Skanti and called Dickie. "Have you charged Garot for the fuel yet?" I asked him.

"No, Captain, I was waiting to get the number of tons from you."

"Thank goodness." I told him in guarded terms what had happened.

"Well, okay, Captain, if that's what happened, just go on to Kingston and refuel there. I could have used the money, but go on to Kingston. I'll call Jack."

I hung up and looked at Yussuf. He looked at me.

"Very strange, Captain," he said.

"Yeah, I know, but what can I do about it? Right now we've got to keep a sharp eye on the fuel burn. We'll go back to the minimum rpm necessary to support the tailshaft. If we run out we'll just have to call a tug from Kingston."

He nodded and went down to the engine room. The engine began to throttle back. When the lights started to surge and wane, the chief bumped it up a few rpm's and left it there. He rang for just over Half Ahead, and I confirmed.

Exactly an hour later I took another measurement of the settling tank sight-glass. The burn rate was down to 1.3 tons a day. I calculated that we had 3.2 days to get to Kingston at this speed. We still wouldn't make it. I found Yussuf in his cabin.

"First, we're going to have to open up the manholes in Nos. 4 and 5 and get some fuel out with buckets. You know there's a couple of tons the pump can't suck."

He nodded his head wearily. "Messy job, Captain, but we can do it. I'll call Lionel and Ricardo." He went down the steps and into the hallway. I heard him knocking on the seamen's doors.

I went back to the bridge, took a quick scan of the radar, and waited for a satellite to pass. The next one was good. We were making about seven knots. I refigured the distance to the Kingston seabuoy, then from there up the length of the bay to the fuel dock. Three days and eight hours. I took a look around the horizon. No ships. The tarp was rolled forward on No 2 hatch, and some of the hatchboards were up. Ian came out of the house with two 5-gallon buckets and lowered them into the hold. A minute later he pulled up a half-full bucket, diesel slopping in it, and then the other. He carried them inside.

Yussuf came up on the bridge two hours later, streaked with dirt, and fished a cigarette out with blackened fingers. "Almost a hundred buckets, Cap'n."

I turned to the chart again. "About one ton. And I estimated we need 1.3." I put the pencil down. "But of course we'll have to go off the tailshaft. Can you get any more out?"

He inhaled deeply and shook his head, smoke leaking from his nose. "I don't think so. Lionel is still scooping it out with a can, but. . .very hard to work in there, Cap'n. The fumes, you know. . ." He took a lungful of the cool wind. "I think that's all. We can open up No. 4, though. There has to be some fuel left there, too."

I nodded. "I'm sorry, First, but we'll have to do it. We're only a little short, but we don't want to run out of fuel in Kingston Bay."

He nodded. "We'll get some more out of No. 4." He took another pull on the cigarette and snapped it overboard. "No worry, Captain. We make Kingston easy."

I pointed a finger at him. "If we spend the night in Kingston, I'll show you a good time."

"I heard it's dangerous."

"That it is," I agreed cheerfully, "but it's a hell of a place. There's a club up in the mountains, called the Willy Nilly, where the big reggae bands play. We can get a taxi to take us up there."

"Okay, Cap'n." He went out. An hour later he was back with a grim expression. "Not as much in No. 4. The suction pipe is close to the shell plating. Maybe 20 buckets."

"Damn! Well, get what you can and button it up. We'll see what we've got when we get to the seabuoy, and if we have to we'll call a tug."

He turned his face toward the northeast, where a wind was slowly building. "If we start getting heavy seas off the bow, that'll slow us down. We might not even make the seabuoy."

"We might not, but that's where we're heading. All right, First, take a shower and get some sleep. Nothing to do now but watch the sight glass and keep steaming."

He went downstairs. I stood on the wing of the bridge and watched the sun set. A crowd of pigmy porpoises threaded their way across the water in the lee of the sun, making tiny black arcs in a river of red. They gained on the ship and disappeared into the gathering gloom eastward. I turned on the running lights. The main engine was turning too slowly. The lights glowed dimly in the dusk, surging and fading as the rpm's wavered.

The ship plowed slowly and steadily toward Kingston. The fuel burn stayed at 1.3 tons a day, and the wind eased a bit. The next evening, waiting for supper before going up to the bridge, I watched as the chief tied a fresh red rag on the hook he kept trailing off the stern.

"One week and no fresh fish," I said. "What we gonna have for supper tonight, Chief? A nice barracuda? Cookie's got stewmeat cooking, but we can have that later. Right, Cookie? *¿Una barracuda fresca,* Cookie? *¿Cocinada con limon y paprika?*"

Victor stuck his face out of the porthole. "*Sí, Capitán.* The stewmeat will keep for tomorrow."

The chief threw the big hook over the taffrail and let the line run out between his fingers. "We'll get something quick," he said. "This is the best speed. If we ran at this speed all the time, we'd have barracuda for lunch every day."

The line ran all the way out. I caught a glimpse of the red rag every once in a while, on the top of a swell. Victor came on deck to throw some onion peels overboard. "*¡Mira!*" he cried, and pointed toward the hook. I stood up.

There was a flash of color streaking across the blue water, coming fast from the north. "Dolphin!" the chief cried happily. "Watch this!"

The streak hit the hook. A silver-blue fish leaped clear of the water with the line in his mouth. He fell back and shot toward the other side. The line tugged against its bight on the bulwark. After the dolphin quit jumping, the chief hauled him in and over the rail. He was about three feet long, streaked with yellow and blue along his shiny sides. The chief hit him on the head with a piece of pipe, and the colors evaporated.

It was 1800 by the time Victor had my plate ready. I took my pangrilled dolphin and french fries up to the wheelhouse. Yussuf was finishing the log for his watch, and had already gotten the old Skanti warmed up for the Notice of ETA to the Kingston agent.

"Ah," he said, "fresh barracuda for supper. I hope Cookie checked him good to make sure he's not poisonous."

"Barracuda?" I said. "Hush your mouth. This is dolphin. Chief got him not five minutes after he put the hook out. You should have seen that big bastard go for the rag. He was shooting through the water at 20 knots."

At dawn of the fourth day out of Cortes, Jamaica was still hull-down off the port bow. Our speed was up to 7.3 knots in a long, shallow swell out of the southeast. We passed The Alley and altered course a few points for the Kingston seabuoy. The serrated spine of the Blue Mountains appeared above the haze.

After lunch I went down to the engine room and checked the fuel. The settling tank was empty, and the level in the day tank had fallen below half. Less than half a metric ton for eight hours' steaming. I shook my head and looked around for the chief, but he had just gone off-watch. Ian was working at the bench with his head down and eyes averted. I went topside.

"If we make it, it'll be a miracle," I told the chief, in the officer's mess. "I figured we need at least .4 of a ton, and we've got about .5."

He nodded somberly. "I'm very sorry, Captain. Perhaps the second turned a wrong valve somewhere. I asked him, and he says he didn't, but I don't know."

"Well, thank God the fuel was surplus, or Dickie would have to pay to replace it. If we can just make Kingston, it'll be okay."

I told Victor to bring my lunch to the saloon and went upstairs. The wind off the starboard bow was starting to pick up, making the curtains at my windows snap. A notebook had blown off the table and lay spreadeagled on the floor. After lunch I finished the Customs declarations and lay down. When I woke again it was late afternoon. The town of Kingston sparkled in the distance against the green hills of the southern coast. I could see the seabuoy with the naked eye.

I went up to the bridge. Yussuf was scanning the reef with the glasses. "I called the pilot station, Captain. They said we will pick up the pilot at 1740 hours."

I looked at my watch. Almost two hours. "That's when we arrive at the seabuoy?"

"Yessir."

"Excellent. How's the fuel?"

"Three hundred liters. Should we order a tug?"

I shook my head. "Let's wait until the last minute."

We slid along the reef, the houses and factories of Kingston shining in the late afternoon sun behind the deep blue water of Kingston Bay. The pilot boat met us at the seabuoy. The pilot was a burly man in his 50's with close-cropped gray hair and a tight uniform. He shook my hand and told Yussuf to follow the buoys. He settled onto the port wing with a cigarette. I stood just inside the door.

We turned north, through the entrance in the reef, and eastward. The sun sank below the western peaks, and the wind gained a chilly edge. Lights started coming on in town. On the street that ran along the shore several large fires were burning.

"What's that?" I asked the pilot.

"Oh," he said casually, "we have little political problem now. Dey burn de tires to stop de cars."

"I see that." I slipped down into the engine room. The chief and Ian were standing in front of the day tank. I came up behind them. We had switched over to the MWM when we came through the reef, so they couldn't hear me. The sight glass showed about 10 centimeters of fuel remaining. I tapped the chief on the shoulder. He turned, saw me, and winced. He shook his head.

"How long now, Captain?" he shouted in my ear.

"About half-an-hour. Think we can do it?"

"Maybe, if not too much maneuvering."

"I'll do my best."

I went back to the bridge. The fuel dock was on the port side now. The pilot called for Half Ahead. The engine slowed. He started giving Yussuf rudder-angle instructions. We nosed up toward the long concrete pier. Two men stood at the end waiting for us.

There was no maneuvering. The water was clear and deep all around the pier. With the bow spring line secured port-side-to, I ordered one last kick of Half Ahead with the rudder Hard-a-Starboard. The stern swung toward the dock and the monkey's fist went sailing onto the pier from the fantail. As soon as the stern line was fast I signaled Finished with Engine. Yussuf looked back from the forecastle and gave me the thumbs-up.

I went downstairs and ashore with the pilot. A ramshackle office building and two dented fuel tanks stood on a narrow strip of land between the road and the rocky shoreline, at the foot of the pier. The pilot went outside the gate and caught a taxi. I went into the office, but there was only a guard with a pistol-grip shotgun inside. He said he didn't know anything about pumping fuel to the ship, and no one would be back in the office until the next morning.

I went onboard and told the crew that we were going to be spending the night. "Jamaica is very dangerous at night," the chief warned the men. "My wife's nephew, her sister's boy, was killed here in Kingston. He was on a ship loading gypsum. He went out by himself, and they found his body in an alley the next morning. His family never found out who killed him or why." He pushed his glasses back with a knuckle to the nosepiece. "Best to stay onboard tonight, *muchachos.*"

The agent arrived, a very tall black man with jug ears. He took the paperwork and said that Jamaican Customs probably would not bother to come to the ship, since we were only stopping for fuel. "Just tell the crewmen to take their passports if they go ashore," he said, "and tell them not to go downtown. There are some. . .some troubles downtown tonight. A big protest rally against the government."

"All right," I said. "I'll tell them."

I went down to the engine room. One hundred liters left. The harbor generator was on, forward in the forecastle, and the engine room was hot and quiet. The chief was working on the air compressor head. I said, "Think we got enough fuel to run the generator all night, Chief?"

He looked up. "Yessir. Harbor generator use 60 liters a day, so we have enough."

"That was a close one, though, wasn't it? Two more hours and we would have run out."

He didn't say anything. I clapped him on the shoulder. "All's well that ends well, Chief. Don't worry about it."

I left the ship in the chief's hands about 2200 and knocked on Yussuf's door. He came out in his best shore clothes, wearing a gold chain around his neck. "Better take that off," I cautioned him. "Somebody could kill you for it in this city."

"Where we're going, is it dangerous?"

"Naw, I don't think so, but better not take any chances."

He put the chain in his cabin. We went on deck and down the gangway. As we approached the gate a taxi stopped and two chunky black girls got out. One was wearing skin-tight yellow stretch pants and a halter-top, and the other short-shorts and a gauzy blouse over a black bra. They stopped us.

"You from the ship?" Black Bra asked.

"Yes," I said. "I'm the captain. May I help you?"

The other girl said, "We come for pa'ty on ship, okay? We get call from somebody. . ." She thought. "From Ian Harrison. He call for pa'ty on ship."

I looked at Yussuf. "We're having a party onboard?"

"Well," he said cautiously, "Ian said he knew some girls from before."

"You know Ian?" I asked them.

"He call my friend," Black Bra said. "She can't come, okay, so she ask we come. It's okay, Captain?"

I shrugged. "Yeah, it's okay." I pointed to the ship. "Be careful going onboard."

They laughed and went off toward the ship. "You want to stay, Yussuf?" I said. "I think the one in yellow pants likes you."

"No, Captain. Plenty time for girls. I'm tired of staying on the ship. Always working on ship, at sea and in port. No place to go ashore in Miragoane. I'm ready to go ashore tonight."

We caught a taxi, a battered black Lada with the left rear door wired shut, and I gave the driver the name of the club. He was a little old black man in a greasy fedora. He craned around to look at me.

"You go to Willy Nilly Club? You know what is this club, friend?"

"Yeah, I've been there before. It's a music club."

He put the taxi in gear. "No white people at this club, friend. Holiday Inn have good club, casino, everything. I take you there."

"We'll check out the Willy Nilly," I insisted. "We don't have to go through downtown, do we? I heard there's trouble downtown tonight."

He shook his head violently. "Plenty problem downtown. Oh, very bad. De people burn de tires in the street. Maybe burn we too. The Willy Nilly Club is op in de hills. Okay, we go dere. You no like, no problem. I bring you back down."

The road turned away from the water's edge next to a giant cement plant, bathed in arc lights, and threaded its way up into the sharp, bare hills. Above our heads the peaks of the mountains were blue in the starlight.

Half-an-hour later we pulled off the road into a huge parking lot in front of a low, tin-roof building that looked like an abandoned factory. The muted thunder of amplified music filled the air. "Stay here for a minute," I told the driver, "while we check it out."

Yussuf and I walked between the cars, stumbling on the rocky ground. A crowd of gaily dressed black people stood in front of the door. They made a path as we came up.

A big man in a spotless white shirt and black slacks stood at the entrance with a wad of Jamaican money in his fist. Music hammered behind the door. "How much to get in?" I asked.

"Twenty dollar. King Yellowman tonight." He waved toward a color-splashed poster on the wall.

"Okay if we go in?" I asked.

The big man laughed. "It okay wit' me, long as you pay de price."

Yussuf went back to pay the cab, then we paid and went in. It was stifling hot in the building, even with two exhaust fans set high in the end walls. A crowd of musicians was pinned by floodlights on a low stage, two women and a man singing behind microphones. The overdriven P. A. sounded like hail on a tin roof.

There were at least a thousand people in the club, and as far as I could see I was the only white person there, but except for an occasional astonished glance nobody paid much attention to me. Yussuf disappeared and came back with two Green Stripe beers, but they didn't last long in the suffocating heat. The only lights in the place came from the stage. Shadowy figures with flashing white teeth lurched in and out of the light. The building shook with the crash of the music and the synchronous pulsing of a thousand people dancing.

Yussuf disappeared again, and a few minutes later I saw him dancing with a yellow-skinned girl in a minidress. He brought her back to where I was standing, but there was too much noise for introductions. They danced away into the shadows.

About 0100 I found them and asked Yussuf if he was ready to go back to the ship. He asked if he could take the girl, and I told him he could. The three of us went out to the road to wait for a taxi, but since people were still arriving, we didn't have to wait long. We got back to the ship a little before 0200.

The party onboard was in full swing. Ian, Ricardo, Lionel, and the chief were on the fantail with four girls and two Jamaican men, seated around a table improvised from a piece of plywood fitted over the capstan. Two rum bottles, one empty and one half-empty, sat on the table next to a pitcher of melting ice. Somebody had brought a boombox from shore, and it was pouring out reggae music at full blast. The chief motioned us to sit down.

"I'm tired," I said. "I think I'll go upstairs."

The Jamaicans were watching me carefully. One of them, a stout young fellow with short braids secured by multicolored rubber bands, jumped up and took my arm. "Have a drink, Captain!"

I shook him off. "No thanks."

He came close. "Captain, I must ask you something. May I talk to you in here?"

He took my arm again and drew me into the galley. Clean dishes were racked by the sink, and two foil-covered plates were on the back of the stove. "Captain," the man said earnestly, "do you want to be rich?"

"Depends on what I have to do."

"I can make you rich, never fear 'bout dat. Dis ship going to Miami?"

"No, it's going to Haiti. This ship never goes to the United States."

The other Jamaican man was slipping past the door, going forward. "Hey," I called to him. He slid out of sight. I started around the Jamaican in front of me, but he dropped a shoulder to block me.

"Yussuf," I yelled, shoving the man aside and running into the hallway. The other man's feet were going up the companionway toward the office. I ran along the hallway and looked up. The door to the office was open. Flashlights waved around in the dark. I went up the steps.

The Jamaican and another man were standing at the forward bulkhead. The hinged painting was ripped off the wall, but the door to the safe was still shut. A crowbar lay on the office desk. The other man, a dark figure with great round eyes and a mouthful of teeth, snatched the crowbar off the desk and raised it. I threw myself sideways into my cabin and slammed the door. I fumbled at the bolt and got it shot home. The two men on the other side started arguing in Jamaican.

I reached up into the air vent above the bunk and stretched my arm in the narrow duct until I could feel the AMT's leather holster. There was yelling from below and hoarse shouts from the men outside the door. The door shivered under a heavy blow.

I pulled the pistol out of the vent and unsnapped the holster. A body slammed into the door. I drew the pistol and jacked a round into the chamber. When the door shook again I pointed the pistol at the middle of it and pulled the trigger.

The .380 sounded like a stick of dynamite in the small cabin. Someone howled on the other side of the door. There was a confused bumping, then feet stumbling down the companionway. The howls faded into silence.

I unlocked the door. The office was empty. The companionway was empty. There was blood on the steps. I crept downstairs with the pistol stuck out in front of me.

Yussuf was stretched out on the floor of the starboard hallway, writhing in pain and holding his head. When I got to him and pulled his hands away, they were covered in blood.

"They hit me with something," he said. "They hit me on the head."

"Are you all right? Can I leave you for a few seconds?"

"Go on, Captain. They went on deck. I'll be okay." He groaned. I eased him back to the floor and went forward.

The Jamaicans were crowding off the ship, the girls bleeting like sheep. They started running across the concrete apron toward the half-open gate. By the time I got to the foot of the gangway they were through the gate and gone into the dark on the other side of the road.

I walked out to the gate with the pistol ready, then went back to the ship, following a trail of blood drops in the dust. I could see the old guard in the office through a window, asleep with his head on a desk, his shotgun laid out in front of him.

Victor and the girl from the Willy Nilly were bending over Yussuf in the crew's mess. A bright, narrow gash gleamed red in his scalp. Ricardo came up from the engine room with a piece of pipe. "Are they gone, Captain?"

"All gone. But go on deck and keep a watch. Let me know right away if you see anybody coming toward the ship."

I went upstairs. There was blood smeared on the bulkhead of the companionway. The lock of the safe was dented, but the door hadn't been opened. A rusty screwdriver and a hammer with a broken handle lay on the floor. I unlocked the safe. The $412 of ship's money and the ship's revolver were untouched.

I regarded my .380 sadly, then went to the boat deck and threw it as far out into the dark bay as I could. I threw the burglar tools overboard as well and wiped up the blood. I went downstairs and wiped up the trail of blood across the deck. There was none on the gangway that I could see. I walked across the apron and used my foot to spread dust and gravel over the blood drops there.

I gave Yussuf some codeine from the ship's medicine chest and he and his friend retired to his cabin. The rest of the crew sat up for a while longer, finishing the rum and talking. Lionel said that they had asked the two girls who arrived first to call for more girls, and that the two men had arrived with the second pair. They'd never seen the man who had slipped upstairs. The girls had brought their own boombox, to cover the sound he made trying to break into the safe. The boombox still sat on the crude table.

I volunteered to take watch and the crew went to bed. I sat in the wheelhouse for the rest of the night, but no one came to the ship until the fuel dock opened for business at 0800. Yussuf's girl came out of his cabin, as neat and done-up as she had been the night before, gave him a long kiss, and left the ship. He said later she hadn't charged him a cent.

We took on 28 tons of diesel, then the pilot arrived and we cast off. Yussuf was wearing a baseball cap that concealed the bandage on his head. When we drew away from the dock and the pilot ordered Half Ahead, Yussuf and I exchanged secret, relieved glances.

The ship cleared the reef at 0910 and we dropped the pilot off at 0935. I sent Yussuf back to his bed and turned the ship toward the southern coast of Haiti. The wind was steady out of the southeast, blowing white spume across the bows, but the ship shook it off and kept plowing ahead under a brassy sky.

At 0700 the next morning we arrived off the Baie des Flamants. I drove back and forth in front of the reef a couple of times, studying the shore through the binoculars. It was steep-to, with a narrow stripe of white sand beach under the brow of the hill. A small village perched on the beach, sailboats at anchor in front of it. The reef ran southwest from a rocky point east of the village and ended in a low coral head awash. The *Sailing Directions* advised keeping the shoreline a quarter-mile off the port side when entering the bay.

I lifted the binocs, but I couldn't find a road to the village, only a path with goats tethered in it leading up over the hills. The nearest town on the chart was Aquin, on the road to Les Cayes. I called for Half Speed and turned the ship around for another pass, dodging the fish-trap floats that dotted the water.

The generator came on and the engine slowed. I brought the ship in to a quarter-mile off the reef and swept the shoreline. Black figures stood on the beach, waving to the ship. One of the boats was putting out, a crew of barechested men hoisting the sail.

Yussuf came into the wheelhouse from breakfast, smoking a cigarette. "Sun too bright," he complained. "We going in, Captain?"

"I guess so. This is the place. Damned if I can see how they're going to discharge, though."

"What about Customs?"

"The charterer promised to send the clearance as soon as we got in, but the only people I can see on the beach are fishermen."

I called for Stop Engine when we got off the western tip of the reef, and we waited, dead in the water, for the fishing boat to arrive. Skimming along under a great ragged sail, it brought up sharply by the pilot ladder, the boy in the bow fending off with his feet as the others took in the sail. I went down on deck and had Yussuf translate.

"Is this the Baie des Flamants?" he yelled down.

They nodded happily. Yes, it was the Baie des Flamants. Nobody knew Jacques Garot, though, and they had not been visited by any strangers recently. Yes, the bay was safe to enter, and very protected from the sea.

The fishermen came onboard and I conned the ship into the bay. Someone had stuck a stick up in the coral head at the end of the reef with a red gallon jug on it. We steamed past at Dead Slow with the fishing boat tied to the side, bumping gently.

The bay got deeper and wider toward the eastern end. We put down three shackles just off the village. The women stood barechested on the beach and stared at the ship. The crew gathered on deck to stare back at them.

Yussuf came down from the bow. I nodded toward the beach. "Is this like Africa?"

He shook his head. "Not the Africa I know, Captain. Maybe down south. This is very primitive here."

I went up to the chartroom and called T & G Shipping in Miami. Jacques Garot was in the office. "I am anchored in Baie des Flamants," I told him. "There is no one here to meet us."

"What? Pierre is not there?"

"No Pierre. There is not even a road here, Mr. Garot. I do not think we can offload here."

"We will discuss that later, Captain. Just stay where you are and call me back in one hour. I will arrange everything."

We signed off. It was a bright, hot day, with the sun glittering like broken glass on the sharp little wavelets. The ship hunted to the anchor, rocking easily. I gave Victor a 12-pack of Schaefer's to cool for the crew, then went upstairs to lie down. I fell asleep listening to Yussuf and the AB's on deck, chipping rust.

Yussuf came for me at 1100, but I was already awake. We went up to the chartroom. Reception was poor, even on 12 and 14 Mhz. I was tuning 22 Mhz when Yussuf clutched my sleeve and pointed through the port windows.

A boatload of policemen was approaching, sculled by a fisherman. I called WOM, but it took almost 10 minutes to get through to the High Seas Operator. I had just gotten Garot on the phone when the policemen came barging into the wheelhouse. The one in front was a bloated little pig with doughnuts of fat around his tiny eyes. He wore a blue uniform of some kind and had a Colt Police Positive in a worn leather holster. The man behind him was a great hulking creature in U.S.-style camouflage fatigues and combat boots. He carried an Uzi in his fist and a baseball grenade on his belt.

"The police are here," I told Garot. "You'd better talk to them."

I handed the phone to the uniformed pig and showed him how to depress the talk button. He and Garot jabbered at each other. The little man quickly grew furious and began to shout into the microphone. Garot's voice was garbled and angry in the tinny speaker.

Piggie dropped the handset and spoke to his men. The big man and two others seized me and dragged me into the wheelhouse. Whiskey Oscar Mike came on the air looking for me, but by then I was being hustled out of the wheelhouse and down the companionway. I saw Yussuf's shocked face in the chartroom window.

The crew were on deck, clustered at the port side. They gave an angry murmur when they saw me brought out, but the Haitian with the Uzi kept them at bay. The Haitians pushed me up the bulwark and onto the pilot ladder. Both policemen in the boat laid hands on me as soon as I stepped into the bottom. They held me as the other policemen got in. The fat little man came last, taking his place in the thwarts, wheezing and patting his chest. He told the scullsman to shove off.

It took only a few minutes to reach the beach. My hands were still unbound, but I was hustled onshore by the whole group of policemen as the ragged inhabitants of the village looked on. There were a dozen or so huts with thatched roofs and bamboo-and-vine walls, and a half-dozen goats tethered on the hillside. The police and I went up the path and over the hill, where the path widened. They released me and spread out. We walked about half-a-mile to the roadhead, where a Nissan pickup truck was parked.

I stopped when we got to the truck and summoned my pathetic French. "*Ou allons nous?*"

The fat man said, "To the police station in Aquin."

"Why?"

He glared at me. "Investigation of smuggling."

"But," I protested, "I wasn't smuggling. I only came here because. . ."

He shook a finger at me. "Say nothing more. We will go to the police station, and then we will have an investigation."

Three of the policemen got in the cab, and the two younger men got in the bed with me. We bounced off toward the west. Thirty minutes later the truck pulled up in front of a fence made out of thorn trees with their branches intertwined. Through the fence I could see a long yellow building with a tin roof. We got out and the two young policemen took my arms and escorted me to the building.

It was cool and dark inside. A desk sat against one wall with an ancient Remington typewriter on it. Two double doors at the back were open, leading onto a wide courtyard with two jacaranda trees in the center. Tiny blue flowers littered the ground under them. On the other side of the courtyard was a jail cell with a cement floor and roof. Three walls were made of 1" vertical pipes spaced about 6" apart. The fourth wall, to the back, was cement. There were about 15 male prisoners in the cell.

The soldiers pushed me into a chair by the typewriter. The pig-man sat in front of me and the others crowded around. He spoke a choppy mixture of Creole and English.

"Why ship here?"

"Charterer tell me to come here." After some time I made him understand what a charterer was.

He scowled. "The Bay of Flamants is not a port of entry."

"I know, but the charterer instructed me to go there. I must do what the charterer says."

"What you ca'go?"

"Cement."

"How many bags?"

"About 31,000."

He laughed. How, he asked, was I to discharge 31,000 bags of cement in a village without even a road? I explained that I didn't know, and that the charterer was responsible for everything. By the end of my little speech my French was getting pretty good.

After 30 minutes of this Piggie announced that he was going to Les Cayes to call Port-au-Prince, and that I would have to stay in jail until he got further instructions. "Per'aps," he said, "you go to jail Po'-au-Pranz, eh?"

He left in the Nissan. A young man in a faded army uniform, wearing a Colt with a chipped wooden handle, took me across the courtyard and opened the cell door. I walked in and he shut it behind me.

My cellmates stared at me curiously. "*Bonjour*," I murmured, and found a spot on the stained concrete floor.

"*B'jour*," came a soft chorus of replies. One of the men, sitting crosslegged, unwound his long legs and eased forward a couple of feet. "Why you here, *blanc*? What you do?"

"I'm a ship captain," I said.

He nodded and translated. They seemed to think that was a good enough reason to be in jail. We exchanged names and started talking. Now my French was really swinging. I explained that I was unjustly accused of smuggling cement, that my ship was in the Baie des Flamants, and that I knew Miragoane very well. As Miragoane was only a few hours away, across the mountains, this made us cousins.

After a few minutes one of the men sitting on a concrete shelf against the rear wall took a seat on the floor and the group invited me to sit on the shelf. I took my place and we continued our conversation.

The only toilet facility was a plastic bucket in one corner. A bucket at the other end of the cell held milky drinking water.

In the afternoon some girls came into the courtyard with baskets on their heads. Another building, at an angle to the cell, was opened by the guard, and half-a-dozen women came out, the female prisoners. They and the girls lit charcoal on the ground and started cooking supper.

Haitian jails don't provide food to their inmates, but my cellmates pressed a plate of rice and plantain on me. I hadn't eaten since breakfast, so I took it gratefully and washed the food down with a cup of questionable drinking water. My cellmates watched me constantly, studying every move I made.

The girls took our plates and washed them in the courtyard, laughing and chattering while they worked. Some of the girls stood outside the cell and talked to the men inside. Two policemen rocked on home-made chairs in the open doors of the station building.

The wind off the sea rustled through the trees strong and sweet. Everybody in the cell settled down for a nap. I and two others got to lie on the shelf, and the rest slept on the concrete floor with their shirts wadded up for pillows. I dozed, but didn't sleep.

The fat little man never returned. At 1700 hours a car pulled up. A big, soft, middle-aged man in a loose shirt and plastic sandals came into the station. I could see him through the open doors talking to the man with the Uzi. The soft man waved to me. I waved back.

The big policeman said something to the young guard, who ambled over and unlocked the cell door. I said goodbye to my cellmates and we shook hands around. I left the cell and the guard locked it behind me. We walked together to the building.

"I'm Pierre Boisblanc," the soft man said. "I am from Mr. Garot."

"Well," I said, "I'm glad to see you."

He laughed. "I am sure you are, Captain, I am sure you are. Have they treated you well here?"

"Very well, thank you."

He handed the big policeman a wad of Haitian money. They shook hands and Pierre escorted me tenderly toward the car. "Very sorry this happen, Captain, but you know Haiti. Mr. Garot did everything to make arrangements, but, well. . ."

"Yeah, right. So what now?"

"You must to go to Miragoane. We have big problem here. Mr. Garot paid Les Cayes police, but they did not share with Aquin police. Now Aquin police call Port-au-Prince, and ship must to leave quick. You must to go onboard and sail the ship to Miragoane." He shook his head. "I told Mr. Garot from the beginning that the ship must to come to Miragoane. This Baie des Flamants is not for ships."

"Hell, you can't even get trucks there. How was the cargo going to get to the road?"

"Well," he said sadly, "I do not think Mr. Garot has seen this place. I think somebody told him it could be done here."

We stopped at the roadhead and he let me out. I told him I would walk back to the village and catch a ride to the ship. He said that Jean Renet would meet us in Miragoane.

I arrived in the village hot and footsore. A U.S. $1.00 note got me a ride out to the ship in a dug-out canoe, where the crew were waiting on deck.

"Captain!" Yussuf said, giving me a hug. "Thank God you are safe. Were you mistreated?"

"Not at all. Chief, get oil up. We're going to Miragoane."

"Yessir," he grinned. "The girls are waiting."

I clapped him on the shoulder. "Let's go clear Customs in Miragoane."

Yussuf went forward with Ricardo, and I went up on the bridge. We turned in the bay with plenty of room and headed for the narrow entrance. The villagers came out again to watch, and some of them rushed to get in their boats. We steamed slowly past the village. I gave them a long, low blast of the horn that reverberated against the hills and tore off in broken notes out over the sea. They jumped and clapped for joy.

Once offshore we settled into our sea rhythm again, steaming westward toward the tip of the peninsula. We turned north during the night and passed between Cap Dame Marie and Navassa Island, and by mid-morning we were steaming in past Miragoane Point. We dropped anchor in the bay.

Yussuf and I surveyed the ships at anchor. The *Dieu Puissant* was there, and the *Gonaives Family*, and a German ship, the *Kara Horst*. The *God Only One* was still swinging to her anchor in the middle of the bay. The tarpaulin that had been stretched over her fantail was now blowing in shreds from the framework. The *Bahia Mar* and two unfamiliar ships were secured stern-to to the shore and discharging. The clanking of their gear and the loaded stutter of their auxiliary engines drifted across the water.

"Here comes Customs," Yussuf said, pointing. A boat full of girls in bright dresses was putting out from shore.

"You see Sonia?"

He picked up the glasses. "Yes, there she is. She cambio from *Bahia Mar*."

"Ah, shit, now I won't see you for three days."

"Captain," he protested, "I do my work, even if my girl is onboard."

"Of course you do. I was only kidding. But do you see my girlfriend?"

"Your girlfriend? Who is that?"

"Amanda."

He laughed. "I don't see Amanda. Maybe she die from AIDS already. No, there she is. Your girlfriend is still alive, Cap'n."

The boat drew up to the pilot ladder. The girls came onboard, greeting their long-lost boyfriends joyously. Victor came on deck and they gave him hugs.

I sent Amanda ashore with two dollars and a gallon jug, since *clairin* is sold out of 55-gallon drums. *Clairin* is Haitian moonshine, a clear distillate that tastes like blackstrap molasses and turpentine, only not as smooth. We had a *clairin* party on deck that night, with half the girls in port onboard. I mixed a wicked punch with mango and coconut juice that had two quarts of *clairin* in it. A German engineer from the *Kara Horst*, who had never tasted *clairin* before, drank four glasses of punch, took off all his clothes, and jumped into the ocean. "The vater is so varm!" he kept yelling up, "the vater is so varm!"

The slim girl with long hair, Lucerna, tried to get me to dance, but I declined. I did hand her a tall glass of punch, which she promptly tossed back. A few minutes later Yussuf came sidling up. "You like that girl, Captain?"

"Which one?"

"The girl who was talking to you. Lucerna."

"Yeah, she's a piece. What you got in mind, First?"

"She wants me to tell you she likes you."

"I bet." I rummaged around on the table, found a clean glass, and poured him a drink.

He shook his head. "I'm drinking Barbancourt. That what-you-call-it, that *clairin* is very bad."

"No," I said, "it tastes good in the punch. Gives it character. Try it."

He sipped and nodded. "Not too bad."

"Take it to Sonia. You'll get what you want after a couple of glasses of this stuff."

He laughed. "I get what I want anyway, Captain."

One of the girls laughed loudly and stumbled against a table. A heavy-set girl named Marta pulled Victor off his chair and started doing a wild prance around him. A Dominicana was dancing with the German engineer. He was now half-dressed, spilling his punch at every lurch. He pawed the girl blindly.

"Yussuf," I said, "these girls are getting plastered. How much do you think it would cost to get every girl on deck to take her clothes off?"

He peered at me. "What's that, Captain?"

"Well, these girls are all whores, right? There's. . .let's see, looks like 12 girls onboard. Ten dollars each is $120, right?"

He laughed and shook his head. "You *are* Captain Loco. These girls aren't going to take their clothes off."

"Aw, come on. You know what they have to go through to earn $10. This is nothing compared to that."

"That's different. This is in public."

"I bet you a case of Beck's that at least half of them will do it for $10."

"I bet none of them do it," he said. We shook hands solemnly.

I jumped up on one of the 55-gallon drums roped against the front of the house. "*Damas y caballeros*," I shouted. The dancers and watchers turned toward me. Victor turned the music down.

"Ladies and gentlemen," I said, "the good ship *Erika* has contributed to a fund to make this party a success. The ship will pay $10 U.S. cash to every girl onboard who will take all her clothes off!"

The party died. The girls drew together. Someone made an angry clucking noise. "Why did you say that, *Capi?*" Amanda demanded. "Why do you want us to take our clothes off? That is *indecente.*"

I climbed down. "Just for a joke. Forget it." I went over and turned the music up. The party resumed. I told Yussuf, "I'll get that case tomorrow, First."

He chuckled. "Yes, Captain, these girls do plenty bad things, but they don't take their clothes off in public."

"You know," I said, "they are *señoritas* after all."

I went up to bed about 0200. I was sitting on my bunk and pulling my shoes off when there was a knock on the office door. I got up and opened it. Lucerna was standing there. The light coming up the companionway lit her long legs below her minidress.

"*Capi?*"

"Lucerna. Um, listen. . ."

She slipped into the office. "Shh, *Capi.* Your crew has taken care of everything."

"My crew has done what?"

She tried to press herself against me, but I managed to get around the corner of the desk. "For us," she said. "For tonight. Your crew wanted me to come to you tonight."

"I see." I armed her off. "Lucerna, that's very nice of my crew, but I can't. I'm married."

She looked puzzled. "Me too, *Capi.*"

I laughed. "Let's do this. . .you can go upstairs and sleep in the pilot berth. Don't say anything to the crew and keep the money." I took her elbow and turned her around. "If they ask, I will tell them it was a night of magic and madness."

She laughed merrily. "Okay, *Capi.* You're a sweet man."

I took her upstairs and unlocked the wheelhouse. There were blankets in the drawer under the pilot berth. The party on deck was finally fizzling out. The German engineer was lying unconscious on the hatchcover with one foot dangling over the deck. Only two Haitian boatmen remained. Victor and his Dominican friend were talking together at the table, sitting in plastic chairs. "Goodnight, Lucerna," I said, and went downstairs.

We stayed at anchor the next day, for unknown reasons, and I gave the crew the day off. A short time after breakfast, while I was having a cup of coffee on deck, Victor's Dominican friend came strolling out of the accommodations. We said good-morning. He hailed a boat and stood leaning against the bulwark as it came over. When he'd gone over the side, I went and found Yussuf on the fantail. Sonia was in the galley washing dishes.

I asked Yussuf in English, "Where did Victor's friend sleep last night? I saw the German engineer sleeping on deck—I guess he must've caught a boat back this morning—and I saw Amanda sleeping in the crew's mess, but where was Victor's friend?"

Yussuf looked toward town. The ships discharging stern-to were clanking and creaking, and cargo nets were going into the lighters. "I think he stayed with Victor, Captain."

"With Victor? In his cabin?"

He nodded.

"Isn't his cabin a single? Oh, no."

Yussuf suppressed a grin. "Oh, yes."

"Victor is. . ."

He made a butterfly with his hands. "*Mariposa*, Cap'n."

"Oh, Lord," I said. "I can't have that onboard. I'm going to have a talk with him." I went to the galley and motioned Victor forward with me on deck. "Victor," I said, "*no importa* if you want to have a man for a friend, understand?"

He didn't say anything.

"But you can't have him stay with you onboard. What you do on shore is your business, but what you do onboard affects the ship. I can't have people saying that the *Erika* has *actividad homosexual* onboard."

He kept his eyes on the deck. "*Sí, Capi*, I understand."

I clapped him on the shoulder. "You're a good cook, and a good man. Don't let this be a problem."

He nodded and went back to the galley.

Shortly before noon I heard a knock on the saloon door. Victor came in with an old man, a tall, stooped *blanc* with a wizened face and a tremble in his hands. He gave me a frail paw to shake.

"I'm Captain Gunnar Johnsen, from the *Dani II*," he said in a heavy Nordic accent, pointing through the window to a red-hulled ship with a Scandinavian knuckle in the forefoot, anchored stern-to. He passed his hands over his face. "I'm sorry, Captain, but a terrible thing has just happened onboard." He swayed heavily.

"Have a seat." I pushed a chair behind him. He collapsed into it. I got a Sprite out of the refrigerator and put it next to a bottle of Scotch on the table. He poured two fingers of Sprite and two fingers of Scotch and downed all four.

"I just had a fatality onboard," he said. "A Haitian stevedore was killed by a slingload of flour. I saw it. I was on deck, and the rope broke. He was standing under it, bloody fool. Broke his neck. Poor chap died instantly."

"How long ago?"

"Two hours. The captain of the *Bahia Mar* said you might be able to help. He says you have contacts with the Haitians."

I laughed. "I do, but they aren't the kind anyone wants. But if you can get to the family before they go to the Justice Court, you might get off cheap." I went down to the deck. Two boys were loitering in a dugout canoe, waiting for someone to take ashore. I threw down a five-*gourde* note and told them to have Ronald Joanel come to the ship as soon as possible.

"I've got a Haitian fixer," I told the old captain when I got back. "He'll take care of you."

We talked for a while. This was his first trip to Haiti—the ship had just come across the Atlantic—but since he was an old Africa hand, he found Haiti tolerable. The death onboard had unnerved him, though, and he dosed himself with two more drinks before Ronald arrived.

"Ronald," I said, "good to see you again. This captain needs help." I explained the situation. "You heard about the accident?"

He shook his head. "I just got back from Petit Goave. What is the man's name?"

"Yves Robun," the captain said.

Ronald looked somber. "Yes, I know him. He is from Petit Riviere. He has a wife and three small children."

"Is his wife a country girl?"

"Yes, of course. She cannot read or write."

"Can you get her to come to town with you? To sign a paper at the notary office? You can take a taxi out to get her."

He nodded.

I turned to the captain. "You might want to go along with him. I suggest you offer her about $800 U.S. That's a year's wages. She might take it. Be sure to get her to sign a paper giving up her rights against the ship, and get it notarized." I looked at Ronald. "Is there a notary here?"

He shook his head. "No, but there is an *avocat* in Petit Goave."

"Then take her there. Take her before people start giving her ideas."

The captain got up to leave.

"And come back to the ship when you're finished," I told Ronald. "I need some help on other things."

They went down to the boat. Just before dark Jean Renet arrived in his polyester shirt and triple-pleated pants. His low-cut loafers were soaking wet. He gave me one shake of the hand. "Captain, why did you not go to Baie des Flamants?"

I told him.

He made an angry gesture. "Those are just excuses. You panicked, Captain. You should have told the police nothing. They would have let you go."

"Bullshit," I said evenly.

"Now plenty problem with the cement. The army controls the port. Every bag that comes off has to be counted by the army tallyman."

"So?"

"So Mr. Garot will have to pay $16,000 in duty for no reason."

I pointed a finger at him. "Was it you who told him he could discharge at the Baie des Flamants? Who came up with that idea?"

"You told Mr. Garot you could take the ship there. He told me you said that."

"Yes," I said, "and I took the ship there. But you never could have discharged there."

I was ready for a good, old-fashioned Haitian argument, but he wasn't in the mood. He left the ship after instructing me to have the vessel secured stern-to and ready to discharge by 0800 the next morning.

After supper some of the crewmen from the *Bahia Mar* came over in the ship's boat. They greeted Lionel happily, and I broke out a case of slop-chest beer for a small party. I sent Amanda to round up some more Customs agents, and by 2100 we had the Christmas lights back up on the front of the house and the Jamaican boombox set up on a table on the hatchcover. The party lasted until 0300, at which time the Nicaraguan chief officer from the *Bahia Mar* had to be lowered into a canoe with the rescue-boat davit. His mates used the deck crane on the *Bahia Mar* to hoist him aboard.

We went in to discharge at dawn, backing and filing between two ships to find our spot. There was an early wind coming off the land, blowing the bow to starboard and compounding the ship's natural tendency to back to port. The crew of the *Hosea Knaughton*, the next ship to the north, came out on deck in a hurry, but went back to breakfast when they saw I was going to make it.

We put out four shackles on each anchor, and I pointed to the boats I wanted to take my ropes ashore. Five or six boats were bobbing under my counter, the boys in them waving and shouting. The two lucky boats fought off the losers and gathered in a heap of hawser each, fed out by Ricardo and Victor on the fantail. By heavy rowing, with the crew paying out through the chocks, they managed to get the lines ashore and dragged up the short beach. One was looped over a twisted piece of I-beam and the other over a crude cement bollard sprouting out of the dusty earth like a mushroom.

We made All-Fast at 0715. I signaled Finished with Engine and went down to breakfast. Sonia and Esmeralda, Ian's girl, were in the galley with Victor, cooking and cleaning. I ate on the fantail, my plate propped on the gunwale. The lighters were starting to gather on the port side, their crews fighting for position under the hook. A donkey engine on the *Dieu Puissant*, to the south of us, started up with a couple of hard piston-slaps. Blue smoke blew across the water.

We had just started discharging when there was a commotion on shore. The stevedores ran to the side of the ship. I went out on the boat deck.

The crowd on the dock was fleeing through the breaks in the rear wall. Some were crouching behind mounds of broken blocks and debris. Two green Army trucks had pulled up in the street in front of the Customs house. A head peered out of one of the open windows in the second story and ducked back down.

I called to Roger, "What's going on onshore?"

"Looks like the army from Port-au-Prince is here, Captain. Maybe they take over now."

There was a short burst of automatic-weapons fire. A collective howl went up from the people still trapped on the dock. They pressed themselves to the earth.

The stevedores onboard flung themselves back from the bulwarks, putting the ship's house between themselves and the shore. Now I could see the barrel of a rifle sticking out from one of the Customs-house windows. Two pistol shots rang out, echoing against the mountains.

Another burst of automatic fire. Chips flew off the masonry wall of the Customs house. Another pistol shot, then a sustained volley of rifle fire from the trucks, pouring into the Customs-house windows and sending clouds of dust and fragments into the air. The firing tapered off and stopped. There was a silence, broken by the crying of children and a couple of hoarse Creole shouts.

A white flag was waving from one of the windows. Soldiers in ragamuffin uniforms stole out from behind the trucks and took up positions facing the open downstairs door of the building. One by one the Customs men came out with their hands up. The soldiers seized them and led them to the backs of the trucks. I saw the port director, his face a black mask in the hard sunlight, his hands tied behind his back, escorted from the building and led into a truck.

They started their engines and drove away. The people picked themselves up from the ground and the chattering began again. Four soldiers came out of the building with M-1's and began herding them toward the back wall. The people howled in protest, and a phalanx of Haitian women rushed to confront the soldiers, but they kept moving forward. Others gathered their meagre belongings hastily. Their voices reached me faintly, high and frightened.

One of the soldiers raised his weapon and fired a long burst into the sky. The scene fell into chaos. The soldiers started kicking the cooking fires apart, spilling food on the dirt. The Haitians ran for the breaches in the wall, carrying whatever they could grab, and within two minutes the dock area was clear of them, the embers from the scattered fires still smoking and the huts in shambles. Another army truck roared through the gate. I could see soldiers moving around in the upstairs offices.

The stevedores lounged on deck for another hour until Jean and two soldiers arrived. Grim-faced, he took me aside. "The Port-au-Prince army controls the port now. No discharging unless a soldier is onboard the ship. If he says stop working, don't argue with him. Just do it."

"Look, Jean," I said, "this is an unsafe port. I'm a hair away from steaming out right now. If these soldiers or anybody else gives me any reason to fear for the ship or the crew, I'm steaming out and Mr. Garot can nominate some other port for discharge."

"No, no," he cried, "It's the same all over Haiti. General Namphy has taken over all ports in Haiti. But do not worry. . .he will be gone soon. We only have to work with them for a while, then someone else will take over. It is not a problem, Captain."

I raised my eyebrows. "We'll see. How many people got killed today?"

"Nobody hurt, nobody. All a big fuss and noise only. Stupid business only."

"Stupid business," I agreed.

Ronald returned late in the afternoon, just as the stevedores were climbing out of the hold. He had taken the old Norwegian captain of the *Dani II* to the stevedore's widow in Petit Riviere, but Madame Robun had proven to be a tough negotiator, and had demanded no less than 13,000 *gourdes*, about $1100 U.S., to release the ship from liability.

The next morning the usual collection of lighters arrived on the starboard side, and when the army tallyman came onboard with his bodyguard at 0800, discharging began.

At about 1000 hours Ronald and I were sitting in plastic chairs in front of the house and laughing about the time I hired a *houngan* to put the powder on the ship, when I jumped up from my chair and ran to the bulwark. "Ronald," I cried, "come here! The *God Only One* is gone!"

He rushed to my side. "She should be right there, Captain."

"But we didn't have any wind last night, did we?" We both scanned the far rim of the bay, where ships that dragged anchor usually ended up. Except for the wreck of the *Palmyra*, which had been on the reef since before the *Erika* first arrived, the rim of the bay was empty of ships.

"Was that old man still onboard?" I asked him.

We looked at each other. His mouth got small and round. "I think he was, Captain."

"Oh, my God," I said. I found Yussuf and the rest of the crew on the fantail, taking their morning break. "Yussuf," I said. "The *God Only One* is gone. She must have sunk during the night. Do you know if the old man was still onboard?"

His jaw dropped. "He was, Captain. I saw him there yesterday. Oh, dear, oh, dear."

We all went forward. There was no sign of the ship.

I hired a Haitian boat to take Ronald and me out to where she had been, but the bay was too deep here to see anything, and too deep to free-dive.

No one ever saw the old man again.

The army from Port-au-Prince soon proved to be eager new members of the Greater Miragoane Chamber of Commerce, and discharging proceeded normally. Five days later we were finished and the holds had been swept clean by a throng of Haitian boys who worked for the bags of salvaged cement they could take ashore. An hour later Jean Renet sent out by canoe a scribbled message to steam for Miami.

We arrived off the Miami seabuoy at 1600 hours on April 10, 1988. Traffic was heavy on Ocean Drive, the bright cars flashing in the sun in front of the pastel hotels. There were a dozen ships in the anchorage, including the old *Gitan Express* with a five-degree list. We put down three shackles north of the seabuoy, and just before dark the pilot station called. We got underway and met the pilot boat at the seabuoy.

The tugs took us to Rollo's dock. There were two other vessels there, the *Bahamas Venture* and the *Gonaives Express*, both brightly lit. We could hear *salsa* from the *Bahamas Venture*'s windows as the tug *Ring Power* pushed our bow against the dock. We were put at the end of the dock, next to an unimproved stretch of coral riverbank.

Customs, INS, and USDA were waiting for us. The ship's agent came onboard, the same florid Irishman, and said that we were going to load bales of waste paper for Rio Haina. After we were cleared in, Yussuf, Lionel, and the AB's got dressed to go out on the town. I went upstairs to sleep. Trusting in Rollo's old watchman and his pump shotgun, I didn't set a watch for the night.

We opened the hatches at 0700 the next morning, and at 0800 bales of waste paper started coming onboard. The ones that burst their wires on the way across the dock were pushed off to the side into giant piles of loose cardboard. I took a taxi to the Alamo office on Le Jeune Road and rented a car, then spent the rest of the day looking for spares and parts. I had to drive to West Palm Beach to get a used exhaust manifold for the MWM, and arrived back onboard just as the crew were closing the hatches for the night.

After we were finished and the AB's had gone to supper, Yussuf came up to me. "Captain, I'm sorry to bother you, but my right ear hurts very bad. I cannot sleep with the pain."

I tried to look into it, but could see nothing. "I'll take you to a doctor tomorrow, Yussuf," I said. I went up and got two codeine tablets from the medicine chest. "Take one of these. If it keeps hurting, take another one. If it still hurts later, wake me up."

The next morning I took Yussuf to an ear specialist on 36th Street, an old Hispanic doctor with a blue chin and sad brown eyes. He studied Yussuf's ear with a light and said, "He has a punctured eardrum. Apparently it has been perforated for some time."

"What could have caused that?"

"Hard to say. Perhaps an infection. There is a great deal of scar tissue around the perforation. He will have to have an operation." He drew his fingernail down Yussuf's head behind the ear. "I will have to cut here and fold the ear forward. I must cut the scar tissue away before I can sew the eardrum back together."

"When can you do it?"

"I must consult my calendar. But he will have to stay in the hospital for a day or two after the operation."

I winced. "We have to sail in a couple of days."

Yussuf said, "I will come with the ship, Captain. I will have the operation next time we come."

"I do not recommend waiting," the doctor said. "You have waited too long already."

"We'll get a replacement first officer for one voyage," I told Yussuf. "You can fly to Santo Domingo to rejoin the ship. No, no, I insist."

The doctor consulted his secretary, and we set the operation for two days later. I took Yussuf back to the ship and left to continue gathering supplies. After three trips to the Jetro warehouse I'd spent my $1500 for the month's groceries. I found a good source for all-cotton rags at a *pepe* place under I-95 by the river. Fifty pounds for $50. I took a scored shaft from the fresh-water hydrofor pump to a shop on North River Drive, where the machinist promised to have it built up and turned down by 1700 hours.

On the way back to the ship I stopped at the agent's office and told the secretary that Yussuf had to get a crewman's medical visa to the U.S. She looked irritated at having her nail-filing interrupted, but managed to jot down a message to the agent. I called Arcadio Munoz and told him I needed a chief mate for one voyage. He promised to send a Nicaraguan he knew personally.

The fuel truck was alongside when I got back to the ship. I hurried onboard to find Garot sitting in the officer's mess waiting for me.

"Captain," he said, taking my hand, "let's go to your cabin."

We went up to the saloon. Victor followed with two cans of Coke and glasses of ice. He set them down and scurried out. Garot poured himself a drink and took a sip. "Captain, I have brought the Bills of Lading for you to sign."

"All right."

He handed the papers to me. I looked them over. "I can't sign these."

He forced a tolerant smile. "Oh, it is nothing but a little game we must play. Of course the ship is not responsible for the number of bales onboard, since it is a time charter. It is just a formality."

"Mr. Garot, of course I will sign all B/L's 'Quantity, quality, condition and number of bales unknown.' But I cannot sign for a number that I know is incorrect."

He slapped the table with the flat of his palm. "Just sign the Bills of Lading, Captain."

"No."

When he spoke again, his voice was quiet. "You cost me plenty money in Haiti last trip, Captain."

"I didn't cost you a penny."

"If you had done what you were told, and discharged in Baie des Flamants, I would have saved $50,000."

"How could I have done that? There's no road there. You were going to hire a thousand Haitians to carry 100-pound bags of cement a mile to the nearest road?"

"That is my concern." He fixed his yellow wolf-eyes on me. "Listen to me, Captain. If you ever disobey me again, I'll make sure you pay for it the next time you go to Haiti. You understand me?"

I stood up. "All too well. Now get off the ship."

He flushed. "You can't order me off the ship. I'm the charterer."

"And I'm the captain. No one ever threatens me on my ship. Get off or I'll put you in handcuffs."

He jumped up. "This ship is off-hire at this moment, Captain! It won't go back on hire until Dickie fires you and gets another captain."

"You've got three minutes to get off the ship." I checked my watch.

"Fuck!" he said, and knocked over his glass of Coke going around the table. He ignored it and stormed out. I saw him get into his Range Rover. The tires squealed as he headed out the gate. That and all other sounds were obliterated by a Concorde jet, streaking skyward on its daily departure for Paris, shaking the shallow earth. An Eastern jet followed it.

I went down and called Dickie. He laughed when I told him about Garot. "Your job is safe, Captain," he assured me. "I'll handle Jack. He's an asshole, but he pays the charter hire."

"Good, because there's another thing. Yussuf has to get an ear operation. The doctor says the total cost will be about $3800, including anesthesia and two days in the hospital."

Dickie didn't say anything.

"Yussuf's got to have this operation or he'll lose hearing in that ear."

He sighed. "All right. I'll wire the money to the agent now."

"What about crew wages?"

"I, uh, I'll wire the wages as soon as I can."

We hung up. I went back onboard and met the chief on deck. The coupling on the Deutz had failed. He had the grimy pieces of the old one wrapped in a rag, a strange-looking European design with tiny steel springs embedded in the rubber. He also had two fanbelts and a bearing for me to match somewhere.

I was in the office doing paperwork when two husky men in casual clothes came in. They introduced themselves as Customs agents and asked if we could go into the saloon. The one who did the talking, a short, dark man with tattooed forearms, was from Breaux Bridge, Louisiana, so we were buddies.

It was the usual proposition. They wanted me to spy on ships in foreign ports. I declined, as always, citing the possibility of Colombian unhappiness with me and my family. They poo-pooed my fears, but didn't press the issue. We shook hands again, they went out, and I started back on my paperwork. A few moments later I heard a noise on the boat deck. I went through the hospital and saw both agents standing in the port lifeboat. Cajun said to the other agent, "Somebody's going to lose his job over this bullshit."

I laughed. Their heads jerked toward me. I said, "We've already been searched, fellows. Besides, I thought you plainclothes guys didn't have to do this kind of dirty work."

They looked at each other, sweat beading their foreheads in the noonday sun. Cajun jumped down and came up to me. "Captain, we're missing something from your ship."

"What are you missing?"

"There was something in your lifeboat, government property, and now it's gone."

"What was in my lifeboat? What are you talking about?"

They looked at each other again.

"Oh, I see. You put a transponder on my ship. Is that what you're talking about?"

Cajun nodded unhappily. "If you've got it, Captain, we need you to give it back."

"I don't have it," I said shortly. "If I'd found it I would have thrown it in the ocean, but I don't have it. And you shouldn't be interfering with a ship's lifeboat."

"We've got to find it," the other man said. He was a tall galoot in a Hawaiian-print shirt and baggy jeans. "We'd be willing to pay some money to get. . ."

"Maybe some Haitian stole it in Miragoane. That's why we don't keep supplies in the lifeboat. I'll have to ask the chief officer."

"Oh, no," Cajun said, "don't say anything to the crew."

"That's your only hope."

"Ask the chief officer, then," he said. "We'll wait here."

I went on deck and found Yussuf. "First, there's a couple of Customs men onboard looking for a transponder they left in the lifeboat. Any idea what happened to it?"

"What kind of transponder?"

"It sends a signal to the satellites, telling the U.S. government where we are. It's to catch drug smugglers."

He stared. "Why on this ship, Captain? Why they put that thing on us?"

"Who knows? Anyway, they've lost it. You heard anything about it?"

"Oh," he said. "Captain, you remember that radio I found in the lifeboat?"

"No."

"When we left Miami the last time. I brought it to the saloon. I thought somebody had left the emergency radio in the boat."

"Oh, yeah, in the canvas case. That was it?"

"I bet it was."

I went up to the boat deck and unlocked the lifeboat locker while the agents watched. I took out the transponder and handed it to Cajun. "This what you guys looking for?"

Cajun looked it over gratefully. "Many thanks, Captain."

They left the ship with their precious transponder. I went back on deck. The loading was still going smoothly. At 1700 hours we were only a few bales away from filling the underdeck. I persuaded Morton to keep the stevedores a few minutes longer in order to finish, but it was almost 1800 when we got the last bale in. The stevedores grumbled as they knocked off, but they were too tired to put their hearts into it.

The next morning, for once, we didn't have to open the hatches. At 0800 hours the stevedores started loading bales on deck. Yussuf came aft from sounding the ballast tanks. "Do you think Dickie sent that money for my operation, Captain?" he asked.

I clapped him on the shoulder. "He'd better have. I'll call the agent at 0900."

"I'll be okay if he didn't. I can have the operation when we come back."

"Nonsense," I said, with more conviction than I felt. But when I called, the agent's secretary said that $3800 had been received by their bank and INS had approved Yussuf's medical visa.

"Was there a second wire?" I asked. "The owner was supposed to send crew wages."

"I'm sorry, that's the only wire transfer we got this morning."

I went back to the ship. Ian and Ricardo were watching me from the fantail. I knocked on Yussuf's door.

"Get dressed, First. The money for your operation is here."

He opened the door smiling. "Dickie sent it!"

"He sure did." I lowered my voice. "But he didn't send the crew wages. Don't tell the crew. I'm hoping it'll come later today."

He nodded and said in a low voice, "The chief is very worried, Captain. If he doesn't make the payment on his house in Cortes, the bank will take it away. And he is close to retirement, Captain. He needs his house."

"I know, First, but don't you worry about those things. Let's get this operation over with."

He got dressed quickly and packed a bag, and we drove out. As I turned onto 36th Street I saw him wiping his palms on his pants. He gave me a quick smile and looked out his window.

"You got your passport?" I asked him. "Good. Now listen, call the agent from the hospital and let him know when you're getting out. He'll have a taxi waiting to take you to a hotel. You should be out of the hospital before the ship reaches Rio Haina, so just rest up in your hotel room until we get there. You can take the first flight down and rest up some more in Haina. I'll keep the Nicaraguan onboard until we leave."

I looked at him. His eyes were damp. "Thank you, Captain," he said softly.

"No problem. It's an Arab thing. We are brothers."

"Yes, Captain, we are brothers."

I took him into the reception area of the hospital and waited as he checked in. A sturdy nurse led him away. He turned back at the swinging doors, but she hustled him through and the doors closed. I went out into the heat and glare of a Miami morning.

When I got back to the ship the stevedores were almost finished with the second tier of bales on deck. I found Morton on the dock. "Two tiers high, right?" I said.

"Mr. Rollo said put three levels high, Captain. You talk to him about it?"

"I don't have to talk to him. I know what the ship will take."

He gnawed on his lip. "Mr. Rollo said. . ."

I patted him on the shoulder. "I'll talk to Rollo about it. But no more than two tiers high until I okay it." I peered at the bales carefully. "Morton, these bales are soaking wet."

He turned around. "Yeah. They was 'spose to have a tarp over 'em, but I guess it blowed off."

The bales were grayish and rounded. Wet scraps of paper littered the deck. The ones that had broken apart on the dock were shoved into a big pile against an abandoned school bus.

I went up to the office and typed out a Note of Protest about the condition of the bales, with carbon copies, and took them to Rollo's office. He was smoking a big cigar and studying some Bills of Lading. Before I could speak he said, "You can take three tiers, can't you, Captain?"

"I'm not sure. I'll have to do a draft survey to see what they weigh. Then I'll do stability and let you know."

"Oh," he said airily, "we load a lot of paper here, believe you me. You won't have any problem with three tiers."

"We'll see." I handed him the Note of Protest and a carbon copy. "Those bales you're putting on deck are in bad shape, Mr. Rollo. I want to make sure the ship isn't held responsible for their condition."

He read the Note slowly, lips moving, and let it fall to the desk. "I know those bales've been out in the weather, but it's no problem. The shipper's been here and looked at 'em. He doesn't have any problem with loading them on deck."

"Then just sign the original. The carbon copy is for you."

"No problemo." He signed it with a flourish and handed it to me. "When can you finish, Captain? I've got another ship coming in at 1900 hours."

"Maybe 1500. But there's the lashing on deck. I doubt if we can get away by 1900 hours."

"No problemo," he said again. "You can have the crew do the lashing on the way downriver."

"Negative. For one thing, nobody's asked them. For another, they've got other things to do to get ready for sea. Hell, it's only 45 minutes downriver."

He pressed his lips together. "Then go to anchor and finish up there. Look, Captain, I've got a ship coming in for an express cargo. Maybe you'd better talk to Jacques."

"I don't need to talk to Jacques. I have four hours after finishing loading to leave the dock. Read the charter-party. If the charterer has to pay extra, that's not the ship's problem. That's between you and him."

He reddened. "Captain, you should be more cooperative. We're all trying to make a living here."

I stood up. "That's no problemo. Just don't try to do it on the crew's back."

He whined some more, but I was already going down the short hallway. Two Haitians were in the lobby, arguing wildly in Creole, hands chopping the air. The Cuban woman behind the desk didn't look up from her work.

Victor was waiting for me in the officer's mess with a dark, heavy-set man. "*Jhonny Garcia, el nuevo primer oficial*," Victor said. Jhonny stood up and shook my hand.

"*Me gusta conocerle*," I said. "So you're the chief mate from Arcadio Munoz?"

"*Sí, Capitán.*"

"What ship you come from?"

"Em. . .the *Carleton Carrier*, sir. A chemical tanker."

"Uh-huh." I regarded him. "What license?"

He opened a small folder and handed me a document. It was a Honduran 1600-ton first officer's license, issued by the Miami consul.

"Humph. This your only license?"

"I have Nicaraguan first mate license, but it is expired. I do not take it with me now."

"I see you've got a Green Card."

"Yessir."

"Good. Come with me." We went up to the wheelhouse. "Do me a favor. Lay out a course from the Miami seabuoy to Bimini Island. Give me the magnetic course-to-steer."

"Yessir." He took the parallel rules and laid off the course while I watched, then walked them over to the compass rose and took the true course. He corrected for variation and wrote the course-to-steer on a scrap of paper.

"Okay," I said, "you're hired for one voyage. I'll pay you $1000, but you will probably be onboard 10 days to two weeks. Is that okay?"

"You don't have permanent job, Captain?"

"I don't think so." I explained about Yussuf. He nodded. "Okay, Captain, I take it. When I get back to Miami I will have some money to look for next job."

After the second tier of bales was finished, I went around the ship taking the drafts forward, aft, and midships, so I could subtract the vessel's weight and find out how many tons had actually been loaded. The stevedore figures said 882 tons, but the mean of means said 912. The midships drafts showed that the ship was slightly sagged. I added 160 tons of ballast water and guessed at 20 tons of constant to arrive at a projected GM of 30 centimeters with three tiers. That was okay. I found Morton and told him to go three high. He grinned. "That's good, Captain. Now we don't have to argue with Mr. Rollo all afternoon."

I had Jhonny and the chief work together to ballast the ship down enough to keep stability without exceeding the river's 14' 6" controlling depth. The fork-lifts kept bringing the bales to the dock, and the crane kept loading them on the tops of the hatchcovers. As the rows of bales crept aft on No. 1, the ship started rolling with every bale that came onboard. I was on my way downstairs when I met Jhonny coming upstairs. "She's getting tender, Captain," he said.

"Yeah, she does feel tender, First. But I just did the stability, and we've still got over 30 centimeters of GM."

The ship rolled under the weight of another slingload. Jhonny gave me a careful look. "That's it," I said. "I'm shutting it down. There's something screwy with these bales."

I went ashore and straight into Rollo's private office. "Mr. Rollo, we've got to stop the loading. I think the weights I'm getting on the bales are off. The ship's all out of GM. I can feel it."

He jumped up. "Oh, no, oh, no, Captain, you've got to load at least 1300 bales. We figured that'll be only three tiers high."

"Doesn't matter. She can't take any more."

He started blustering. I said, "Mr. Rollo, I did my load plan according to the weights you supplied. But the bales in the hold are dry and the ones on deck are soaking wet. I want to see what those bales actually weight. I know you have a scale in the north warehouse."

He finally gave in rather than weigh the bales, and we ended up with three tiers high on No. 1 and two high on No. 2. I called the agent from the dock phone, but no more money had arrived. I called Dickie. "The agent says he hasn't received the crew wages yet," I told him.

"Oh, I'm sorry, Captain," he said easily, "I just haven't gotten around to it. It's too late for the crew to send money home now, anyway."

"No, it's not. There's a DHL office right across the river that's open 'til 10. You mean you haven't wired the money?"

"Uh, actually, I haven't, Captain. I'll wire it to the agent in Rio Haina."

I sighed. "Well, maybe I can get them to sail. And get your buddy Jack to pay you $500 for lashing, because I'm adding it to the wage accounts."

"All right, Captain. Tell the guys I'm sending everything to Rio Haina. Have a safe voyage and call me when you get there."

Once more I had to ask the crew to sail without getting paid. I was embarrassed, and waited until Jhonny had gone to drop his car off before calling them together. Once more, bitter and depressed, they agreed to sail.

The workshop delivered the reconditioned hydrofor shaft at 1630, and an hour later wire and fittings arrived. The crew started lashing the bales down to the staples in the bulwarks. It was late in the evening, and the cargo planes were starting to fly. Old Convairs and Martins mostly, overloaded and trailing blue smoke. And the big boys, cargo 747's with their windows taken out, shaking the earth as they struggled toward the ocean.

By 2200 hours a gusty wind was building from the east, heavy with the smell of rain. The crew had gotten the bales lashed down, but instead of polypropylene tarps Rollo had bought 4-mil plastic sheeting. I told the crew to go ahead and put it on top of the bales for show. The vessel had about a three-degree list to port, and Ricardo was spreading sawdust on the port side where one of the many pipe-repair clamps was leaking.

I patted him on the shoulder. "Good thinking, Ricardo."

"*Gracias, Capitán*. Yussuf used to tell me to do this every time in the United States. To keep from the fine, you know." He gave me a worried look.

"Don't worry," I assured him, "Yussuf will be back in Rio Haina. We'll all go up to the Manila Sunrise together."

Hercules arrived and nosed up to the bow, and Ricardo passed the hawser down. I could hear *Ring Power* at the stern, gunning her engine. Two hangers-on at the dock, Haitians who lived in a shipping container, threw off the lines from the bollards. We eased away from the bank.

The 27th Avenue Bridge opened, bells ringing and lights flashing, and we slid between the spans. I stood in the darkened wheelhouse as we slipped downriver. Under the I-95 overpass derelicts fought for whiskey and drugs in the half-light, darting shapes between the cardboard shacks. Then we went through the Brickell Avenue Bridge and out into the bay where the pilot boat was waiting. The pilot stepped across to the bulwark and climbed over the bales to the house.

There was a chop in the narrow bay as the ship neared the breakwater. "Rough out there tonight," the pilot said. He was a blond man about my age, wearing a white shirt with epaulets. "Loaded like you are, though, you won't have a problem."

"We're going south," I said. "It'll be smooth as a lake."

We dropped him off at the seabuoy and Jhonny came up on the bridge. "I take midnight shift, Captain?"

"Naw, that's only an hour away. I'll stay on until 0200, then I'll get you up. How about that?"

"Very kind, Captain, but I do not mind. . ."

I sent him downstairs to eat and get some sleep. With the ship on course and the tailshaft on, I went out on the wing of the bridge to check the running lights. The wind was snapping the flag at the stern. Short, hard waves were thumping against the port side of the hull, directly abeam. Now the ship was listing four degrees to starboard.

I went down to the engine room. "Chief, are two and three full?"

"Yessir."

I shook my head.

"Problem, Captain?"

"I don't like the way the ship feels. She's topheavy."

"Maybe we go back?"

"No, I don't think so. We'll be okay. I just hope it's not too rough when we get south of Cap Dame Marie."

I went up to the wheelhouse and closed the door on the wind. Spray was bursting over the port bulwarks, and the thin plastic sheeting that had covered the bales was already starting to shred. Now and then spray flew over the tops of the bales and tore across the ship into the blackness.

The wind kept building as the ship rolled southward. We left the lights of the Florida Keys dwindling off to pinpricks to the southwest, and by 0200 we were at the mouth of the Santaren Channel. Cuba was 100 miles ahead. The list had increased to five degrees under the press of the wind.

When Jhonny came on watch, I went on deck and crawled forward over the bales to sound the tanks again. The ship was rolling easily, but she was sluggish coming back upright. I hung over the starboard bulwark, looking aft, and saw very little water draining out of the scuppers. I didn't like that. I didn't like that at all.

Back in the accommodations I went along the hallways knocking on doors. "Everybody up," I yelled. "We've got a problem. We've got to get rid of deck cargo."

The off-duty crew came out of their cabins, groggy and wrinkle-faced.

"Men," I said, "the bales on deck are soaking up water and getting heavier. We've got to cut some of 'em loose. Ricardo, get the wire-cutters. You and Lionel and Jhonny go forward and cut the lashings on No. 1."

"Yessir." They went back in their cabins to get dressed.

I went up on the bridge and checked the clinometer. Now six degrees. The ship swayed under a gust of wind, rolled to starboard, and struggled back to six-and-a-half degrees.

"Oh, shit," I said. I went to the autopilot to turn the vessel's bow into the wind, but I was one wave too late. The next one was stiff with spray and shoulders above the rest. It slammed into the port side and sent solid sheets of water pouring across the tops of the bales. The ship heaved to starboard, shuddered, and started rolling. I lost my footing and fell to the deck, sliding into the steering pedestal.

The ship kept rolling. Things flew off the chart table and crashed to the floor. There was a muffled yell from below, and more crashing. I struggled up, hanging onto the binnacle. The clinometer said 25 degrees. It went no further. I looked down at the deck.

The second and third tiers of the deck cargo on No. 1 had slid to starboard and were hanging on the lashing wires. The bales were soaked black in the flood-lights, the wires buried in them.

I found the crew scrambling for the port side, struggling into their life jackets. "Stay onboard!" I yelled. "Stay onboard! We've got to get those bales off."

They stared at me with wild eyes. Ian came tumbling out of the engine room, clawing for purchase against the bulkhead.

"The ship is stable for the moment," I said. "Ricardo, where are the bolt-cutters?"

"I. . .I left them on deck."

I went forward and found them lying against the hatchcoaming. The black ocean was washing through the scuppers on the starboard side, carrying hundreds of clotted lumps of paper rearward with every heave.

I took the bolt-cutters into the accommodations. "Ricardo, you and Jhonny go forward and cut the wires. You have to do it from the port side. And be careful. Those wires are under a lot of tension."

He stood there. I held out the cutters. He did not take them.

"What's wrong?"

"Captain, it's too dangerous. When I cut the wires, the bales will be flying. Maybe the wire will cut my head off."

"We've got to save the ship," I said, my voice rising. "Crouch down by the bulwark when you cut. Hold the cutters up like this." I raised them over my head. A blast of spray blew into the hallway and plastered my shirt to my back.

Ricardo stepped away.

"All right," I said, "I'll do it. But I need someone to come with me. Who's coming?"

I looked at Lionel. His stolid face worked in the hard overhead light. The ship rolled to starboard and lost another degree. A wire groaned under the strain. Lionel stepped out of the light.

So I went outside and climbed up on the bales on the port side, using the lashing wires for hand-holds. Warm spray stung my head and ears and turned cold in the wind. I clambered over the crane and onto the No. 1 hatchcover. The top bales had shifted more than six feet. On the starboard side the outermost bales were hanging over the ocean.

I worked my way forward to where the first wire was shackled to a staple in the port bulwark. The deck was dry here, and I was able to wedge myself between the bulwark and the forecastle ladder. The light was cut off by the forecastle, and I was in the dark. Bright spray flew past the floodlights on the bridge.

I reached the cutters up and secured the wire between the jaws. The wire trembled in the handles. I pulled my head down between my shoulders and pulled the handles together.

It took only the slightest force to sever the wire. The cutters fell clear as the wire sang off into the dark. There were some heavy splashes on the starboard side, but I couldn't tell if we lost any list. I crawled aft to the second wire. Here I was exposed to the wind and spray shooting over the bulwark and the ocean surging in through the scuppers. The ship rolled again, and struggled back. I cut. Again the wire tore off with a sound like rushing air, and bales fell unseen into the ocean.

I had to get on top of the bales on deck to get to the next wire. It was sunk into the bale. There was nowhere to hide here, nothing to put between me and the flying wire. I stretched myself flat on the soaked bale, as far from the wire as I could get, and reached the cutters out. I got the wire between the jaws, closed my eyes, and pulled them together.

The wire whirred up in the air. The ship shuddered as bales fell off. I opened my eyes. Maybe a little less list. I crawled aft to the next wire and cut it. Again it flew up and away, and more bales fell off.

I stopped when I'd cut all the wires forward of amidships. I went aft on top of the bales on No. 2. Ricardo and Lionel were standing in the spray forward of the house, dripping wet, holding flashlights and rope. They didn't say anything as I came off the bales and went into the house. I dried myself in my cabin, changed clothes, and went up to the wheelhouse.

The ship was steady at 10 degrees of list. About half the cargo on the No. 1 hatchcover had fallen off. The rest of the unsecured bales had jammed themselves against the starboard bulwark.

The chief came up to the wheelhouse. "Captain, you want me to pump out No. 3 starboard? That would probably bring us back even."

"Negative, Chief. We need all the weight below we can get. If we did that we might roll to port. No, we'll continue like we are. In the morning we'll turn into the wind and try to use the crane to get some more bales off."

"Yessir."

I followed him downstairs. The crew had gathered on the fantail, still in their lifejackets. I looked them over. "Go back to your cabins. Keep your life jackets handy. If she rolls again, more bales will fall off and she'll come back with no problem."

The crew went forward, one at a time, until only Victor was left. "Captain," he said, "the crew feel very bad. They are sorry they did not help you."

I grunted. "I wish to God I had Yussuf here now."

"Yes, Captain," he said, "this old *buque* needs Yussuf."

I stood watch with Jhonny for the rest of the night. Dawn came slowly. The wind continued at the same force. Whitecaps marched out of the rising sun and hurled themselves against the sloping side of the ship. The loose ends of the severed wires trailed along the starboard side.

About 0900 hours the wind fell off to a steady breeze. I gathered the deck crew and turned the ship into it. The chief took the ship off the tailshaft generator and slowed to Half Ahead. We chugged slowly eastward toward the Bahamas.

There was still too much roll to use the crane, but with everybody on deck except the chief, we were able to heave the loose bales overboard one at a time. By 1200 hours we had cleared all but a dozen of the second tier of bales on No. 1 hatchcover. The first tier was jammed against the bales on the starboard deck. I told the crew to leave the rest, and Jhonny and I went up to the wheelhouse. The clinometer said five degrees.

"You can turn back on course," I told him wearily. "I've got it marked where you turn into the Old Bahama Channel. It should be about 1300 hours. Wake me up if anything happens. Otherwise, I'll come on watch at 1800 as usual."

"Yessir."

I went downstairs and took a lukewarm shower to rinse the salt off, then tumbled into my bunk. It was cool enough that I didn't need the fan.

CHAPTER EIGHT

WE ARRIVED OFF THE RIO HAINA SEABUOY JUST AFTER DAWN on the sixteenth. The sea was running high in a light wind that came in from Africa through the Windwards, rolling the ship heavily in the troughs. It had rained again during the night. Limp strands of plastic sheeting lay stuck to the tops of the bales on No. 2.

The pilot took us in at 0710 to berth at the same unimproved dock next to the sally port. The clouds had cleared, and a hot Dominican sun was well up in the sky over the shipyard across the river. We docked bow-upriver and Jhonny led the deck crew in lowering the gangway. The pilot, a spry little oldster with bushy white eyebrows, took his Scotch and cigarettes in a paper bag and scampered off the ship. The officials trooped on and cleared us in.

Gustavo, the same ship's agent, brought the receivers with him. Mario was a tall, dark man with thin black hair combed in greasy tendrils over his bald pate. He handed me a faxed copy of the Bill of Lading and asked if all the bales were onboard.

I handed him a carbon copy of the Note of Protest I had prepared. "We lost about 120 bales overboard," I said. "I had to jettison them to save the ship in heavy weather."

The other receiver, a squat black man with gray hair named Owen, pulled the Note of Protest from Mario's hands. "Over 100 bales!" he said in a Jamaican accent. "The ship will pay for these bales?"

"Not at all. Deck cargo is always shipper's risk."

He frowned. Mario said, "Except for those 120 bales, you have all the rest of this Bill of Lading onboard?"

I shrugged. "How would I know? We're on time charter. The ship took no tally."

"But. . ." Gustavo persisted anxiously, "you are sure you loaded 1302 bales, right?"

"I told you, I have no idea. The tally is not the ship's responsibility. This ship is under time charter to Mr. Garot."

Gustavo said to Mario, in Spanish, "We must try to get a count as soon as possible. Dompapel will kill us if there is a shortage. The Letters of Credit were released yesterday."

"When can we get the count, then?" Mario asked me in English.

"Maybe two days. There's going to be a hell of a mess in the hold after you're done, you know. A lot of the bales broke apart during loading."

Mario winced. "Broken bales are a big problem, Captain."

"A big problem for the stevedores in Miami, maybe. No problem for the ship."

They didn't seem so sure about that, but they got up and shook hands with me again. Gustavo said, "Oh, Captain, you are changing chief officer in Haina?"

"Yeah. Remember Yussuf? He had to have an ear operation. I took another man for the voyage. Yussuf will rejoin the ship here."

"Yes, I have a fax from the agent in Miami. Mr. al Karim is arriving this afternoon on American 1778. I will have a boy pick him up and bring him to the ship."

"Great. Also make arrangements to sign off the present chief mate, Jhonny Garcia. He's going to Miami. He has a Green Card."

They went out and down to the dock. A giant crawler crane was inching toward the ship, the hook swinging wildly from the tip. Four flatbed trucks were already parked on the verge, their drivers squatting in the shade of the trailers. Jhonny came into the saloon. "Which hatch do you want to discharge first, Captain?"

"Discharge No. 2 hatchcover. I want to keep from getting the bow too high. After that, discharge the rest of the cargo from No. 1 hatchcover."

He started to say something, but changed his mind and went out. I finished my paperwork and went to the bridge to complete the logs. About 0930 I went ashore and took a motorbike ride to the center of town, where I found a *notario* to put his seal on the Note of Protest. I called my house from the telephone office, but my wife wasn't home. I called Dickie's number and left a message on his answering machine. Then I went back to the ship.

The No. 2 hatchcover and the decks alongside it were cleared when I arrived, piles of wet paper making a gluey mess on deck. Jhonny had gathered the loose wires from the starboard side, and the crew were busy unlashing the bales on the No. 1 hatchcover. A tallyman for the receivers was sitting on the hatchcoaming with a grimy notebook in his lap.

A car taxi pulled up at the foot of the gangway. Yussuf got out with his bag, paid the driver, and came slowly up the gangway. I met him at the boarding ladder.

"Captain!" he said. We hugged. His head had been shaved behind the right ear.

"Welcome back, First," I said, taking his bag. "Your cabin's ready for you. I made your replacement sleep in the spare cabin." We walked across the deck. "Man, I sure needed you coming down. We almost turned over in the Santaren Channel."

He stopped. "What?"

"The cargo got wet and shifted. The ship went over to 25 degrees and didn't come back." I spat on the deck. "And no one on the crew would help me cut it loose. I had to go forward with the bolt-cutters and cut the lashings myself."

He looked stricken. "Ricardo, Lionel. . .they wouldn't help you?"

"Nope. The cowards hid in the accommodations until I was finished. It was hairy, too, let me tell you. Those cables were so goddamned tight they snapped like piano wire."

We started walking again. "Very bad, Captain," he said sadly. "Very bad. I wish I had been with you. You know I would not have let the captain do that himself. It is not right."

"At least you would have gone with me." I unlocked his door and opened it. The cabin was hot and dark and smelled of damp bedding. I put his bag on the table. "Get some rest, First. We should be finished discharging tomorrow." I stepped out and turned around. "How do you feel? Can I sign the other chief mate off here, or should I keep him for another voyage?"

"Oh, no, Captain, I'm fine. You should sign him off before we leave."

"Good. If you need anything, I'll be onboard."

At 1600 hours the agent arrived with the receiver, Mario. The stevedores had reached the floorboards at the forward end of the hold, wading through waist-deep piles of paper scraps and tangled loops of baling wire. Gustavo and Mario nodded to me and went to stand by the coaming, talking with their heads together. I stood on the other side and watched the bales come out, trailing scraps and dust.

After a few minutes Gustavo and Mario went to talk to their tallyman, then they came up to me. We shook hands.

"Captain," Gustavo said gravely, "there is a very big problem. The cargo is very short."

I nodded. "I figured it would be. Plus the broken bales. There's a bunch of them."

Mario said curtly in Spanish, "Very big problem, Captain."

I looked at Gustavo. "Problem for the ship?"

Gustavo put a hand on my arm. "Let us finish discharging and we will see. Do not preoccupy yourself now, Captain. "

"Okay, fine," I said. "I'll just occupy myself when the time comes."

They went down to the dock and stood on the gravel arguing for five minutes before leaving in Mario's van. Two hours later the stevedores finished discharging and left the ship. The foreman told me without bothering to put any conviction in it that they would be back the next morning to clean up the loose paper. I called Gustavo on VHF and told him that we were ready to sail.

"Em, Captain, it is too late today," he said. "I must go to the Captain of the Port, you know, and they are already closed."

"Why didn't you get our clearance earlier, then? You knew we were going to finish today."

"I'm sorry, Captain," he said smoothly, "I must take another call. But don't preoccupy yourself. . .I will be there in the morning."

He signed off. I went to the saloon and ate a solitary supper, washing it down with a cold Presidente. Later I went downstairs, but Yussuf was asleep, so I left the ship and walked up the hill to the Manila Sunrise. Hanio had a fresh crop of Filipinas in, not a one over 20. He was holding court from behind the bar, entertaining a group of Yugoslav seamen with an energetic rendition of "Having My Baby." He waved to me and sent a short, plump girl to my table with a one-liter Presidente. She sat down and tried to rub my leg, but I squirmed away. A group of Peruvian seamen, already drunk, came staggering in, and she went to them.

I drank two one-liter Presidentes and left a little before dark. Hanio wanted to send a girl with me— "on the house," he said—but I declined. The air was cooling off, and the sound of music from the other bars floated across the street in the light wind. A fat black girl in a tube top, with a bulge like a Tootsie Roll, tried to waylay me, but I swerved and kept going. I could see the *Erika* far below, lit by the deck lights, a thread of blue smoke drifting up from her stack.

The crew were in their cabins. I found Yussuf and Jhonny in the officer's mess, drinking Schaefers. "Jhonny," I said, "you'll be signing off tomorrow. I'll pay you in the morning. The agent said he'll call and let me know when he's coming to get you."

"Thank you, Captain."

"Yussuf, how do you feel?"

"A little tired, Captain, but I'm okay." He smiled wanly. "I need some of Victor's cooking. That hospital food was terrible."

"You need some *pollo desnudo*," I said, and explained the joke to Jhonny.

I took the first watch, until 0200, then Lionel came up to relieve me. I was about to go down when he cleared his throat. I stopped in the door. "Captain," he began, "de odder night, when you had to go on deck by you'se'f. . ."

"Yes?"

"I'm sorry. I should ha' gone wit' you. You know I am not afraid, but de odders. . .dey was talking about how de owner do not pay, how we should not risk our lives for soch an owner. Now I t'ink dat was wrong. You had to risk your life instead. Dat is wrong, Cap."

"Don't worry about it, Lionel. I'm not firing anybody because of it."

He shook his head. His face was obscured by the dark in the wheelhouse and the brilliant floodlights on the dock behind him. "I no worry 'bout dat," he said. "Good welder get job on any ship. I talk to Guyanese captain today offer me one good job on container boat. Dey go from here to Rotterdam wit' pineapple."

"Are you going?"

"No, Cap, unless you tell me to. If I can stay on *Erika*, I stay wit' you."

"Then stay, Lionel. You're a good man."

"T'ank you, Cap." He left.

I went downstairs for a snack. Victor heard me in the galley and came out in a tee-shirt and shorts, his feet slapping along in plastic sandals.

"*Capitán*," he said, "I have something very important to tell you."

"What is it, Cookie?"

He was not ducking or grinning now. "I went to see Ysadora today, *Capi*. You remember, the little one with the. . ." He pantomimed large breasts.

"Yeah, *los tetones*. The chief's girlfriend."

"Yes, Captain. She is a friend of mine. I called her and went to see her. She has a good job in Haina now. She will never go back to the ships."

"I'm glad to hear that," I said patiently. I took a piece of chicken from the back of the stove.

"Ysadora told me that Humberto is Sonia's husband."

I stopped with the drumstick half-way to my mouth. "What? Humberto, the Dominican musician?"

"Yessir."

"I'll be damned. And I remember one night after a party, Sonia was with Yussuf and Humberto slept in the crew's mess."

"That's right, *Capi*. And Humberto put the *polizontes* onboard our ship."

I dropped the chicken back on the plate. "The hell you say! The ones in Miami? How did he do that?"

"They paid him $700 each. They came from Santo Domingo just to stow away on the *Erika*. Humberto looked all around the ship and figured out how to hide them. He had some short pieces of wood cut onshore for the stowaways to bring onboard in sacks." He smiled sadly. "He makes plenty money putting stowaways on ships. That is why he stays in Miragoane even when the band is not there."

"Sonofabitch. Thanks, Victor. I'll talk to Yussuf in the morning."

I ate the chicken and went up to the saloon. It was brightly lit and hot. I threw open the windows, turned on the fan, and sat down to read, but the words crawled across the page like ants. Finally I went to my cabin and lay down, sweating and naked, on the bunk.

The next morning I set the crew to sweeping up the deck. Yussuf said, "The charterer must clean the holds, right, Captain? Plenty trash still in the holds."

"Hah. Don't hold your breath for the stevedores this morning." I moved up close and told him what Victor had told me. He dropped his broom.

"No, Captain! It is not possible!"

"Yussuf," I said gently, "she's a whore. What does a husband mean to a whore?"

He shook his head in dismay. "It's not that. But I cannot forgive myself for bringing trouble to the ship. I cost Mr. Dickie $9000 and almost got you fired."

"Hell, Yussuf," I said, "it wasn't your fault. I knew Humberto was a snake and I still let him on the ship. Without him none of it would have happened."

"I'm sorry, Captain. I will have nothing more to do with Sonia."

"I'll take care of it when we get back to Miragoane," I said. "I'll have Kokimo break his fucking fingers. We'll see what kind of music he plays after that."

"And I will pay for it," Yussuf said, without a smile.

Eight o'clock came, then nine, and still no stevedores. I was in the chartroom, about to call the agent on the radio, when I saw a small detachment of soldiers and police walking toward the ship from the port offices. Yussuf was wrapping scrap wire into a bundle forward. I leaned out the window and whistled to him. I pointed my chin toward the boarding party.

They came up the gangway single-file. I met them at the foot of the steps.

"¿Capitán?" the lead man said. He was a small, neat civilian with a doll's head, his slick black hair combed tight to his round skull. I nodded.

He handed me a paper in Spanish. I scanned it. The ship was *detinado por debtos*. I tried to hand it back, but he waved it away. "The ship is detained at the port, Captain," he said. "By order of the court in Santo Domingo, you cannot sail."

"But what is this all about?"

"Your cargo, Captain. The ship is accused of taking the cargo."

"We're accused of stealing waste paper? Is this a joke?"

"No, Captain, it is not a joke. It is very serious." He summoned one of the soldiers. "A guard will be put onboard for security. You do not have to give him any food. He will not interfere with your crew if you do not try to leave."

"I understand."

The little man hesitated. "I am sorry about this, Captain, but it is the way of shipping, no? I am the director of the port. . .if I can help you in any way, please call on me in my office." He pointed to the gray building. "Good luck, Captain. Let us hope this problem is resolved quickly."

"Yes," I said, "let us do that."

All but the guard went down the gangway. He was a sallow young man with a hairline mustache and a shabby, ill-fitting uniform. He carried a pistol-grip shotgun and wore a cartridge belt. I smiled at him. He returned a sullen look and went to sit on the edge of the hatch.

"Ricardo," I said, in Spanish, "get the guard a chair to sit on."

I went up to the wheelhouse and called the agent on VHF. "Gustavo, what is this about the ship getting seized?"

"Oh, Captain," his tinny voice said, "very big problem. All the missing bales . . .Dompapel has gone to the court and gotten an order seizing the ship for the missing bales."

"This ship is on time charter," I wailed. "We aren't responsible for short-loads. And deck cargo is always shipper's risk."

"Very sorry, Captain, but Dompapel is powerful company here. Maybe your owner will have to get a lawyer and fight them in court."

"Oh," I said, "fight a Dominican company in a Dominican court. That's a good one. I'm going to tell that one to all my friends."

I signed off and went ashore to call Dickie, but his answering machine picked up again. I relayed the news and left. It was almost 1000, and the air was already hot under puffy brownish clouds racing westward. It took a while to find a *moto* to take me back to the ship. I bought a tepid Coke to wash down the dust while I waited.

A group of men came surging up the street with a door held above their heads. An enormously fat woman was lying on it, writhing in pain. With traffic backed up behind them into the distance, they carried her up the hill and into a ramshackle little building with *"Cirujano"* scrawled on the wall.

I finally snared a beat-up dirt bike with the tank wired to the frame and made it back to the ship. The crew were on the fantail. Yussuf said, "The agent was here. He said he will come back at 1400 to take Jhonny to the airport."

"Did he say anything about crew wages?" I asked. "Dickie is supposed to wire crew wages. I can't sign Jhonny off until I get some money."

"No, Captain. He said nothing about receiving money."

I sighed. He moved up closer. "What will happen, Captain? To the ship, I mean?"

"Nothing. It's going to sit here."

"But how long? When can we sail?"

I sat on a bitt. "Fellows, this may be it for the old *Erika*. Rio Haina is where ships come to die. You see all those wrecks upriver?" I pointed to the hulks lining the banks ahead of us. "They came in, got seized, and never left. There is no law in this country. It's as bad as Haiti."

Ian said, "But Captain, what about us? When do we get paid?"

I regarded him somberly. "Frankly, Ian, when an owner knows he's going to lose his ship, he doesn't care what happens to the crew."

"But we get paid when de ship is auctioned, no true?" he asked.

I shook my head. "No crewman has ever seen a dime from a ship auction in Dom Rep, even when it was the crew that had the ship seized in the first place."

They sagged like leaky balloons. *"Oh, Capitán,"* Ricardo said, *"muy malo, muy malo*. My wife has no money, no food in the house. I must go home."

"I know, Ricardo. I know. I'll try to call Dickie again after lunch and see if he sent the money. You can sign off if you want to. I don't blame you."

"Oh, no," he said in anguish, "I don't want to leave the ship. You are *buen capitán*. But. . .my family. . ."

I looked around the others' faces. Their eyes searched mine hungrily, but there was nothing for them there. I went upstairs.

At noon another guard came onboard, a skeletal young man with angry boils on his wasted cheeks. I watched from the saloon as he took the shotgun and cartridge belt from the first guard, pulled the chair over to a small rectangle of shade, and settled in.

I went to the phone office. This time I got Dickie on the first ring. "I know, I know," he said, before I could say anything. "The ship's seized for the fucking missing bales. You know how much they want? Two hundred thousand dollars. Can you believe that?"

"Sure I can believe it. But don't think that's all it's going to cost."

"What do you mean?"

"It'll take a month to get the ship released. By then there'll be another 40 or 50 in port charges and dockage. They've got us by the balls here, Dickie. You'd better get the P&I club to post a bond."

He hesitated. "The ship. . .doesn't have P&I."

"What? We're under Manchester P&I, aren't we?"

"No," he said, "they dropped the ship after that cargo claim in Mobile. Assholes."

"And we've been running without cover since then? Jesus Christ! Jacques know about this?"

He said in a small voice, "He never asked."

Static crackled in the wires. I said, "Then you can forget about the *Erika*. She's finished. By the time this thing goes to court she won't be worth the money it'll take to get her out. It's not the missing bales on deck, you know. That's shipper's risk. It's the short-load. The receiver has already paid the shipper for 1302 bales, and now they've paid off some judge to seize the ship."

He didn't say anything. I couldn't even hear him breathe.

"You've got to find the money somehow to send the crew home," I said. "You can't let them rot away in this Godforsaken place."

"And where do I get the fucking money?" he yelled into the phone. "Every goddamn trip I get further behind. The fucking *Veronika* just blew a generator and I've got to ship a whole rebuilt generator to Santo Tomas. And that sonofabitch Garot deducts so much money from the charter hire I can't even pay ship's expenses."

"That's your fault. Every time I come into port I fax you the ship's accounts, logs, and Notes of Protest. There's nothing else a captain can do. Hell, this ship is a cash cow. We hardly ever go off-hire."

He didn't say anything. Finally I said, "Well, there is something we can do."

"What's that?"

"Steam out. Just cut the dock lines and go."

"Can you get away with that?"

I looked through the glass wall of the phone office, toward the towering gray clouds rushing up out of the southeast. "Maybe," I said. "There's a storm coming. Maybe we can hide in it."

"Go ahead, Captain, go ahead," he said. "Do your best. Call me on the SSB when you get out."

I got back to the ship just before 1400 hours. Black clouds raced out of the southeast across the lead-gray sea. The salt wind blew clouds of scrap paper along the dock as I went onboard. I nodded to the guard, sitting slumped in his chair with his feet propped on the hatchcoaming, but he just stared at me. I went upstairs and into the chartroom.

The coast to the east followed the latitude line, straight to Santo Domingo about 15 miles away. Along the route I was interested in, the coast ran south-southwest about 30 miles to Punto Nizao, then southwest to Isla Beata, the great rock, then westward to Haiti.

I went out on the port wing of the bridge. One of the little wooden ferries was pulling up behind the ship, filled with people coming from the shipyard. They held onto their hats in the rising wind and looked over their shoulders at the scudding clouds. About a kilometer behind the ship, down the wide river, the breakwater bracketed the entrance to the port, two lines of concrete boulders piled about a meter above the water. The entrance was marked by beacons on lattice-work towers. Between the beacons was the entrance, not more than 200 feet across, and beyond that was the open sea.

I went forward and looked down. The guard was sitting with his head on his chest, but as I watched he put his feet down and stretched his back, arching his shoulders one way and the other. Two girls came walking down the hill, Dominicanas in bright blouses, their wide skirts blowing in the wind. The guard went to the bulwark and whistled at them. They looked his way, but didn't respond. He called to them. They turned into an alley. He returned to his seat and slumped into it.

I found Yussuf in his cabin, lying in his bunk with his shirt off. He struggled up when I came in. "Yussuf," I whispered, closing the door, "I think we're going to try to sneak the ship out."

He pulled his shirt off the chair. "Sneak out? You mean, without a clearance?"

"Yeah. Just cut the dock lines and go."

"But Captain, what about the guard? You're not going to. . ."

"No, I won't hurt him. I'll give him a drink with something from the medicine chest to put him to sleep, then I'll put him on the dock."

He grinned. "Of course you can count on me, Captain, but what about the Dominican Navy? There's a big base in Santo Domingo, you know."

"Yeah, I know. They could get here in minutes. But you see that storm coming?"

"Where?"

"Out of the southeast. If we take off in the storm, the navy ships won't be able to find us in the rain clutter."

He got out of the bunk, buttoning his shirt. "Only if it is very heavy rain, Captain. Otherwise. . ."

"Otherwise the crew gets taken off the ship and I go to jail. Come on."

We went on deck together. The guard cast his eyes at us for a moment, then sank back into his reverie. A dark gray band of rain was spreading across the horizon. Yussuf and I nodded to each other and went up on the bridge.

"Look," I whispered, "if we wait until the storm is almost here, we can cut the dock lines and steam out before anybody on shore knows what's up. We head right for the thickest part of the storm and pray that the Dominican Navy has old radars."

"What if the guard won't take the drink? What if he tastes the medicine in it?"

I thought for a second. "I've got another idea. Come on, let's go up to the Manila Sunrise."

I left the ship under the chief's command and we walked up the road to the bars. Dust-devils whirled in the street and scooped trash from the gutters. The Manila Sunrise was open, but it was still early, and only a couple of girls were on watch. Hanio was drinking a Presidente and reading a Tagalog newspaper. He put the paper down and started to rise, but I held up a hand and we joined him at his table.

"Hanio," I said, "we've got a problem. My ship's been seized."

He raised his eyebrows politely.

"It's bullshit, but you know what that means here."

"Maybe she never leave," he said.

"That's right. We've got to sneak her out."

He grimaced. "Very dangerous, Captain. Dominican Navy very close. Maybe you go to jail for long time."

"Yeah, maybe. But I need your help. You got any Dominican girls working for you?"

"No sir. Only Filipinas."

"You know a Dominicana you can trust? I want a girl to snuggle up with the guard onboard and feed him some alcohol. I'll pay her $100."

"I know just the girl. She works at the Rincon, on the corner. Wait here."

He left one of the Filipinas in charge and went out. Five minutes later he was back with a short, buxom girl in her early 20's, wearing a silver lame tank-top and black velvet short-shorts. She had long black hair piled up on her head and falling around her shoulders. She gave me a crooked smile.

"This is Dolores," Hanio said. "She used to work for me."

"Good. Dolores, I've got a job for you. I'll pay $100, but you've got to keep your mouth shut and stay out of sight afterward."

She frowned. "What is this job?"

"Do you know any soldiers at the port?"

She shook her head. "Soldiers can't afford me. I only date *marinaros*."

"Excellent. This is what I want you to do. . .there's a soldier on my ship. I want you to get comfortable with him, make him think you like him. Take a bottle with you. I'm going to put some sleeping powder in the bottle. You get him to take a couple of drinks, and when he's asleep we'll carry him ashore. You sneak out of the port and the ship sails off. Sound okay?"

"The soldier, he will not die?"

"Oh, no. I will give him just enough medicine to make him go to sleep. *No te preocupues*."

"When do I come?"

I went to the door and looked to the east, where the storm was still building. "As soon as you can." I gave Hanio a 10-dollar bill. "Give her a bottle of rum." Then, to the girl, "Come down the road in 10 minutes. Yussuf here will meet you outside the port. I'm sure you know the place where girls crawl under the fence. Yussuf will take you to the ship."

"No problem, *Capitán*."

"Then you and Yussuf will pretend to have a fight in his cabin. The guard will hear you fighting. You come on deck and make friends with the guard. As soon as. . ."

"What if he doesn't like girls?" she asked. "Some soldiers are like that, you know."

"This guy'll like you just fine."

"Okay, *Capi*," she said. I get my money first, okay?"

"As soon as you come onboard, I promise."

Hanio said to her, "Don't worry, Dolores. I know the captain. He is a friend of mine."

I shook his hand. "Thanks, Hanio. I may not see you soon, but when I do, we'll have a blow-out."

"I will be watching, Captain. When you are beyond the breakwater, I will sing a special song for you."

I looked through the french doors. We could see the breakwater in the distance, with gray rollers battering it from the ocean side. Yussuf and I hurried down the hill to the ship.

"Yussuf," I said, "tell the crew to come up to the bridge. I want to give them a chance to get off."

"They will come with the ship," he promised. "No one wants to be stranded in this outhouse of a port."

"Well, I wouldn't blame them for staying, two months behind in wages and the chance of going to jail if we get caught. But bring them up without telling them what it's about."

I went up first. The crew filed onto the bridge and looked at me curiously.

"Men," I said, "I'm going to take this ship out without a clearance. I'm going to do it without violence, but I'm not going to let these Dominican pirates steal my ship." I looked around. "I want to leave in the middle of the storm that's coming."

They glanced back through the chartroom windows.

"There's a chance we all could go to jail if we get caught. Probably it would just be me, but who knows? If you want to get off, I don't blame you, but you probably won't get your back wages if you do. If you stay, I believe you'll get your wages in the next port. Now, who wants to get off?"

They looked at each other. No one moved. Jhonny said quietly, "I think I should leave the ship, Captain."

I nodded. "Okay, Jhonny. That's fine. I have only about $500 onboard, but you might as well take it. I promise you as your captain that as soon as we reach the next port, I will wire the rest of your wages to you. I know the agent already has your ticket."

He nodded. I looked around. "Anyone else?"

No one moved. "Okay," I said, "let's get going. Ricardo, take a fire axe up on the forecastle. Lionel, get another axe and take it on the fantail. When I give the signal, chop the dock lines and do it quick. We won't have much time before they see what we're up to from the port office. As soon as the dock lines are free, get back in the accommodations in case some asshole starts shooting. That's all you have to do."

"What about the guard?" Ian asked.

"I've got him taken care of." I outlined the plan.

They started grinning. "Good plan, Captain," the chief said, "but make sure you don't give him too much. If you kill him, maybe the U.S. police send you back here to jail."

"I won't. He'll be sleeping like a baby. Let's go. Yussuf, go meet Dolores and bring her back. Try to keep the guards at the gate from seeing her."

I went into the hospital and searched through the narcotics until I found a bottle of benzodiazepan. The label said, "Benzodiazepan is a powerful sedative. Do not give to persons under the influence of other sedatives. Dosage: 2 tablets. Induces sleep within 30 minutes. Maximum 4 tablets in 24 hours."

I took four pills and closed the bottle, then opened it again and took out two more. I went down to the galley. Victor was washing dishes. He rolled his eyes at me, but I shushed him with a finger to my lips. I crushed the tablets on the countertop with a spoon and scooped the powder into a folded piece of paper.

I found Jhonny in his cabin, packing. I pressed $400 into his hand. "I'm sorry, Jhonny, but I have to save a hundred to give to the girl. I promise to send you the rest. Do you have an address for me?"

"Send it to Arcadio Munoz. He'll hold it for me." He gave me a worried look. "Good luck, Captain."

"Thanks. Get ready to go now. As soon as we put the guard ashore, you gotta go."

Ricardo appeared in the door. "*Capitán*," he whispered, "Yussuf and the girl are coming."

I went out on the fantail and craned my head around the bulkhead. Yussuf and Dolores were coming up the gangway. I looked over at the gate. A truck was coming through and the guard shack was hidden behind it.

I nodded to Victor in the galley and slipped forward along the starboard hallway. Yussuf and the girl were in his cabin, arguing.

"*No soy una puta*," Dolores cried out. "I only came to the ship to be friends."

Yussuf said, "*¿No eres una puta?* All Dominicanas are whores! Take your clothes off."

"No!"

"*¡Desnude!*" There was the sound of flesh on flesh. The girl cried out. Yussuf's door flew open and Dolores ran out on deck with a hand to her cheek. Yussuf told me later he had slapped himself.

I went up to my saloon and leaned out the window. The girl was standing on deck with the bottle of rum in her hand. The guard was getting out of his chair with the shotgun in his fist, turning toward her.

"What is the problem, *muchacha*?" he asked.

"*El primer oficial*, he wants to violate me. I told him I am no whore."

The guard moved up to her. "Want me to teach him a lesson?"

"No, no," she said quickly. "You would get in trouble."

He struck a pose. "I am the guard on this ship. I can have him thrown in *el jusgado* if I want."

She put a hand on his chest. "Please, no trouble." She moved closer. "What do you call yourself?"

"Adorno. Adorno Reyes. And you?"

"Mercedes, but my friends call me Quiti. You can call me Quiti." She glanced up toward my window. I drew back. I heard her say, "Adorno, may I sit down with you for a while?"

"Of course." He pulled the chair over for her. She sat down and he sat on the hatchcover, his ravaged face intent on hers.

"Adorno, the cook is a friend of mine. I will fix us two drinks, no?"

He glanced toward the port office. "Em, no thank you. I am on duty, you know."

She pouted. "No one is thinking of you here. This duty of yours, it is very boring, is it not? We should have one little drink, so you can tell me about yourself."

He fingered the shotgun and hesitated. "You are from Haina?"

"*Sí*. I have lived here all my life. And you?"

"Santo Domingo," he said proudly. "One more year, and I will be finished with the army. My uncle has a big store in Santo Domingo. Domsasa. Do you know it?"

"Ooh, that is a very nice store. I buy clothes there sometimes." She patted his hand. "Now I will fix our drinks. Do not worry, though. . .I will put your drink in a tall glass with ice, so it will look like lemonade."

He didn't argue. She stood up. I ran down the companionway and into the hallway. She was behind me, but I didn't stop until I got to the galley. "Victor," I said, "get two glasses of ice and a Coke."

He had them ready in the refrigerator. I dusted the sleeping powder in the taller glass and poured Coke over it. The powder floated to the top in clumps. Dolores came in. "He is ready to drink," she whispered, handing me the bottle.

I poured a healthy slug of the amber rum over the Coke and stirred the mixture with a spoon until the powder broke up and sank. I took a tiny sip, but couldn't taste the medicine.

"You think he'll see that?" I said, holding the glass up to the light. Whitish specks swirled in the bottom.

She laughed softly. "I'll make sure he doesn't." She poured a light splash of rum into her Coke. "Now?"

"Now. We don't have much time. Try to get him to drink it all."

"*Bien*. But first, my $100. And put more ice in the glass. It will help conceal the powder."

I had her money folded up in my shirt pocket, a single bill. She unfolded it, studied it carefully, and tucked it away. Victor filled the glasses with cracked ice and she took the drinks forward. I went up to the saloon.

Dolores slid onto the hatchcover next to Adorno. She handed him the taller glass. "*Sante*," she said.

He held the glass up, but he was looking at her. "*Sante*, Mercedes. I mean, Quiti."

They drank together. She snuggled up to him. "Put your *arma* down for a moment. No one will steal it."

"Why?"

"I'll show you why." She pushed the shotgun off his lap, and he reluctantly laid it on the hatchcover. Then she reached up and kissed him. His hand wandered toward her breast, but she brushed it aside, broke free, and picked up her drink. He drank also.

"Take a man's drink," she said. "When do you get off duty?"

"At seven."

"Ah," she said. "It is six now. We will have two drinks here, then we will go to my apartment. My roommate will be at evening school."

"But. . .I must report to my sergeant before I leave. . ."

"So? I will wait for you up the hill." She rubbed his leg. "Unless I do not please you. I know you must have many girlfriends."

He licked his lips. "Not so many," he confessed. "And you? A boyfriend?"

She pouted. "He broke up with me. For another woman. A *gringa* he met in his job at the casino."

"Ah," he said angrily. "A *gringa*!"

"But let us forget about him and drink our drinks." She pushed his glass up toward his mouth. He took a drink. She held her finger under the bottom so he couldn't lower it. His adam's apple worked. She let the glass down and laughed merrily. "I thought soldiers were trained to drink!"

"I can drink," he protested, "but you would not let me breathe."

Her hand crept higher on his leg. "Later, Adornito, I will teach you how to breathe."

This time he took a long pull of Dutch courage, and when he put the glass down, it was almost empty. He took her glass from her hands and said thickly, "You are '*mosa*, Quiti."

"Then touch me," she murmured. He leaned over, went too far, and jerked himself upright.

"Oh," he said, "oh, I drank too quickly. My sergeant. . ." He slid off the hatchcoaming and fell in a pile on the deck. I ran down to the galley, got the bottle of rum, and went forward. Yussuf was already there.

"Captain," he said, "you gave him too much. He is dead."

"Bullshit." I looked around. No one was watching from shore. I knelt down and felt his pulse. It was strong and steady. "He's okay. He's sleeping like a baby." I unscrewed the cap and poured a couple of ounces of rum on his blouse.

Dolores was standing a few feet away. She peered down at him calmly. "His sergeant will give him heavy blows for getting drunk on duty." She straightened her top and smoothed her hair in the wind. "Am I finished?"

"Yeah. Many thanks. You did a wonderful job. Maybe soon you will be an *estrella* in Hollywood."

She laughed.

"Take care you are not seen leaving. Yussuf, go with her to the fence and make sure she gets through okay. Hurry back."

They left the ship together, Yussuf keeping his body between her and the guards at the gate. I called Jhonny and told him to go ashore. We shook hands. He hurried down the gangway with his bag and boombox. I went to the hallway and hissed for help. Lionel and Ricardo came out of their cabins and stared at the fallen soldier.

"Is he okay?" Ricardo asked. At that moment the soldier blew out a long, blubbery breath and turned on his side, snoring softly.

"Just *boracho*. Drunk on duty. Come on, let's get him over by the gangway. We'll leave him onboard until we're ready to go."

Yussuf came hurrying up. "First," I said, "you've got lipstick on your lips."

He wiped at them quickly and gave a shy grin. "She gave me her number."

"You sly devil. Now let's get going. Ricardo, go tell the chief to get oil up, but don't ring the telegraph. You can hear that thing all the way to the guard shack. Ricardo, you've got an axe forward?"

"*Sí, Capitán.*"

"Lionel, got an axe aft?"

"Yassar, Cap."

"All right, go to your stations, but don't do a thing until I give the signal. As soon as the lines are cut, get into the accommodations and stay there until I call for you. Yussuf, you and Ricardo stand by at the gangway to help me get the guard overboard."

I ran up to the bridge. The wind was whistling in through the open starboard door, but the rain was still to the east. The cranes of the shipyard glowed cream-colored in the dim light. A jagged crack of lightning shot down into the sea. The air was fresh and sharp. Stevedores at the sally port were clamoring for motorcycles to take them to town before the rain struck.

Ian appeared at the door. "Captain, oil is up."

"Okay, Ian. I'll ring for Half Ahead. Tell the chief for God's sake don't get confused."

He ran downstairs. I swung the rudder from lock to lock, then set it amidships. I made sure the VHF was turned all the way up. I hesitated for a moment, then went ahead and turned on the radar, even though the spinning antenna might alert someone.

A flurry of raindrops, as big as ball bearings, clattered against the starboard wing. The leading edge of the rain was over the shipyard, a gray curtain sweeping in from the misty sea. Another burst of raindrops. In the ferryboat, heading for the near shore, people were getting out newspapers and pieces of plastic to cover their heads.

The cranes of the shipyard blurred into spider shapes as the rain marched over them. I looked at the beacon towers bracketing the entrance to the river. The rain was just reaching them. The sea outside was boiling under the press of the wind.

I ran down to the deck. Yussuf and Ricardo already had the guard by the arms and feet. I checked the dock, but there was no one around. No one looking from the guard shack. I slung his shotgun over my shoulder and helped Ricardo with the man's other foot. We hustled him down the gangway to the gravel surface and laid him there with his weapon, soaking wet and stinking of rum. He cried out softly.

"To the bow," I told the men. "Get ready to cut the lines."

"Captain," Yussuf said, "we've got to get the gangway in."

"No time. Cut the ropes and let it fall. We'll buy another one later." I ran up to the wheelhouse. Yussuf and Ricardo had already cut the gangway ropes and were on their way to the forecastle. I signaled them to cut the dock lines and slid down to the boatdeck. "Lionel," I called aft, "cut the lines, cut the lines. Hurry!"

There were a couple of heavy thuds forward. I went back on the bridge in time to see the bow spring line fall into the water between the hull and the dock. Another couple of whacks, the axe-blade glittering in the last rays of sunlight. The bow line fell. I ran to the port wing and saw the stern spring line and stern line already lying limp on the dock.

I was afraid the wind would pin the ship, so that I would have to grind along the rocks until we could get clear of shore, but the current was already swinging the bow out. Another quick glance at the guard shack. No one looking. Then the rain arrived, a solid mass of water pouring onto the ship and blowing across the wheelhouse through the starboard door. No time to shut it. A rattling crash as the gangway fell onto the rocks.

Now the other side of the river was almost invisible. The bow was gaining speed. The ship turned port-side to the current. I rang for Half Ahead, and within two seconds I got the confirmation. The ship shuddered. The engine caught with three short pops, coughed, and started turning up. I gave the helm five degrees of starboard rudder, careful not to put the stern into the bank.

The bow swung past the hazy outline of the far bank. I gave the rudder another five degrees.

A yell from shore. I looked back through the chartroom windows. The lights of the port were yellow and watery in the rain. Two soldiers were running along the edge of the dock waving their hands, their rifles bouncing on their backs. I put the rudder Hard-a-Starboard.

I could barely see the beacons as the bow swung past the other shore. The lights weren't lit, and while I watched the towers themselves disappeared into the mist. I stuck my head into the radar hood, but the breakwater and towers were lost in the rain clutter. All I could do was steer for the mid-point between where they had been a few moments ago.

Now, with our starboard side to the dock, I could see more soldiers running from the port office, a couple of civilians with them. The VHF crackled. "Captain of the *Erika*, Captain of the *Erika*, stop your engine at once. Your ship is detained in port."

We were still half-a-kilometer from the breakwater, rain sluicing down the windows. I caught a glimpse of the towers, but again they disappeared in the downpour. The world turned gray and hazy.

There were two gunshots from shore. I kept steering with tiny, nervous corrections. I dared not order any more speed without being able to see where I was going. Yussuf appeared in the port door, drenched to the skin. He took his station at the radar.

"Nothing, Captain," he said. "Too much rain clutter."

"Go on the wing. See if you can see the beacons. I can't see anything."

The world was white around us, gusts of rain sweeping across the front of the house. I could hardly see the foremast.

"Shit, Yussuf, we're going to hit the breakwater. I've got to slow down." I rang for Dead Slow Ahead. The chief forgot to confirm, but the engine slowed to 100 rpm. A few seconds later I saw the western side of the breakwater dead ahead, the wet rocks about 200 yards away. I had overcorrected.

"Captain," Yussuf cried, "port your helm! I can see the rocks."

I spun the wheel hard over. The angle indicator crept across the midships mark. The bow swung. Another glimpse of the western side, now only 100 yards away. The beacon, still unlit, loomed out of the rain.

A flurry of Spanish on the VHF, but I was concentrating too hard to listen. Yussuf said, "It's a Navy ship, Captain. They're leaving Santo Domingo now. They're asking where we are."

"Holy shit. Fifteen miles. . .they'll be here in half-an-hour. We've got to stay in the rain or we're sunk."

We steamed through the gap in the breakwater with the western side close enough to spit on. The bow hit the first swell, rose into the air, and caught the wind. With the ship empty, the bow swung violently to starboard, but I racked the wheel over and caught it. The bow fought its way back into the eye of the wind. Now we were past the breakwater, into the open ocean, with 15-foot waves slamming into the port side. The rain continued to hammer the windows, spurting in through the casings where I'd forgotten to dog them down.

I rang for Full Ahead and turned the ship south. The engine came up to speed, shaking the ship in heavy tremors. I looked back. Only the weak yellow lights of the port could be seen. Within minutes these too disappeared, and the ship was alone in a cocoon of rain and fog.

The radio crackled again. "Haina Port, Haina Port," a Spanish voice said, "this is the Frigate *Puerto Plata*. Where is the gringo now? Can you see him?" Stupidly, they were still on channel 16.

"He is going south, going south, *Puerto Plata*. We cannot see him, but he is going south."

"We can see nothing in the radar because of the rain," the frigate's officer complained.

We steamed through a light patch, the sunlight bright above us, but again the rain closed in. The center of the storm was still ahead. I left Yussuf at the helm while I studied the chart.

"Steer 195, Yussuf," I called through the chartroom window. "That'll take us into international water in about 50 minutes."

The radio hissed. "*Motonave Erika, Motonave Erika*, what is your position? This is the Navy Frigate *Puerto Plata* calling."

Yussuf and I grinned at each other. The frigate called a couple of times more, then fell silent. We kept steaming southward through the driving rain. A foot of water was rolling around at the aft end of the main deck, where sodden paper had clogged the scuppers.

Then we came out of the rain, suddenly, like opening a door. The dying sun shone red and huge above the western hills. I glanced at my watch. Seven-thirty. Behind us the horizon was hidden by the storm. "What's our position, Yussuf?" I asked.

He went in the chartroom. "I can't get a satellite fix, Captain. Dead reckoning says we're 13 miles off the coast."

I slumped at the wheel. "International water. Thank God."

He came forward and pulled out a cigarette. It was soaked, and fell apart in his fingers. He tore open the pack, looked in, and threw it overboard. "We are safe, Captain?"

"Not exactly. There's still the law of hot pursuit. If the frigate sees us now, it can claim it was following us all the way from Haina, so it has the right to stop us."

We looked back. No sign of the frigate. I checked the radar. The bottom third of the screen was bright with rain clutter, and even tweaking the gain couldn't bring out the frigate.

"Can he see us?" Yussuf asked.

"Not if we can't see him. His radar can't shoot through the rain yet."

When dark fell we were still steaming south-southwest toward Isla Beata. We never did see the frigate on radar, and never saw its lights. There was some more radio chatter, but by then we were almost out of VHF range and couldn't understand the garbled transmissions. I took a turn around the ship to check that the lights were out, then went down to the pantry to turn off a single bulb glowing in the porthole. I returned to the darkened bridge. Yussuf was smoking a borrowed cigarette and conning the ship by hand.

"Put her on the pilot," I said. "After we pass Beata, steer for the tip of Haiti."

"Aye aye, sir." His teeth gleamed in the dark. "Congratulations, Captain."

"Thank you, First. Now let's see what Dickie has to say."

I got the crew to string up the longwire antenna, which we'd dropped during discharging. Dickie answered on the first ring. "We did it," I said. "We're in international water. Where to?"

"You're safe? You got out?"

"Affirmative. Do you have the next port of call?"

"Uh, Captain, steam for Miami and call again tomorrow."

"Roger, will call tomorrow same time."

"Congratulations, Captain," he said belatedly. "And give my thanks to the crew."

"You can thank them yourself," I said, "when you pay them in Miami."

At 1600 hours on April 24th, we were 15 miles off Punto Manati on the Cuban coast. A string of low green islands was backed by sere mountains inland, their peaks buried in cloud. I went up to the bridge as soon as I woke and sent Yussuf to take the AB's down in the hold to clean up the paper. He, Lionel, and Ricardo went forward and down the stevedore hatch.

The ship rolled easily in the long, low swells. A light breeze, moving only a little faster than the ship, wafted past the wheelhouse from the northeast and fluttered the curtains in the chartroom. I took radar bearings on a couple of points on the Cuban coast to make sure we were still in international waters, marked our position on the chart, and caught up the log.

After half-an-hour Ricardo and Lionel came topside and opened a corner of No. 2 hatch. I watched idly as Lionel lowered a rope into the hold. They hauled out a great bundle of wadded-up paper and stowed it on the port deck, then lowered the rope again.

A giant white cruise ship, the *Song of Norway*, came barreling down the channel from ahead, gleaming in the sun, throwing white water from her bows as she sliced past us. I could see the bright clothing of the passengers lounging on the starboard rail. After that I went back to the chartroom and cranked up the Skanti to give my 48-hour ETA. Traffic was heavy on the afternoon frequencies, the cruise-ship operators fighting each other to get their call signs in first. I got right in there in the hog-calling contest, but Whiskey Oscar Mike always gave cruise ships priority over lowly freighters.

I finally got through to Dickie. He sounded wan and distant. He instructed me to continue steaming for Miami and promised to relay our ETA to the agent. I had just signed off when Yussuf came running into the wheelhouse. "Captain, Captain, Ricardo fell!"

"What?" I jumped to the telegraph to call for Stop Engine, but he grabbed my arm. "No, Captain, not overboard. He fell in the hold. He's at the bottom of the hold. He's hurt bad."

"Jesus." I scanned the horizon quickly, saw no traffic, and ran down with him to the deck. I slid down the stevedore ladder and landed heavily on the floorboards.

Ricardo lay on his side near midships. His face was a mask of blood. Lionel was kneeling by his side, not touching him. I bent down and peered into his face.

His eyes were half-open, unfocused, above his smashed nose and mouth. Dirt and paper clung to the blood on his face.

"Did you guys move him?"

"No sir. This is where we found him."

"Ricardo," I said. "Can you hear me?"

He didn't answer. His face had a bluish tinge. His jawbone was broken into pieces, and when I opened his mouth two bloody teeth fell out. He wasn't breathing. I reached into his ruined mouth and pulled some more teeth out. He vomited suddenly, spewing blood and broken teeth onto my pants. His chest heaved and he started breathing again, gargling blood. Risking further damage to his neck and spine, I turned his head so the blood could run out. After a couple of minutes his breathing subsided to a ragged gasping and the blue tint went out of his skin.

"What happened?" I asked Yussuf and Lionel. I looked up. The hole they'd opened in the hatchcover was about five meters farther forward than where Ricardo was lying. "How the hell did he fall and land over here?"

"I don't know, Captain," Yussuf said. "Lionel and I were in the forecastle. When we got back we found him here."

"He was on deck?"

"He was in the hold when we left."

"Jesus. Lionel, go get some wet towels from Cookie."

"Here, Cap. I already brought some." He handed me some wet rags. I wiped the blood away from Ricardo's forehead and cheeks. His nose was flattened into his face, the nostrils swollen shut. His eyes looked through me blankly.

I wiped his neck. He was bleeding from both ears. He seemed to come around a little, and started moaning, but when I tried to question him, he didn't respond.

"Don't move him any more," I told them. "I'm going to call the Coast Guard."

I ran up to the bridge and called WOM on the radio. The same cultivated young man was on 8 Mhz. He cleared the channel and put me through to the Miami Coast Guard.

"Stand by, Captain," a woman said. "We're going to patch you through to a Coast Guard surgeon."

A rough-voiced man came on the frequency. I described Ricardo's condition.

"Does he respond to you, Captain?"

"Negative."

"Does he seem conscious?"

"I don't know, sir. His eyes are open, but he doesn't seem to be looking at anything. He's moaning a little."

"Are his pupils the same size?"

"I don't think so."

"Stand by one." The air went dead, except for the drifts of other conversations bleeding across the frequencies. The surgeon came back on. "Captain, how far are you from Great Inagua?"

I made a quick estimate. "About 10 hours, sir."

"Stand by one." Then, "Captain, does he seem to have any other injuries?"

"He's bleeding from both ears."

He didn't like that. "Captain," he said, "we're going to send a helicopter from Guantanamo Bay to take him off the vessel. Can you rig a litter on deck?"

"Roger, sir. We have a litter onboard."

"Okay, Captain. Guantanamo Bay says the chopper'll be there in 45 minutes. Can you get him up on deck?"

"Yessir. We can use the crane."

"Okay, Captain. We're going to keep this frequency open for you. Stand by."

I went out on the port wing, about to go down, when I saw a white speck coming toward us from Cuba. I jumped inside and grabbed the binoculars. It was a Cuban gunboat, a .50 caliber machine gun on the bow, coming head-on. I called the Coast Guard again. "Sir, I think I may have gone into Cuban waters. There's a Cuban gunboat coming toward me."

"Roger that, Captain. How far away is he?"

"Maybe five miles."

"How far are you from international water?"

"I can't be but a couple of miles. I was 15 miles offshore when this happened."

"Okay, Captain. Keep your men off the deck. We're sending a Falcon from Guantanamo as well."

I checked the ship's position. Right inside the 12-mile limit. I turned the auto-pilot to the north, the shortest course to international water. The gunboat was still coming, the deck crowded with men in white uniforms. The radar showed it as three miles away and closing.

Yussuf came up. "He's having trouble breathing again, Captain. He might still have some teeth in his throat. Lionel's trying to help him."

I relayed the information to the Coast Guard. While I was waiting for the surgeon to come back on the line, I heard a roaring sound and looked out the window. It was the gunboat, plunging through the low sea on the port side. A man in a white uniform was hanging onto the .50's on the foredeck, his body swaying. All the men onboard had long, wild black hair streaming out from under their white caps.

The gunboat roared past the ship at about 100 meters' distance, turned in front of the bow, and came back along the starboard side. One of the men in its wheel-house pointed toward the sky. I looked up. A Falcon jet, painted in blue-and-white with the U.S. seal on the side, was streaking toward us at 100 feet off the water. It made a tight turn over the ship, wings vertical, and shot back in the other direction.

A new voice came on channel 16. "Motorvessel *Erika*, this is Customs Jet 437. Do you read me?"

"Roger, Customs."

"Captain, we have you in sight. Has the Cuban boat made any threatening moves toward your vessel at this time?"

"Negative, Customs. But be advised they are manning their deck gun."

"We see that. You're in international waters, Captain. Maintain your course and speed. The chopper is 10 minutes out. Can you get the man on deck?"

"Affirmative. I'm going to have to leave the bridge to help, though."

"Go ahead, Captain. We'll keep an eye on things."

The jet was making tight circles around the ship at mast-top level, filling the air with the screaming of its engines. The Cuban boat had dropped to a quarter-mile back, and had throttled down to stay with the ship. I got the litter out of the hospital and took it on deck. Yussuf was already unlashing the crane boom.

Lionel lowered the litter into the hold, and he and I went down. Ricardo's legs were moving spasmodically, his shoeless feet kicking. We put the litter by him and lifted him into it. I fastened the straps. Lionel went up to help Yussuf take off more hatchboards.

The crane engine started and the boom swung into view. The headache ball and hook spooled down through the hole. I hooked it onto the lifting wires and signaled Lionel. He made a signal to Yussuf in the crane, and the slack slowly came out of the runner. I fastened two ropes for guy-lines.

With the litter out of the hold and on deck, I went back up to the bridge. The Falcon was still screaming around the ship, a little higher but still making tight circles. The Cuban boat was now half-a-mile astern, off the port quarter. A dot appeared between us and the Cuban mountains, and grew into an orange-and-white Coast Guard helicopter. The whapping of its rotor blades joined the whining of the jet's engines and the low rumble of the gunboat.

The chopper pilot came on the VHF. "Captain, we're going to lower a line for you to fasten to the litter. Have you ever done a medivac by helicopter before?"

"Negative, Coast Guard."

"Roger, Captain. Now listen carefully. When the hook is close enough, have your men hook it to the litter and stand clear, but this is very important. Under no circumstance are your men to fasten the hook to anything on the ship. Is that clear?"

"Understood, Coast Guard."

"Okay, Captain, let us know when you're ready."

I looked down on deck. Yussuf and Lionel were kneeling by the litter, shielding their eyes as they looked up. "Ready?" I yelled down to them.

Yussuf gave the thumbs-up.

"We're ready," I told the chopper.

"Reduce your speed to the minimum necessary for steering."

I rang for Dead Slow Ahead, and the telegraph answered. The generator finally cranked and the engine slowed.

"Steer into the wind, Captain."

I turned the bow to the northeast. The chopper was right overhead, pointing in the same direction. The line came down slowly, making small circles in the air. When the hook came within reach Yussuf stood up and grabbed it.

"Make fast to the litter, Captain," the chopper pilot ordered.

I yelled to Yussuf, "Hook it on, First."

He hooked the litter's wires to the chopper's line. The litter rose with a sudden smooth motion. Yussuf had forgotten to remove the guy-lines, which went trailing off downwind. The chopper angled to the port side and rose a few feet, blowing down thin trails of black smoke. The litter continued upward. A minute later a man in a flight helmet reached for the litter as it came level with the open door, then it was inside. A minute later the empty litter came spooling down and Yussuf unhooked it.

"Okay, Captain," the chopper pilot said. "We're taking him to Great Inagua, where the jet will meet us. It'll fly him to Miami."

I sagged against the bulkhead. "Thank you, Coast Guard. Thank you, Customs. Thank God you came."

"No problem, Captain," the chopper pilot said. "That's what we're here for."

The jet pilot came on. "Captain, Customs 437 will be going now. Stay on the SSB. If you have any problem with the Cubans, let them know in Miami."

"Roger that. Many thanks, Customs."

The jet peeled off in a steep wing-over and headed northeast, followed by the chopper. Within a minute they were out of sight. I looked around for the gunboat, but it was already a speck against the Cuban coast, showing its stern.

Yussuf and Lionel came into the wheelhouse. "Knock off for the day, men," I told them. "We've had enough."

Yussuf nodded, lighting a cigarette. "Okay, Captain. We can leave the hold open?"

"Yeah, that's fine. It won't rain today."

They went out, but a second later Yussuf came back in. "Captain, I didn't want to say anything in front of Lionel, but I think there's somebody in the hold."

"What?"

"I think we have stowaways. I heard something moving around in the hold when I found Ricardo."

"Oh, fuck. Hiding in the paper."

He nodded. I started. "Oh, Jesus, Ricardo didn't fall. . .he was attacked by stowaways. That's why he wasn't under the hole in the hatchcover."

Yussuf's mouth dropped open. "I bet you're right, Captain. I'd better get the crew together."

I grabbed his shoulder. "No, First. I'm going to take care of this myself."

"No, Captain. You can't go down there by yourself."

"Remember what I told you when I shot that thief in Miragoane with the Wrist-Rocket? This is something I've got to do by myself."

His brown eyes got wide. "You're not going to kill them, are you, Captain?"

"No, First. I'm going to put them overboard on the paint raft."

"But Captain, they'll die out here."

"Bullshit. They'll drift into Cuba. What happens to them after that is their problem."

He shook his head. "Very bad, Captain. You could go to jail, you know."

"Nobody else onboard is going to know. You won't tell on me, will you?"

He stared at me levelly, threw his cigarette away, and advanced toward me. He put his hands on my shoulders. "Let us go get them, Captain. I will die before I say anything to anyone. That is my word. I am an Arab."

"Me too," I said. "*Allahu akbar!*"

He gave a strained little laugh. "*Allahu akbar*, Captain."

"Okay, go downstairs and tell the crew no one is to leave his cabin for any reason." I looked at my watch. "The chief's on duty. Tell him to stay in the engine room. Tell him I'm going to signal for Stop Engine. And don't answer any questions. Don't even hint that we have stowaways on board."

"Yessir."

"And get some rope to tie them up with."

He went downstairs. I got a can of mace from my cabin and retrieved the ship's .38 from the safe. I loaded six rounds into the cylinder. Yussuf met me in the main deck hallway with a grim expression. He had several lengths of rope looped around his waist and a galley knife through his belt.

We went on deck and forward. I peered into the hold through the hole in the hatchcovers, but there was no movement below. I nodded to Yussuf and went down the stevedore ladder first, the pistol in my belt. I kept looking around as I descended, but could see no one.

When I got to the bottom I pulled the pistol and held it ready as Yussuf came down. The crew had been cleaning aft, and there wasn't enough loose paper there to hide a man, but the hold forward was full of waist-deep piles. We moved through them cautiously.

Yussuf got a broom and started poking the handle into the piles. Water gurgled against the sides of the hull. Something metallic was rolling around on deck above our heads, but the hold was hot and still. I could hear Yussuf's quick breath.

He approached a big pile of paper shoved against the port side about 10 feet aft of the collision bulkhead. He froze, listened, and pointed at the pile. I nodded.

He inched the pole forward and into the paper. A cascade of scraps slid down the pile as a shape rose out of it. Yussuf jumped back with a sudden sharp cry. I raised the pistol and shouted, "*¡Sube o yo tiro!*"

A man's head appeared as the paper fell away, a square black head with a thick black beard. The man's hands shot into the air. "*No tire, no tire*," he cried.

"*Venga, venga.*" I kept the barrel on him. "Come out here."

He pushed out of the pile, bare-chested, wearing only a pair of filthy running shorts.

"Lie down on the floor," I said. "Lie down, *culo*."

He threw himself forward with his arms stretched out.

I stood over him with the pistol pointed at his head. "Watch yourself, Yussuf," I said in English. "I bet there's more of them." I said to the man, "*¿Quantos?* How many are you?"

"Only me, Captain," he rasped. "I am *soltero*."

"*Mentiroso*," I growled. "If I find more men, I will shoot you."

He cocked an eye up. "*Capitán*, there are two more."

"Where? Here?"

"Yes. In the paper."

Yussuf jumped back and snatched his knife from his belt.

"The rest of you come out," I said in Spanish. "If you don't come out by the count of five, I'm going to start shooting into the paper. *Uno, dos, tres...*"

Two shapes rose out of piles on the other side of the hold. One was just a boy, a teenager, and the other was a middle-aged man with gray hair. They were both black, like the first, filthy, barefoot, and nearly naked. They raised their hands into the air.

"Lie down on the floor," I said. "Over here."

They lay down beside their comrade.

"Yussuf, tie their hands."

The first man started to protest when Yussuf grabbed his wrist, but I shouted, "Don't move, *culo*, or I'll blow your head off."

He let Yussuf tie his wrists behind his back. The others did not resist. I let them roll over and sit up, their chests heaving, their eyes rolling wildly.

I looked at them for a long time. "Who beat up my AB?" I asked quietly.

They looked at each other and said nothing.

"Somebody almost killed him. Who was it?"

The three of them shook their heads violently. "We did nothing, I swear," the older man said. "He must have fallen from the deck."

I motioned with my head for Yussuf to follow me up on deck. As I went aft to the stevedore ladder I could see the puddle of congealing blood, black in the pale light from overhead, lumpy with pieces of broken teeth in it. I spat angrily and climbed up the ladder into the cool wind.

Yussuf followed me and lit a cigarette. I scanned the horizon ahead, but it was empty. The Cuban coast was below the horizon, the mountains behind it soft and blue as the sun set. The ship was still steaming ahead at Dead Slow, rolling slightly in the low swell.

"We should keep them onboard, Captain," Yussuf said. "We can finish the brig."

I swung on him. "I told you...I'm going to put them on the paint raft. The Cubans will know how to deal with murdering scum like them."

"It is many miles to Cuba." He read my stony face and put a hand on my arm. "Captain, you are not a murderer. Take them to Miami where they will go to jail for attacking Ricardo."

I shook my head. "Don't be too sure what I am. They're going on the paint raft."

"But, Captain, the crew...they might tell the police."

"They won't know anything about it. They're in their cabins."

"How will we put these men on the raft without the crew's help? They might start fighting us."

"I hope they do," I said savagely. "You and I will put them on the raft, unless you'd rather not help. Then I'll do it myself."

He shook his head sadly. "Of course I must help." He blew out a long stream of smoke that drifted slowly toward Cuba. "We can use the crane to lower them down, but what can we put them in?"

"A cargo net. We'll pick them up and swing them over the side. We'll have the raft tied under the pilot ladder. I'll go down the ladder and unhook the net, then I'll cut the raft free. When the net falls loose they'll be all right."

"But. . .water? Life jackets? Will you give them anything to take?"

"I'll give them plenty of food and water. No life jackets. They've got the ship's name on them. But I will give them plastic water jugs to hold on to in case the raft sinks. Hell, I'll even give 'em a box of flares." I gauged the wind. "They'll be ashore by daybreak."

He nodded and snapped the cigarette over the side. It made a long, slow arc to the water.

"All right," I said briskly, "let's go up on the boat deck and get the raft over the side."

I signaled for Stop Engine and we went aft to the boat deck. We unlashed the paint raft and I tied the bitter end of the painter to the ship's railing. When the ship had lost all way, we lowered the raft to the water and maneuvered it forward.

I went to the lifeboat locker and got one case of water and one case of rations. I put them and a box of hand-flares in a canvas bag and took it down on deck. I found three five-gallon jugs of detergent in the steering flat. I emptied them into the engine-room bilge, screwed the caps tight, and took them topside.

Yussuf was standing-by at the pilot ladder. I went down to the raft and he lowered the canvas bag to me. I tied it to one of the crude cleats welded to the frame. Then I taped a galley knife in the center of the deck, covering the edge with duct tape so the men wouldn't get cut when they landed. I tied the handles of the plastic jugs to another cleat.

I climbed up to the ship's deck. "All right," I said, "let's get those assholes up. Go get a net and some rope from the forecastle. Light stuff."

He hesitated. "You sure, Captain?"

"Dead sure."

He went forward and came back with one of the cargo nets and some light rope bundled in his arms. He threw them down into the hold.

I went down the stevedore ladder. The stowaways were where we'd left them. They had been talking in low voices, but they shut up when they saw me. Yussuf came down above me.

I spread the net out under the hole in the hatchboards. One corner fell into the pool of Ricardo's blood. I moved close to Yussuf. "We'll use nooses around their necks to control them," I said. "We'll keep them between us."

He nodded grimly. I took out the pistol and went up to the stowaways. "Okay, men, we're going to take the three of you up on deck. I have a cabin with a lock to put you in. If you give me any trouble, I'm going to beat the shit out of you. Understand me?"

The bearded man shook his head violently. *"¡No, señor, no!* You are going to drown us, I know. Please, for my mother's sake!"

"Chingale tu madre," I said. "If you give me any trouble, I'll knock you unconscious." I turned to Yussuf and muttered in English, "Let's take this one first, so he won't see what's coming. He's the dangerous one."

I tucked away the pistol and went behind the man to make slip-knots in the ends of two ropes. I threw the nooses over his head and tossed one rope-end to Yussuf. We both took a light strain on him at the same time, but when he started throwing himself around we pulled the ropes tight. He choked and gave up.

We guided him carefully aft toward the net, keeping a strain on the ropes. He stumbled once, gagging as the nooses tightened, but he regained his feet and kept going. When we'd gotten him positioned on the net, Yussuf tied his end to a frame and I tied my end to a midships beam. "Sit down," I told the man. He dropped to his knees, then sat. I took up the slack in my rope. He sat there, staring stolidly aft, the nooses around his neck, his hands tied behind his back, as I secured my end.

The boy was crying, tears rolling down his cheeks, as we looped the nooses around his neck and led him to the net. He fell heavily against the bearded man. Yussuf tied off his end and went over to straighten the boy. After that the two stowaways sat side-by-side, the boy sobbing in the quiet of the hold.

The gray-haired man managed to jerk his head free, his eyes rolling like a horse's, when I tried to put the first noose around his neck. When I stepped closer he lashed out with a leg and hit my shin with his bare foot. His lips drew back in a snarl.

I hit him hard, once, on the side of the head, with the barrel of the pistol. His head snapped back and fell forward. He raised his head again, eyes cloudy. A small sound escaped from Yussuf, but I didn't look at him. I got the nooses around the stowaway's neck. He was able to walk unaided when we led him back to the net.

With the three of them pinned in the middle of the hold, I sent Yussuf up to lower the hook. I waited a few feet away. The two men watched me silently, but the boy had his eyes screwed shut, his mouth open and gasping. The crane started with a heavy knock and a roar. The men's heads snapped up. The boy opened his eyes and turned them up to the hole. The hook came snaking down.

I yelled when the hook was about four feet from the floor, and Yussuf set the brake. I waited until the ship's roll swung the hook toward me, then I looped the corners of the net over the hook and had Yussuf raise it until the netting closed around the men's outstretched feet. I untied their nooses and fastened a guy-line to the net.

The crane rumbled again, and the hook lifted. The net tightened, and one by one their feet went through the interstices until the men were suspended four feet from the floor. They cried out as the net pressed them together like a load of sheep.

I gave the signal again, and the net rose into the air. They started thrashing, shaking the net, and the hold was filled with desperate yells. Yussuf stopped, but I told him to keep going. The net rose through the hole in the hatchcover with its struggling cargo. Yussuf stopped it just above the hatch, to give me time to get on deck. The crane engine slowed to idle.

Even the fading twilight was bright after the darkness of the hold. I took the guy-line to the starboard bulwark and signaled to Yussuf. The stowaways kept howling. I could hear the boy's voice, a ragged scream for mercy, as the net swung past the starboard deck and out over the water. They were squirming so violently the guy-line jerked in my hand like a live thing.

Yussuf lowered the net slowly past the bulwarks. Even with his smooth touch the net bumped the hull several times on the way down. I stood leaning over the side, guiding him with hand signals, until the cargo landed on the raft. Even with their hands tied they managed to get a grip on the boards through the netting, and hang on.

Within a minute I had climbed down the pilot ladder and unhooked the bridle. The net fell loose in the water. "*Señores*," I said, "there is a knife taped to the deck of the raft. Someone must pull it loose to cut you free." I climbed up on deck and pulled up the pilot ladder.

The gray-haired man found the knife with his bound hands and pulled it out from under the netting. He managed to get the bearded man's hands free, and handed him the knife. The bearded man cut his raftmates' bonds. The raft bobbled in a wave. The bearded man had to hold onto the boy to keep him onboard. The raft and the ship rolled together in loose embrace. The point of night was upon us.

I untied the painter. The raft spun away from the ship. "*Adios, amigos*," I called to them, an ugly edge of glee in my voice. "*Digale a Fidel '¡Hola!'*"

The sun was gone. Its last pink glow painted the three men in a soft light that hid their faces. Yussuf centered and lowered the boom, turned the crane's engine off, and came down to the bulwark beside me. We watched silently as the raft dwindled to a speck in the darkness.

"Okay," I said, and heaved a sigh. "I'll go up on the bridge. It's my watch anyway. Tell the crew they can come out of their cabins." He didn't say anything. I glanced at his face. He wasn't looking at me. I said, "And no matter what they ask, don't say a word about the stowaways. I know they'll figure it out, especially after what happened to Ricardo, but don't admit anything."

He nodded, still without looking at me. "I won't, Captain. I will never say anything to anyone."

Back in the wheelhouse I rang for Full Ahead. The telegraph answered and the engine began to rev. A few minutes later the lights flickered and the generator rattled to a stop. Quiet washed over the ship. I looked aft, but the raft had long since disappeared.

I checked the chart but made no marks. Already the Cayo Lobos light was peeking above the black horizon. The ship, now running at full speed, heaved through the dark water toward Miami. To the south, shrouded in night, the coast of Cuba waited for the stowaways.

The next morning I went down to breakfast before going on watch. Victor started when I stepped into the galley, ducked his head, and moved out of my way. I poured a cup of coffee and went into the officer's mess. Ian and the chief were sitting over their second cups, their plates pushed away. They looked at me curiously. I nodded to them and sat down.

The chief said, "Miami tomorrow, Captain?"

"Miami tomorrow."

"What cargo?"

I shrugged. "Don't know. Won't be paper for Haina, I know that."

Ian laughed. "We were very lucky, Captain. Yussuf said there was a Navy ship looking for us."

"Yeah, we were lucky. I thought when we came out of the rainstorm that they would find us for sure. I still don't know where they were."

The chief said, "Strange things happening on this ship, Captain." He slid out from behind the table. "Maybe plenty trouble in Miami."

"Maybe. No trouble for you, though."

He looked down at me, his eyes owlish behind his thick glasses. "And for you? I hate to see you have problem, Captain."

I smiled thinly. "Nothing I can't handle."

Ian said, "And Ricardo? Have you heard about him? Is he going to be all right?"

The smile, such as it was, faded. "He's not going to be all right, Ian. He'll never be all right again. How his family in Honduras is going to manage, I don't know."

The chief shook his head. "I know his family, Captain. He has three sons, all in school." He hesitated. "He won't be able to work again?"

"Maybe someday, Chief, but not soon. His jaw was broken into pieces. All his front teeth were knocked out. Maybe worse, I don't know. He was bleeding from both ears."

"He fell, Captain?" Ian asked. "He fell from the deck into the hold?"

"That's right."

"Yussuf said we should not ask questions about what happened."

"Yussuf was right. Ricardo fell into the hold, and that's that."

"What if he remembers what happened?"

"Ian," I said, "he fell on his head. He'll be back in Honduras in a few days anyway, and nobody will care what he remembers."

"What do you mean?"

"You're a professional seaman. You know what happens when you get hurt on one of these ships. You go to the hospital, you get patched up just enough to travel, and you get sent home. He'll be lucky if Dickie gives him a month's extra wages."

The chief shook his head angrily. "Very bad, Captain. Very bad. Ricardo is my countryman. I hope somebody paid for this." He looked at me steadily. "A captain should trust his crew."

Victor brought my plate of eggs and ham. I ignored the chief and started eating. He went out and Victor hurried out behind him.

After breakfast I went up on the bridge to relieve Yussuf. He was smoking on the starboard wing. It was a bright, clear morning, the sun warming the handrail as I went up. The wind was still steady out of the east-northeast, hurrying the ship along. Yussuf threw away his cigarette half-smoked.

"Good morning, Captain."

"Morning." I went into the wheelhouse. He followed. I checked the position and the log for the night. We had just turned into the Santaren Channel. I could see the sandy dunes of Cay Sal Bank to the west, a lumpy yellow thread above the blue-green water.

"Captain. . ." Yussuf began.

"Yes?"

"The crew is asking me what happened. Why we had to stop engine. Lionel said he knows we had stowaways onboard. He asked me if the stowaways beat up Ricardo."

"What did you tell him?"

"Just what you said. That Ricardo fell, and there were no stowaways. He asked me where the paint raft is. I told him it must have fallen overboard. He knew I was lying."

"You told him the right thing. The same thing you're going to tell anyone else who asks." I gave him a steady look. "It doesn't matter if they think you're lying. It doesn't matter if they think we killed the stowaways." I spat through the front window. "They're a bunch of cowards. Who cares what they think?"

There was a long silence. Yussuf said, "They're only human, Captain. Their families have no one else to depend on. Why should they risk their lives for an owner who won't pay them?"

I turned on him. "Because I gave them direct orders. And because any crewman who won't risk his life for the ship isn't worth having onboard."

He went to the starboard door and turned around. "Sometimes captains make mistakes when they think like that," he said quietly. He slipped out.

I went to the wing, but he had already gone down and into the house.

We arrived at the Miami seabuoy at 0645 the next morning and dropped anchor into water the color of a parrot's back. Several ships were already at anchor, including the *Bahia Mar* and the *St. Joseph.* The pilot came onboard at 0800 and took us into Government Cut, and by 0935 the tugs were nosing us up against the dock at the All Seas Terminal, this time at the concrete wharf. Behind us were the

Grimaldo, a half-shelterdecker, and the *Seven Stars*, a battered old 1000-tonner, Dutch-built by her bow. The *Seven Stars* was alongside the coral rocks where we had been docked the last time, loading bales of paper.

Dickie came onboard with Customs and Immigration. I had to type out and sign an affidavit regarding the ship's unorthodox departure from Rio Haina. After the officials were gone Dickie shook my hand. "You saved the ship again, Captain."

"You don't even know." I told him about almost turning over off the Keys, and finished with, "Anyway, the ship survived. But how is Ricardo?"

His face fell. "I had to give Jackson Memorial $25,000 already. They're going to try to rebuild his jaw, but he has brain damage."

"Can he remember what happened?"

He shook his head. "His jaw is wired shut. He fell in the hold, didn't he?"

"That's right. They were cleaning out the paper the stevedores left. There's still a shitload down there. After the accident we just didn't have the crew to finish. It's to charterer's account, anyway."

"Ha!" he said. "Garot has disappeared. I think it has something to do with the short-load. Plus he owes me $11,000."

"Well, I hope you've got the crew wages. Otherwise it's ITF time, I can promise you. So, what about the next charter? I assume we won't be carrying waste paper to the Dominican Republic any time soon."

He laughed. "No, no, Captain. You're taking general cargo to Miragoane."

"For whom?"

"A Haitian named Robert Jermaine. A young guy, about 25. Seems pretty sharp."

"You get the first charter-hire yet?"

He hesitated. "Yeah, some of it, but the money's all spent."

"On the *Veronika*?"

He nodded. "The engineers let the main engine overheat on the way to Coco Solo. Cracked three heads. I'm having to get them flown in from Holland. Fourteen thousand dollars."

I nodded unsympathetically. "That's shipownership. And don't forget the *Erika*'s class certificates. Drydocking's due in July."

"Oh," he said lightly, "I'm going to drop Lloyds and go with Honduran certs. I'll get another year before drydocking."

"This ship needs drydocking," I said. "It's looking for a hole in the ocean right now."

He didn't say anything.

"Well, you'd better pay the crew what you got so they can wire it home."

"I don't have the wages right now. I've got to go over to Jermaine's office. Don't tell the crew I'm going to pay both months, though. I don't know how much I'm going to get."

We shook hands and he left. I went out on the boat deck to watch the stevedores loading bales of waste paper on the *Seven Stars*. They were starting on the second tier on deck. Morton waved to me from the dock.

I went back to the office to do paperwork. The chief came up with a long face. His arms were black to the elbow. "Captain, we've got a problem with the lube-oil pump. I couldn't get oil pressure up when we came in from the anchorage, so I had to use the stand-by pump. Ian is taking it apart now, but it looks like the cylinder's cracked. We'll probably have to get another pump."

"Okay. Let me know when Ian's got it apart, and we'll take a look at it."

He scuffed his feet. "And we can't strip the No. 3 port ballast tank. The pump is working, but it won't pull from that tank."

I sighed. "Why not?"

"Probably a hole in the stripping pipe."

"Okay. I'll get the crew to open the manhole and we'll pump it out with the trash pump. Anything else?"

"No sir. Here's the stores list." He handed me a grimy sheet of yellow paper. The list covered the whole front and half the back. He went to the door and turned around. "I'm sorry to have to say this, Captain, but if we don't get paid for two months, I'm going to leave the ship here in Miami. It's nothing against you, Captain, but. . ."

"I've already told Dickie, Chief. It's all I can do. He promised to pay the crew wages before we sail."

"Both months? I'm not going to take some bullshit advance."

"I wouldn't either, Chief. But it'd be better if you tell him yourself. He doesn't seem to believe me."

"I'll tell him. You can believe I'll tell him." He went out and stamped down the companionway. I looked at his list and started marking the items that would be easy to get and the ones I was going to have to chase down. Half-way through I pushed it aside and laid my head on my arms. The world contracted to a small place between my temples, a small hot place like the engine room, filled with impossibility.

There was a yell from below. I didn't move. Another yell. It was Yussuf. I forced myself to get up and go into the saloon so I could look down on deck. The crew were at the starboard gunwale, leaning over and looking aft.

"Yussuf, what's going on?" I called.

"The *Seven Stars*." He pointed. "She's about to turn over."

I ran down to the deck and slid down the pilot ladder. The *Seven Stars* was lying at an angle of about 15° toward the dock, her gangway hanging down into the river. The crew and stevedores were in the water, swimming for shore. As I watched an old man, the captain, clawed his way along the starboard hallway and down the ladder to the deck. He staggered a little, his face bright red above a shaggy white beard.

Morton was at the edge of the dock, dangerously close to the taut dock lines, a walkie-talkie held to his lips. He shouted something to the captain. The old man climbed up on the gunwale and jumped in the water. He paddled to shore and two of his crewmen helped him up onto the rough coral bank. He sat down, streaming water, his head in his hands.

A car came driving along the dock at reckless speed, a little sports Mercedes. It skidded to a stop and a short, dark man jumped out holding a cellular phone to his ear. He was wearing a dark-blue business suit. He hurried toward the ship, still talking into the phone. He spoke British English with an Indian accent.

"Captain," he said, "what happened? Have you done your stability?"

The old captain staggered to his feet. "Yessir," he said, wringing water from his beard. "I don't know what happened. We just started on the third tier when she took a roll."

"What's your GM now?"

"Eh, er, I don't remember. Sorry, Captain, but I'm still a little in shock."

The Indian stepped forward and sniffed his breath. "You're still a little drunk, actually, Captain. Go into the office and get yourself cleaned up before the Coast Guard arrives. Get some breath mints or something. And tell Mr. Rollo to come out here immediately."

The captain mumbled something, eyes downcast, and trudged off toward the office. The short man looked at me.

"Hello," I said. "I'm the captain of the *Erika*."

"The what?"

"That ship there."

He glanced over. "I see." He walked to the edge of the dock. I followed.

"Sir," I said, "if you send someone onboard to cut the lashings, some of the bales will fall off into the river. Then the ship will lose some of her list and the crane might be able to reach the rest."

He looked at me. "That is so." He saw the crew huddled against the shipping container that served as a dock office. "Thanks." He walked over to them. They were black men from St. Vincent, half-a-dozen of them, faces stiff with fright. They responded to the Indian with wild swings of the arms and vigorous shakes of the heads. The man came back to me.

"They refuse to go onboard. I'm sure the stevedores won't go. I may have to get. . ."

"Are you the shipper?"

"Yes."

"I'll go onboard and cut the lashings. I've got bolt-cutters onboard."

He thought for a second. "How much will you charge to do that?"

"A hundred dollars."

He gave a little smile. "Excellent, Captain. Would you be able to do that now?"

"Yessir."

"Do you need help?"

"No, I can do it."

"Fine."

I went back to the ship and got the bolt-cutters from the forecastle. Yussuf came forward from the fantail. "Captain, what are you doing?"

"I'm going to cut those bales loose on the *Seven Stars*. The shipper can't get those cowardly crewmen from the ship to do it."

"I'll help." He reached for the cutters.

I pulled them away. "No, Yussuf, but thanks. It only takes one person." I grinned. "Besides, I've got experience."

He followed anyway. We went down to the dock. Rollo was arguing with the Indian from the seat of his golf cart. I used a rope to make a sling for the cutters and got a piece of pallet-board for a paddle. Yussuf and I got into the water, standing on a narrow ledge of coral rock, and pulled over a bale that had fallen overboard. It was floating with the top a couple of inches out of the water. I told Yussuf to stay on shore, got on the bale, and paddled across to the foot of the gangway. It was hanging straight down into the water, but with the cutters slung over my back I was able to pull myself up by the stanchions and get on deck.

The bales had shifted to starboard, hanging against the lashing wires. I made my way forward over the bales to the No. 1 hatch. I crouched down, just as I had done two weeks earlier, and reached up to cut the first wire. It whirled into the air and a dozen bales tumbled past me to splash into the river. I climbed up and managed to kick another half-dozen after them. The ship came up a couple of degrees. Then I went to the next wire and did the same thing. It was a lot easier in the daylight.

After I'd cut all the wires on No. 1, the ship righted to about seven or eight degrees. The ship had moved closer to the dock, and the shore-crane operator was already climbing up into his seat. I slung the cutters across my back and went down the gangway to the point where I could jump across to the bank.

The Indian was standing next to his car, talking on his cellular phone again. He hung up when I approached and shook my hand. "Good job, Captain." He gave me a hundred-dollar bill. "How long have you been onboard your ship?"

I hesitated. I had not thought of it lately. "About five months," I said. "I came onboard in November."

"What license do you have?"

"Panamanian Unlimited."

"Would you be interested in a port captain's job?"

"Yessir."

He smiled. "Do you have a family?"

"Yessir. A wife and two children in New Orleans."

"I see. Would you be willing to move your family to Miami?"

"I'll have to check with my wife, but I'm sure the answer is yes."

"Very good." He handed me a card. "Our office is in Hialeah, only a few blocks away. I would like you to come over this afternoon. We can discuss the details then."

"Good." We shook hands again. The stevedores had secured the *Seven Stars'* gangway. He went onboard.

I went onboard the *Erika* and up to my cabin to shower. When I came out Yussuf was waiting for me in the saloon.

"Yussuf," I said, sitting across from him at the table, "I'm leaving the *Erika*."

He nodded. "It's time for you to go, Captain. We'll miss you."

"I want you to take over as captain."

His eyes widened. "I don't have a captain's license."

"This is a Honduran ship. All you need is a Honduran license. I'll take you over to the consulate this afternoon and get you all fixed up. Do you have $150?"

"Yessir."

"Well, that's what it'll cost. Got any more passport photos?"

"Always, Captain."

"I'm sure Dickie will be glad to have you take over. He knows what a good man you are."

He leaned across the table and put his hands over mine. "Captain, we will always be friends."

"Yes, Yussuf. We are Arabs. You'll be a good captain. Just don't let Dickie take advantage of you. And always keep enough cash hidden away for airfare home."

"Good advice." He left, grinning broadly.

I went down to the dock and called my wife. She answered on the first ring.

"Darling," I said, "would you move to Miami if I left the ship?"

"What do you mean?"

"I've been offered a port-captain job in Miami."

There was a silence on the line. "You're leaving the *Erika*?"

"That's right."

"Well, come home and let's talk about it. I'm sure we'll make it work."

We hung up and I went back to the ship to start packing. The *Seven Stars* was upright again. Morton was on deck arguing with the old captain. The stevedores had gotten a battered jo-boat into the river and were trying to corral the runaway bales.

Dickie appeared about an hour later with one month's wages for the crew. He took the news of my departure calmly, and agreed that Yussuf would make a good captain. He was able to pay me for 24 days of April, and we parted on good terms. He even gave me $600 for Jhonny Garcia after a little prodding. The Hondurans were not so happy, but they finally agreed to wait for the rest of their money.

Yussuf and I arrived at the Honduran consulate just before they closed. The girl took his application and photos and disappeared. A few minutes later the consul himself came out to congratulate Yussuf, hand him his license, and take his $150, which seemed to give him the greatest pleasure of all. Then I took Yussuf back to his command and went to see my new employer.

The offices of Cartones del Sud, Inc., were only a few blocks from the ship, in a low, modern office building with a guard in the parking lot. The Indian captain came out of an office marked Vice President to introduce me around. He gave me a week to go home and prepare for the move, and even had his secretary arrange my flight and pay my ticket. I went back to the ship to find Yussuf in the hold with Lionel, tying up bales of paper. I called him on deck.

"Captain," I said, "I've got the phone number of a crewing agent here in Miami named Arcadio Munoz. He can find you a chief mate and another AB."

He grinned. "I've already gotten a chief mate from the *Gitan Express*. She's at the Trujillo dock. And Lionel says we can get a Guyanese AB from the *Bahia Mar* when she comes in. She's going to the Caribe Terminal."

I laughed. "Then you're the right man for the job, Captain Yussuf. Here's Jhonny Garcia's money. Call Arcadio to come get it." I looked at my watch. "Well, my flight leaves at 1900 hours. We still have time for a little *clairin* party before I go. I know there's a gallon or two somewhere."

He gathered the crew on the fantail. Now the whole ship knew I was going. Victor got so upset he started making hors d'oeuvres. We had no mangos, but Lionel mixed up a Guyanese spiced punch with frozen pineapple juice that finally taught the *clairin* some manners.

I held up my glass. "Calm seas and pretty girls!"

They laughed and drank the toast.

"To the *Erika*!" I said. "May the old girl roll on for years to come!"

"To the *Erika*!" they chorused.

"Well, Captain Yussuf," I said, "do you think the Customs boat will meet you in Miragoane?"

"De Custom boat come," Lionel answered for him. "Never fear dat, Cap. When de ship reach Miragoane, de Custom boat come."

At 1700 hours the agent's boy arrived to take me to Customs and INS. Yussuf lowered my bags to the dock with a rope and came down the pilot ladder. The chief, Ian, Lionel, and Victor leaned over the gunwale and waved. I waved back. Yussuf and I hugged.

"*Insh'Allah*, Yussuf," I said.

"*Insh'Allah*, Captain. It is the will of Allah that we meet again."

I got in the car and told the agent's boy to drive up along the dock so I could look back at the *Erika*. She was a long, slender needle of a ship, painted pink by the setting sun. The boy drove out on North River Drive.

"Going home, Captain?"

"That's right," I said. "I'm going home."

EPILOGUE

The MV *Erika* sank in August, 1989, on a voyage from Cartagena to Miragoane, under the command of Capt. Yussuf al Karim. There was no loss of life.